...ERS · ART DEALERS · AUCTION HOUSE...
...S · CULINARY SCHOOLS · EMPLOYMENT...
...AUTY · HOTELS · JEWELRY AND WATCH...
...S POLO CLUBS · PORTRAIT PAINTERS AND PHOTOGRA...
...SCHOOLS · SECURITY CONSULTANTS · SPAS AND CLINI...
...GEMENT · WINE MERCHANTS · WINE MAKERS · YACHTIN...
...DEALERS · AUCTION HOUSES · CHAUFFEUR SERVICES · ...
...SCHOOLS · EMPLOYMENT AGENCIES · EVENTS · FASHI...
...ELRY AND WATCHES · LANDSCAPE ARCHITECTS · LAW...
...BS · PORTRAIT PAINTERS AND PHOTOGRAPHERS · PRIV...
...RITY CONSULTANTS · SPAS AND CLINICS · SPECIALTY S...
...S · WINE MAKERS · YACHTING · AIRCRAFT · ANTIQUES · ...
...ES · CHAUFFEUR SERVICES · CIGAR BARS AND CLUBS · ...
...AGENCIES · EVENTS · FASHION · FITNESS · FLORISTS · ...
...NDSCAPE ARCHITECTS · LAWFIRMS · MUSEUMS · PARTY...
...HOTOGRAPHERS · PRIVATE CLUBS · PROPERTY CONSULT...
...AND CLINICS · SPECIALTY SHOPS · TRAVEL CONSULTAN...
...ING · AIRCRAFT · ANTIQUES · ARCHITECTS AND INTER...
...R SERVICES · CIGAR BARS AND CLUBS · COLLEGES · COS...
...EVENTS · FASHION · FITNESS · FLORISTS · GOLF CLUB...
...RCHITECTS · LAWFIRMS · MUSEUMS · PARTY ORGANIZE...
...GRAPHERS · PRIVATE CLUBS · PROPERTY CONSULTANT...
...AND CLINICS · SPECIALTY SHOPS · TRAVEL CONSULTAN...
...TING · AIRCRAFT · ANTIQUES · ARCHITECTS AND INTER...
...R SERVICES · CIGAR BARS AND CLUBS · COLLEGES · COS...
...EVENTS · FASHION · FITNESS · FLORISTS · GOLF CLUB...
...RCHITECTS · LAWFIRMS · MUSEUMS · PARTY ORGANIZE...
...GRAPHERS · PRIVATE CLUBS · PROPERTY CONSULTANT...
...AND CLINICS · SPECIALTY SHOPS · TRAVEL CONSULTAN...
...ING · AIRCRAFT · ANTIQUES · ARCHITECTS AND INTER...

AMERICA'S ELITE 1000

THE ULTIMATE LIST

2001 EDITION

Publisher & Editor in Chief
Kevin Kelly

Deputy Editor
Michael Slimmer

Managing Editor
Lynda Weatherhead

Associate Publishers
Mark D. Kelly
Francine S. Stessel

Art Director
Victor J. Brunetti

Picture Editor - UK
Nicole Bettelley

Picture Editors - US
Lili Beneda
Sondra Weimar

Printed and bound by Mondadori Editore, Verona, Italy

First Published in November 1999 and **revised in October 2000** by Cadogan Publications Inc.
27 West 24th Street, New York, NY 10010, USA
Telephone: +1-212-414-8776

UK Address:
7 Verney House, Hollywood Road, Fulham, SW1O 9HS, UK
Telephone: +44-207-823-7445

America's Elite 1000 - The Ultimate List
Copyright © Cadogan Publications Inc. 2000

British Library Cataloging in Publication Data
A catalog record for this book is available from The British Library.

ISBN0-9671694-1-0

AMERICA'S ELITE 1000
2001 EDITION

EDITED BY
TREVOR WHITE

CP

CADOGAN PUBLICATIONS

FOREWORD

I am delighted to say that the launch issue of *America's Elite 1000* met with great acclaim. In publishing it is often difficult to create a new concept – a green field project – which can really only be judged when a publication reaches the market. I believe with *America's Elite 1000* we had an original idea (often the hardest to find) and we felt that provided the idea was executed to a high editorial standard we could create a publication which would be beautiful to look at and interesting to read – the sort of book which would proudly sit on the finest coffee tables across America.

Like our sister publication, *Europe's Elite 1000*, it is our ambition to improve each issue year on year. This new issue of *America's Elite 1000* includes 200 new entries. Each of the 1000 entries has been revisited for new information, new ideas, new updates. Our journalists have interviewed the owners of the establishments, we have incorporated the latest information and every single image in the book has been changed. Those who have seen the early proof copies of *America's Elite 1000* tell me the result is a superb publication, but really only you can be the judge of that.

Our feature on American museums illustrates the amazing treasures that exist in museums in every city and large town in the United States of America. These selections are a small sample and an endorsement of the collecting skills of previous generations and the judicious choice and scholarship of curators and directors of leading museums. As a country becomes increasingly affluent a measure of its sophistication is its commitment to providing for the whole population an opportunity to understand, to view and appreciate the talents of not only American artists but creative geniuses from the earliest days of civilization. The names of American benefactors of the arts encapsulate the families who have made America great - the Fricks, the Mellons, the Rockefellers, the Gettys and in contemporary times the Mahoneys, the Wrightsmans, the Newhouses, the Gates, the Cantors, amongst many more. America, the richest economy the world has ever seen, reflects its huge commitment to the appreciation of history and beauty.

Christopher Lawrence had the enviable task of speaking to and interviewing our leading ladies for our keynote feature. The range of women profiled reflects the style, talent, energy and commitment of contemporary American women. Our list includes very many successful career women and others actively involved in philanthropy. These busy women each agreed to be interviewed and photographed and the end result represents a vibrant cross section of American women in the first year of the third millennium. *America's Elite 1000* has been an exciting project and I hope you the readers will enjoy the publication and find it as informative and stimulating to read as we have found it stimulating in its creation and production.

KEVIN KELLY
CHAIRMAN AND EDITOR-IN-CHIEF

AMERICA'S ELITE 1000

THE LISTINGS

The 1000 names on our list are the editors' choices of the finest shops, services and luxury goods that America has to offer. Every company or individual proposed for inclusion has been checked and cross-checked by our network of contributors, advisors and contacts, to ensure that inclusion is merited. The names have been selected on the basis of the current excellence of their products and services, rather than simply a high profile or impressive past reputation. Equally, all names have been judged against a pan-American standard of excellence, rather than being selected on a state-by-state basis. All of the entries will be reviewed and updated annually.

While the *Elite 1000* naturally includes the acknowledged greats, it also contains many less predictable names. Readers may be surprised to find certain famous names missing from the list. If they did not qualify, it is because they appear to have succumbed either to the temptation of resting on their laurels, rather than constantly reviewing and upgrading their standards, or to the temptation of becoming too commercial and populist.

Entries described as *Best Kept Secrets* are specialty shops and services. Many of the names are already well-established but deserve to be more widely known. Some of them are hardly known outside the inner circle of America's cognoscenti. All of them offer outstanding quality and an indefinable 'something special'.

We have also highlighted *Rising Stars,* those firms which, in our opinion, will soon make it to the very top in their particular field. Some of these firms may not have yet fulfilled their potential or proved that they have real staying power but their commitment to excellence is unquestioned.

HOW TO USE THIS BOOK

The *Elite 1000* is published in alphabetical order, across all product categories. The names are cross-referenced in three indexes, to enable you to use this book in a variety of ways. For example, if you are traveling to a particular city, you would use the city index to discover the best of everything in, say, Washington D.C. On the other hand, if you are the best in a certain field—say jewelers or antique dealers—you would use the product category index, which will list all names under the relevant category heading. In addition, there is a straight alphabetical index of all names which have been included in the Listings section of the book.

CONTENTS

C
LIVE
EARN
LOCATE
LOVE
I
N
E

TALKING PICTURES

Edited by Michael Slimmer

American museums house many of the world's greatest works of art. Here, some
of the country's leading museum Curators and Directors introduce
a favorite piece from their collections.

John Singer Sargent

The Daughters of Edward Darley Boit, 1882
Museum of Fine Arts, Boston, MA

The Museum of Fine Arts, Boston, is home to many world-famous collections - of Asian art, Egyptian art, prints, and French Impressionist paintings - and its American paintings are particularly renowned. The Museum owns one of the finest concentrations of the work of John Singer Sargent, including his masterpiece - and perhaps the most beloved painting in the entire collection - *The Daughters of Edward Darley Boit*.

Sargent was only twenty-six and at the beginning of his international career when his friend and fellow artist Edward Boit asked him to paint a portrait of his four daughters. The Boits were wealthy Bostonians then living in Paris; the girls (who range in age from 4 to 14) are shown in the family's apartment in the fashionable Avenue de Friedland. Sargent, who intended to exhibit the painting at the Salon, drew upon various old-master compositions, notably Velazquez's Las Meninas, in creating his daring composition, which one critic described as "four corners and a void."

The Daughters of Edward Darley Boit, caused a great deal of comment when it appeared at the 1883 Salon - critics were impressed with Sargent's virtuosic paint handling, and intrigued by his characterizations of the girls. Unlike most fashionable group portraits, in which sitters are given equal prominence, Sargent has separated the children from one another and scattered them among the shadows of a dark, cavernous room.

The painting remained in the family until 1919, when the daughters, none of whom were to marry, gave it to the MFA. Since then, its charm and mystery have made it a favorite, well deserving of its recent estimation as "one of the best American pictures."
Malcolm Rogers,
Ann and Graham Gund Director

Page 9: John Singer Sargent, Madame X, ca. 1884,
Courtesy of the Metropolitan Museum of Art, New York, NY.
Below: John Singer Sargent,
The Daughters of Edward Darley Boit, 1882.

Albert Bierstadt

A Storm in the Rocky Mountains, Mt. Rosalie, 1866
Brooklyn Museum of Art, Brooklyn, NY
Albert Bierstadt returned to the United States in 1857 from four years of study in Europe to begin his career as a landscape painter. A trip to the Rocky Mountains in 1859 established him as the primary interpreter of the western wilderness landscape.

A Storm in the Rocky Mountains, Mt. Rosalie was inspired by Bierstadt's 1863 overland expedition to California. En route he made numerous on-the-spot sketches and studies in the mountains north of Denver, Colorado. Returning to his New York studio, he incorporated them into this panoramic vista.

For all its careful detail, the painting is not a literal rendering of a specific site. It is a highly subjective visual essay on the natural wonders of the New World executed on a scale commensurate with the vastness of the land. Bierstadt's use of such large canvases invites comparison of his work to that of Frederic Church as well as to the then-popular theatrical attractions of moving panoramas and dioramas. Mount Rosalie (now Mount Evans) was named by the artist in honor of the woman he would marry in 1866. This monumental landscape dropped from public view after purchase by an Englishman in 1867. Until its rediscovery in 1974, it was known only by a chromolithograph.
Ellen Reeder,
Deputy Director for Art

Above: Albert Bierstadt,
A Storm in the Rocky Mountains, Mt. Rosalie, 1866.

Rembrandt Harmensz van Rijn

Self Portrait, 1658
The Frick Collection, New York, NY

Arguably the most forceful portrait by the most forceful artist, Rembrandt's image of himself done in 1658 brings enormous human emotion to the unsuspecting visitor and expert alike. One need not know the details of the suffering and loss the artist endured in his life to see it in his eyes or sense it in the aged but solid hands. Dressed in Oriental finery he in fact wears the last remnants of his formerly impressive possessions most all of which have been sold to satisfy his creditors. But the spirit remains proud and moving and we can not deny our visceral reaction to his self-knowing gaze.

It has been my great pleasure as an art historian to experience this great masterpiece not just as the Director of The Frick Collection, but for so many years as a visitor. Today it remains tremendously satisfying to see the faces of the public - among them New Yorkers as well as art lovers who travel from across the planet to our doorstep, and of course, the students involved in our Education program - as they react to this breathtaking masterpiece. This painting is one of the many treasures that grace the walls of The Frick Collection - works assembled with knowledge and precision by Henry Clay Frick and generously left to the public to forever enjoy.

Samuel Sachs, II,
Director

Above: Rembrandt Harmensz van Rijn,
Self Portrait, 1658.
Right: Rembrandt Harmensz van Rijn,
Joris de Caulerij, 1632.

Joris de Caulerij, 1632
Fine Arts Museum of San Francisco, CA

The California Palace of the Legion of Honor, one of the two institutions that comprise the Fine Arts Museums of San Francisco, is situated on a breathtaking promontory overlooking the mouth of San Francisco Bay and the Golden Gate Bridge. The distinguished collection - including European old-master paintings, sculpture, decorative arts, textiles, and graphic works - contains treasures of great beauty, quality, and rarity collected over the Museums' one-hundred-year history.

Dutch painting of the seventeenth century is a particular strength of the collection, as represented by Rembrandt's *Joris de Caulerij*, signed and dated in 1632. This exceptional work illustrates why the young Rembrandt van Rijn, having only just established himself in Amsterdam the previous year, soon displaced that city's leading portraitists. Rembrandt's early mastery of the portrait idiom combines the sympathetic and direct characterization of the sitter with striking three-dimensional and atmospheric effects, a descriptive style well suited to the requirements of his prosperous clientele.

The different techniques Rembrandt employed to achieve this convincing realism are evident here because of the painting's excellent state of preservation. Paint passages vary from thick impasto to delicate transparent glazes, with areas of scumbling - where one broken layer of paint reveals patches of another color underneath - used to differentiate textures across the face. The result is an image of extraordinary vitality that thrills the viewer with the sheer joy that looking at pictures can bring. Rembrandt's painting is just one of many exceptional objects on view in San Francisco's Legion of Honor.

Dr. Lynn Federie Orr,
Associate Department Head for European Art
and Curator of European Paintings

Frederic Edwin Church

The Icebergs, 1863
Dallas Museum of Art, Dallas, TX

Of the many outstanding examples of painting, sculpture, and other works of art in the comprehensive collection of the Dallas Museum of Art, no work is more representative of the Museum's high standards of beauty and quality than *The Icebergs*. Frederic Church was known for traveling to the far reaches of the earth to find examples of unspoiled nature that reflect the pristine innocence of a Garden of Eden. This painting is one of America's great contributions to the landscape tradition and is an integral part of the DMA's collection of art of North America, which includes *The Fountains of Vaucluse*, a major landscape by Thomas Cole, Church's teacher and one of the founders of the Hudson River school of painting.

In the summer of 1859 Church embarked on a monthlong sketching trip aboard a chartered schooner exploring the waters off the coast of Newfoundland and Labrador. Buffeted by high seas and afflicted with seasickness, Church sketched icebergs as they appeared on the horizon until the moment they threatened to capsize the small boats used to draw near them. These sketches inspired Church as he embarked on what was his largest canvas to date. He completed the painting, initially entitled *The North,* in 1863 he shipped the canvas to London, where it was retitled *The Icebergs.* The painting was bought by a member of Parliament and vanished from sight for a number of years. It was purchased for the DMA by an anonymous donor in 1979 for the highest price paid at auction at the time for an American painting.

Dr. Charles L. Venable,
Deputy Director, Chief Curator and Curator
of Decorative Arts

Giovanni Domenico Tiepolo

The Storyteller, ca. 1865
The Jack S. Blanton Museum of Art, Austin, TX

From the moment the Blanton Museum of Art acquired the Suida-Manning Collection in 1998, *The Storyteller,* an oil on canvas painted by Giovanni Domenico Tiepolo circa 1865, captured my attention. The manner in which the artist provides a "snapshot" of eighteenth-century daily life, depicting a cross section of the population interacting within the composition, is quite clever. At first, it may be difficult for the modern eye to view such a composition as innovative, given the role the camera has played in art since the nineteenth century, but Tiepolo has very cleverly manipulated the space. He placed the foreground characters off-center and a casual group of onlookers just in front of the church façade in the right background. These elements, on the opposite side of the piazza from the storyteller himself, balance the weight of the composition and enhance the feeling that this is a real space.

As Tiepolo was Venetian, it is not surprising that he takes advantage of the manipulation of brilliant colors in his compositions. However, the artist's use of black and white elements to lead the viewer's eye across the canvas is striking. His very nervous, fine black lines define the figures, draw the eye across their contours, and guide it to the most important elements of the composition. And the draftsman-like aspects of the architecture lend a bit of mystery to the narrative. The Suida-Manning Collection is one of the finest privately assembled collections of Old Master paintings and drawings in existence. I feel fortunate to have the opportunity to experience such a magnificent work and share it with the public for the first time.

Jessie Otto Hite,
Director

Above: Frederic Edwin Church,
The Icebergs, 1863.
Right: Giovanni Domenico Tiepolo,
The Storyteller, ca. 1865.

Winslow Homer

Right and Left, 1908
National Gallery of Art, Washington, DC

Homer painted *Right and Left* in 1908, in the small coastal town of Prout's Neck, Maine, where he had been living since 1883. At the time Homer was painting nothing but the inexorable power and beauty of the sea itself, and the coldness and austerity and solitude of the Maine coast. He would make only one more oil before his death two years later.

He wrote to his brother, "I am painting...a most surprising picture..." and surprising it is. At first glance the two birds appear to be flying above the torrid sea. In fact, they are both targets of a double-barreled gun - hence the title, *Right and Left*. The bird on the right has already been hit, its wings have gone limp and it is falling towards the water. A lone feather floats in the air beside it. The bird at the left, however, has a millisecond of life left - it stares out at us with one clear, bright orange eye.

Immediately below that bird, in the distance, we can just make out a boat emerging from the waves, and the tiny figure of a hunter, his gaze obscured by the smoke of a gun, and a flash of fiery red. Perhaps most unusual is our vantage point. We share with the artist the same physical space as the doomed creatures - directly in the line of fire. Homer confronts us with both the horror of death, and its beauty.

Right and Left is just one of the many considerable holdings in the National Gallery of Art created in 1937 through a gift from financier and art collector Andrew J. Mellon, who began accumulating art in the 1920s with the intention of creating a gallery for the people of the United States.

Earl A. Powell, III,

Director

Edgar Degas

Portrait of Mme. Rene Degas, 1872
New Orleans Museum of Art, New Orleans, LA

The Portrait of Madame Rene Degas is a remarkable souvenir of the visit of Edgar Degas to New Orleans, the city of his mother's birth. It is perhaps the most poignant of the small handful of paintings he made when he came to spend the winter with his Louisiana relatives. The artist had a special affection for the sitter, who was his cousin Estelle, dating from her visit to France when she was newly widowed by the Civil War. Degas's youngest brother Rene had fallen in love with Estelle at the time and followed her back to New Orleans where they were married.

When Degas painted Estelle, the family was happily ensconced in a handsome house on Esplanade Avenue which still stands today. He shows her arranging flowers in a tall vase, which ought to make a pleasant subject, yet Degas seems to have sensed the dark clouds gathering in Estelle's life. She had already lost the sight in one eye and would soon be completely blind. What Degas painted most sensually is what she would understand from her own sense of touch and smell. The flowers are very much alive as they are torn apart on the tabletop or inserted into the vase by those deft fingers. Not long after this portrait, her husband, Degas's brother Rene, would elope with the next-door neighbor, abandon Estelle and their children, and bring emotional and financial disaster to the family on both sides of the Atlantic.

Degas kept the portrait of Estelle in his studio until his death. In the 1960s the New Orleans Museum of Art was able to acquire it by public subscription. Many visitors still come to see the painting that they gave pennies to help buy when they were children, and among these visitors are the descendants of Estelle and Rene, the great grandnephews of Edgar Degas, the only French Impressionist to have painted in the United States.

The portrait is just one example of the extraordinary works in the New Orleans Museum of Art, which has particularly outstanding collections of painting, decorative art, photography, African and Asian art.
Gail Feigenbaum,
Curator of Painting

Above: Winslow Homer,
Right and Left, 1908.
Right: Edgar Degas,
Portrait of Madame Rene Degas, 1872.
Pages 18-19: Juan Sánchez Cotán,
Quince, Cabbage, Melon and Cucumber, ca. 1603.

Juan Sánchez Cotán

Quince, Cabbage, Melon and Cucumber, ca. 1603
San Diego Museum of Art, San Diego, CA

Quince, Cabbage, Melon and Cucumber is one of the most famous Spanish works of art in the United States. It is one of a small number of documented still lifes by the seventeenth-century still-life painter Juan Sánchez Cotán.

When this picture was painted, in Toledo, Spain sometime before 1603, still-life elements only appeared as decoration in paintings usually depicting religious or classical stories. The picture is first mentioned in an inventory associated with the will Sánchez Cotán made prior to entering a Carthusian monastery. It has been suggested that the austerity of his still lifes is in some way associated with his religious calling. Whatever the connection it is certain that the Carthusians practiced contemplation and self-denial.

The subject is a small collection of fruit and vegetables arranged in a window setting, possibly a cantarera, or "cooling space," in a Spanish house. The hanging fruit may look strange to modern eyes but in Spain at that time this was a common way of preserving produce from pests.

All of the produce is ordinary, but Sánchez Cotán carefully considers the composition, arranging the fruits and vegetables in a precise curve moving both vertically and horizontally. Descending objects project successively outward until the cucumber, which extends over the ledge, seems to thrust forward into the viewer's space.

The painting has had an interesting history since its first mention in the museum's inventory in 1603. In 1809 it seems to have been a part of a group of paintings confiscated from the Spanish Royal Collection by the French under the command of Joseph Bonaparte.

When Bonaparte fled Spain in 1813 he took with him 1,500 wagon loads of booty. In 1815 he moved to New Jersey under the assumed name, "Comte de Survilliers," a year later a collection of some 200 paintings taken from Spain were sent to him. Three years later, the Pennsylvania Academy of Fine Arts displayed a work by Sánchez Cotán entitled *Still Life-Quince, Cabbage, Melon, & C* [sic].

In 1844 Bonaparte died, the following year, his grandson began to sell off paintings belonging to the estate, the Pennsylvania Academy of Fine Arts again displayed a still life by Sánchez Cotán that was said to be for sale. The painting disappeared for an entire century and reappeared, to be purchased by Anne R. and Amy Putnam for the San Diego Museum of Art.

Don Bacigalupi,
The Maruja Baldwin Director

Therman Statom

Glass House, 1997
Scottsdale Museum of Contemporary Art, Scottsdale, AZ

Therman Statom is well-known for his elaborate glass constructions which often take the form of ladders, chairs, tables and houses.

Glass House, built from hollow blocks of plate glass, contains an odd collection of hand-painted images and found fabricated objects.

Shards of glass, bottles filled with blue liquid, handwritten messages and a glass orb are assembled, thus creating a rich and multi-layered collage of random exuberance.

These internal elements are either found or fabricated by Statom and are further enhanced by colorful paintings which he applies to the objects and the surface of the glass. As if by magic, Statom's houses often appear to float without a visible means of support.

Statom's Glass House is one of the first significant donations to the Scottsdale Museum of Contemporary Art's collection. Since 1997, over 300 pieces of art have been donated to this venerable institution.

Robert Knight,
Director

Above: Constantin Brancusi,
The Kiss and Bird in Space, 1916 and 1923-24.
Right: Therman Statom,
Glasshouse, 1997.

Constantin Brancusi

The Kiss and Bird in Space, 1916, 1923-24
Philadelphia Museum of Art, Philadelphia, PA

A serene, chapel-like space within the Galleries of Modern and Contemporary Art at the Philadelphia Museum of Art frames the breathtaking sculptural group that reveals Constantin Brancusi's search for essential forms.

Brancusi carved a series of stone versions of *The Kiss* throughout his long career, of which Philadelphia's is the most geometric. The tall block of stone is divided vertically down the center, the woman differentiated from the man by her rounded breast and the long hair falling down her back. The flat horizontality of the arms, the overall regularity of the stone, the joined mouths, and the single arc of the two hairlines present a unified whole far more powerful than the two individuals within. Graced with an ideal form that literally transcends the imperfections of earthly existence, the bird was a predominant theme for Brancusi, and was the subject of more than 25 marble or bronze sculptures that he made during the course of four decades.

In *Bird in Space* all the parts of the creature become one soaring movement, made especially elegant by the slight swell of its chest and the graceful undulation of its slender footing. Brancusi considered his bases integral to his sculpture. The pedestal supporting *Bird in Space* is comprised of a variety of textures and shapes - oak and limestone, cylinders and sawtooth forms - that provide a counterpoint to the smooth unity of the yellow marble bird. The harmony of the whole achieves Brancusi's mystical goal of unifying opposites.

Brancusi was born in Romania in 1876 and moved to Paris in 1904, where he remained until his death in 1957. After graduating from the Ecole des Beaux-Arts in 1907, he began as an assistant in the studio of Auguste Rodin, but left soon after because, as he explained, "nothing grows under big trees." That same year he turned to the technique of direct carving in reaction to the Western tradition of modeling and casting in plaster or bronze. Working directly with stone, wood, and plaster, he began what would become a lifelong exploration of a few primary themes - women, infants, birds, and fish - which he developed in increasingly simplified forms.

Anne d'Harnoncourt,
The George D. Widener Director and Chief Executive Officer

Adriana Varejão

Carpet-Style Tilework in Live Flesh, 1999
Museum of Contemporary Art, San Diego, CA

While working on an exhibition for the Museum of Contemporary Art, San Diego (MCA), I have made several trips recently to Latin America. During these visits, I became particularly interested in Brazilian artist Adriana Varejão, who lives and works in Rio de Janeiro. Her layered and nuanced work incorporates the history of colonization, the introduction of European art and religion to the region, and the ensuing mixture of cultures. These interests are exemplified by a piece recently acquired by the MCA, her poignant *Azulejaria "De Tapete em Carne Viva (Carpet-Style Tilework in Live Flesh),"* 1999.

In this striking work, Varejão simulates in paint the glazed blue and white tiles imported to Brazil during the 18th century from Portugal. Her painted wall of tiles, a reference to Portuguese colonial heritage, appears to be buckling, as if in an earthquake. Its center is ripped open, exposing a large mass of eviscerated flesh (again, simulated) that oozes out from the gaping wound. It is as if the beautiful hand-painted tile work, the by-product of European civilization and symbol of Iberian colonizers, cannot contain the violence and trauma that accompanied the colonization of Brazil.

Below: Adriana Varejão,
Carpet-Style Tilework in Live Flesh, 1999.

The acquisition of this work, the first piece by Varejão to enter a museum collection in North America, reflects the MCA's commitment to supporting young artists early in their career. It joins the company of work by other artists, such as Kiki Smith and Byron Kim, who have also used the body as a metaphor in their art. It finds context, as well, in the Museum's holdings of work by Latin American and Latino artists. For me, it is an exemplary work that brings together virtuoso artmaking with poignant imagery that reflects on our history and culture.

Elizabeth N. Armstrong,
Senior Curator

Mark di Suvero

Are Years What?, 1967

Hirshhorn Museum and Sculpture Garden, Washington, DC

Housed in a concrete, donut-shaped building that surrounds a sculpture garden, the Hirshorn Museum and Sculpture Garden is the only museum in Washington, D.C. devoted exclusively to modern art. The Hirshhorn houses over 6000 works including masterpieces by Picasso and Matisse.

Are Years What? (for Marianne Moore), a monumental steel sculpture created in 1967 by American artist Mark di Suvero, working with a crane and a blowtorch, communicates the innate strength and power and dynamism of steel. That - and the brilliant red color - makes up the work's obvious power. But look again. Despite being made of intractable, industrial materials weighing several tons, this behemoth sculpture manages to communicate a fragility that is poignant, graceful, and almost tragic.

Watch it over time as nature's forces enact a transformation. The lightness and independence with which the free-hanging element slowly moves - and draws itself into and out of an almost musical dance with dynamic but earthbound diagonal steel beams - seems emotionally charged, visually compelling, and ripe with meaning all at once.

Below: Mark Di Suvero,
Are Years What?, 1967.

Part metaphor, part dynamic abstraction, and part poetic object, di Suvero's sculpture is multidimensional in the broadest sense. Small wonder that the artist - broadly respected for his contributions to contemporary sculpture - titled the work as an homage to a poem by American writer Marianne Moore (1887-1972). The last lines of "What Are Years?," Moore's paean to humanity, might be said to provide a fitting analog to di Suvero's masterwork: "Though he is captive,/his mighty singing/says, satisfaction is a lowly/thing, how pure a thing is joy."

James T. Demetrion,

Director (A)

CHRISTIE'S

LotFinder: Click and Explore

Introducing LotFinder, Christie's online search engine.
LotFinder allows you to find art and objects from
Christie's auctions around the world.

www.christies.com

A Texan Renaissance

By Trevor White

La Colombe d'Or and Villa d'Este are born again in Texas, where America proves itself truly cosmopolitan. Here we introduce the people and places behind the Texan Renaissance.

Texas begins with Stanley Marcus. The 95 year old icon is a perfect lunch guest, tossing opinions around like a witness who knows that he is only telling the truth. From Israel's involvement in Palestine to the vagaries of e-commerce and every subject in between, the Honorary Chairman of Neiman Marcus has something provocative to say.

Stanley Marcus carved a reputation for quality by challenging preconceptions: back when cotton socks sold for a dollar a pair, he introduced Lisle socks for $7.50. As America's premier purveyor of fine men's and women's clothing, he has always specialized in upping the ante. "For a lifetime," he says, "I have bought and sold luxury, constantly searching the world's markets for goods and services that represent the highest standards of man's ability to produce." That is no idle boast. In Europe his name alone is a byword for good taste. When Mohamed al Fayed wanted to reinvigorate Harrods, he turned to the Texan retailer. And to this day Stanley Marcus wears his Legion d'Honneur, the highest civilian honor in France.

How appropriate, then, that old-world institutions like La Colombe d'Or and Villa d'Este are born again in the Lone Star state. Yes, the Texan Villa d'Este is actually a block of apartments, and La Colombe d'Or has little of its French rival's charm. But America proves itself truly cosmopolitan in a state that has served under six flags: Spain, France, Mexico, the Republic of Texas, the Confederacy and the United States.

Spanish conquistadors landed on the shores of this much-contested land in 1519. 150 years later the French arrived. Swiftly booted out by the Spanish, Texas went on to win a battle for independence from Mexico in 1836. But the new republic, led by General Sam Houston, lasted less than a decade before becoming the 28th state in the Union. After a few years of peace, Texas became embroiled in America's bloody Civil War.

Given this turbulent past, it is hardly surprising that the state has produced more than its share of heroes. Chief among them was Houston, legendary war hero, Governor of two states and President of the Republic of Texas. At the end of his life he predicted that "Texas will again lift its head and stand among the nations. No country upon the globe can compare with it in natural advantages." 40 years after Houston's death a huge oil well blew, launching a famous (and much documented) race for black gold.

Quite literally, then, oil provided the foundation for the state's current prosperity: the population quadrupled in the 20th century, and living standards changed beyond all recognition. Even today, after a century of drilling, there are still estimated to be reserves equal to some eight million barrels of oil.

This stark, sun-scorched slab of God's rich earth is larger than New York, New England, Pennsylvania, Ohio and Illinois combined. As a result of its vast size – 7.5% of the nation's total land area – the largest state in continental America enjoys a density less than that of the nation as a whole. But statistics like these only hint at the intrigue, iconoclasm and fierce independence of Texas past and present. And they do not even touch on anomalies like the fascinating relationship between Dallas and Fort Worth, some 30 miles apart but getting ever closer, or the rivalry between Houston and Dallas, in a state which boasts "Friendship!" as a motto. The residents of Texas' two largest cities unashamedly claim precedence in almost every arena: the best opera company, the grandest party, the tallest building and even, of course, the number of resident billionaires.

Is this competitiveness a form of sibling rivalry? Or is it a function of history in a state where land has always been proudly defended? Probably a little bit of both. Today, Houston and Dallas are among the most culturally pampered cities in the United States. They are each home to world-class museums, art galleries and symphony orchestras.

As the man responsible for bringing the Japanese Kibuki Theater, the Kirov Ballet and pianist Evgeny Kissin to Texas, Toby Mattox has done more than most to establish the state as an artistic powerhouse. The Executive Director of Houston's Society for the Performing Arts, a leading not for profit arts facilitator, has raised almost $17 million to stage such performances. "There is a long tradition of giving something back in this part of the world," says Mattox. "If there is some sort of competition between Houston and Dallas, and frankly, I don't think there is anymore, then it has to be described as healthy."

Another beneficiary of local generosity is the Museum of Fine Arts Houston, which has just opened an extension designed by Rafael Moneo. The Spanish architect has been widely acclaimed for his work on Stockholm's Museum of Modern Art and the Miró Museum in Mallorca. His $83 million Audrey Jones Beck building effectively doubles the exhibition space, complementing a 1924 Beaux-Arts structure and a Mies van der Rohe masterpiece.

Texans' voracious appetite for culture is coupled with a slightly less noble obsession. Imposing skyscrapers harbor hordes of high-end arcades and malls. In Houston, a city which bears no scars from zoning, these sentinels of commerce provide a curious constant, fostering and fueling the famous passion for shopping. Smart visitors flock to the Galleria, a vast, high-end mall within the 610 Loop (the mythical heart of Houston affluence) which boasts impressive outlets for giants like Saks Fifth Avenue, Cartier and Tiffany. Developer Gerald Hines – who now lives in London – was inspired to build the Galleria when he saw Milan's Galleria Vittorio Emanuelle. Not to be outdone, Dallas has its own Galleria, as well as two miles of walkways, accessing 250 shops and restaurants, underneath the Financial Center. And for ultimate Texas sophistication, there is the excellent Neiman Marcus in Dallas and Houston considered by many to be the best department stores in the world.

Where, then, do Texans go to flaunt their baubles? A handful of exclusive private clubs keep the mortals at bay. Beware, however, of social pariahdom, an affliction which besets even the most ambitious arrivistes if they happen to join the wrong club. The resolutely old school Bayou Club, River Oaks Country Club and the Houston Country Club, in the chic enclave of Tanglewood (which boasts President George Bush among its members) are the most prestigious clubs in Houston. A host of young pretenders are snapping at their heels, but these three fortresses of style and substance remain impregnable. Country clubs are also a vital part of Dallas' social fabric. Highland Park luminaries like Trammell and Margaret Crow, and oil millionaire Edwin L Cox, are members of the Dallas Country Club.

Houston is a relentlessly social town, with a staggering array of balls, benefits and opening nights. Highlights in the calendar include the Best Dressed Luncheon, benefiting the March of Dimes, the Houston Grand Opera Ball and the Museum of Fine Arts Ball. Social stardom is taken very seriously in a city where Chanel is the uniform of many working women – even when the work is on someone else's checkbook.

The undisputed Queen of Houston society is Lynn Wyatt, whose easy charm and grand entertaining have seduced everyone from the Rolling Stones to Princess Margaret. Even the recent sale of her River Oaks mansion is unlikely to hurt her status. Syndicated columnist Liz Smith, who was born in Fort Worth, says of the socialite, "She is beautiful, rich, fun, easy going, accomplished and energetic. Lynn Wyatt has truly helped to put Houston on the map."

Chief among a new generation of Houston's social superstars are couples like John and Carroll Goodman, polo-playing jet setters, and Gregg and Elena Davis, whose mineral interests cast them firmly in the mold of Texan oil barons – except for the little matter of 20th Century Fox, which Gregg's father sold to Rupert Murdoch for $575 million. The best emblem of Houston's emergence from the 1980s, when oil prices tumbled, is a phoenix-like entrepreneur called Andy Beal, who borrowed $3 million at the age of 35, to launch a bank days after the savings-and-loan debacle, at the very moment when many venerable institutions were taking a nose dive. Beal now stands atop an empire with tentacles which stretch across the world.

Page 25: The incandescent Dallas skyline at night.
Page 26-27: Texas retail legend, Stanley Marcus.
Above: A gusher at Burkburnett, circa 1920.
Page 29: A typical day in Fort Worth.

Not to be outdone by all this success, Dallas has its own bright young things, and a host of lavish galas. Chief among them are the Dallas Museum Beaux-Arts Ball, the Cattle Baron's Ball, the Sweethearts Ball and the Crystal Charity Ball. Although it is a little less flashy than Houston (new money is always louder than old) Meatloaf's home-town is usually awash with glitter. At the time of writing, for instance, Dallasites were falling over themselves to spread the news: "Richard Gere's in town!" The matinée idol was filming Robert Altman's *Dr. T and the Women* alongside Liv Tyler, Helen Hunt, Shelley Long and Laura Dern.

Stars come and go, and Dallas affords them a great Texas welcome. However, it will always be remembered, tragically, as the city in which President Kennedy was slain. The Camelot era is saluted in a poignant exhibition on the sixth floor of the Texas School Book Depository on Dealey Plaza – the very spot where Lee Harvey Oswald fired the gun which killed the President. This sensitive record of a great man's life and his senseless murder is well worth seeing; the curators have wisely avoided the temptation to turn it into a gaudy shrine.

Philanthropist Ruth Altshuler, who today sits on the board of Southern Methodist University, was on the grand jury that indicted Jack Ruby. "It took a long time for the city to get over being blamed for John Kennedy's death," she says, "although Los Angeles never suffered from its connection to Bobby Kennedy's death. And no-one blamed Memphis for Martin Luther King's assassination. Dallas got a raw deal on that one."

With all this talk of Houston and Dallas, the casual reader from another planet may well imagine that Texas has nothing else to offer. This could not be further from the truth. For residents of Austin, for instance, the rivalry between Houston and Dallas-Fort Worth seems almost frivolous. As the state capital, this beguiling college town will always have more than a whiff of authority, and its reputation as one of the most liberal towns in the state looks secure in the wake of a recent $26 million donation to renovate Palmer Auditorium, creating a multi-venue center for the Performing Arts. The donation was made by Joe Lozano Long, a banker and lawyer who once saw Arturo Toscanini conduct the New York Philharmonic at the University of Texas. Together with his wife, Teresa, the Longs also gave over $6 million to their alma mater last year. It is a pattern which is repeated state-wide. Schools were the largest beneficiary of the $340 million donated by Texan philanthropists in 1999.

San Antonio is not without its own claims to greatness. This cultural crossroads has over 300 days of sunshine a year, and a tour of downtown reveals literally centuries of history, including the largest Mexican marketplace outside Mexico and the King William Historic District, an elegant residential enclave settled by prosperous German businessmen in the 19th century. The past and the future blend seamlessly here; the fastest growing city in the country is home to many innovative young firms in the booming high tech sector.

What, then, of Texans? The myth of television suggests they are larger (and louder) than life itself: oil-man JR Ewing in his big, brash Stetson, a bitter wife, her expensive face. These are caricatures, not people. Yes, the state boasts great wealth. 10% of the *Forbes 400* list of the richest Americans are Texans. And much of this wealth comes from oil. But in truth, Texans vary as much as this vast, disparate land itself.

Socialite Laura Hunt, whose daughter, Gannon, married Ted Turner's son, Beau, in one of the most talked about weddings in recent years, notes that "the greatest hostesses in the world come out of Texas because there's that southern hospitality mixed in with great creativity and exuberance." But she also knows that while many Texans are delightfully independent, some are merely insular. "I know people in Dallas," she says, "who never leave a three mile radius. They're born in Highland Park, they go to Southern Methodist University, get married, join Dallas Country Club and Brook Hollow. They never leave that space in their whole lives."

The inimitable Caroline Rose Hunt (no relation), who created the Mansion on Turtle Creek and designed London's Lanesborough Hotel, has a different perspective. A confirmed Anglophile,

Waving or drowning? By the time you read this, the 46th Governor of Texas will either be a gallant loser or President of the United States.

Hunt now runs a successful business offering Dallasites genuine reproductions of English antiques. "Texans have always been very well traveled," she says. "And nowadays, of course, there are so many Europeans here."

Witness, for instance, the ascent of Public Relations man Clive Watson, a suave Englishman who is carving a reputation as the unofficial doorkeeper to Houston society. "You can't choose the place you were born in," says Watson. "And I wasn't born in Texas. But I got here as soon as I could." Like many "imports" to the state, the Englishman cites a "can-do" attitude and genuine hospitality as reasons for staying.

While Europeans flock to the Lone Star state, Texans remain equally inveterate travelers. In certain circles a ranch in Wyoming and a home in the Hamptons are simply "essential," while socialites like Lynn Wyatt, who used to summer in the old Somerset Maugham house on the French Riviera, are leading the charge back to Europe. Nowadays a lavish retreat in Villefranche is the venue for many of Wyatt's soirées.

Generosity is an integral element of the Texas character. In 1982, when Laura Hunt founded the prestigious Sweetheart Ball to raise funds for heart research, she could count on the support of Dallas' high rollers. By the end of the decade, those same tycoons were in trouble: "When the economy collapsed in the latter half of the 1980s, first in Houston and then in Dallas, there were so many who were hurt and they didn't have anything." Hunt explains that "some of the men wouldn't even come to the party because they were embarrassed, but they would still write that check for charity. Now, to me, that says a lot."

Liz Smith puts the Texan mindset in a sound historical context when she explains that "this was a frontier state wrested from the Indians and the Mexicans by a lot of WASPs who had probably been ordered to get the hell out of Virginia and the Carolinas, or else. So a very rugged kind of brave and foolhardy individual immigrated to Texas and there is still that whiff of individualism."

Smith cites Texans like reporter Molly Ivins ("an important voice in an illiberal state") and Governor Ann Richards ("one of the finest females ever to enter politics") as perfect examples of "what a Texan might be in the 21st century." Finally, like many people who achieved success outside the state, Smith also champions Stanley Marcus, who turned "a soul-less city dedicated to insurance, banks, cotton and cattle into a bastion of art and culture in the middle of nowhere."

Texas ends with Stanley Marcus. After a light lunch, the veteran purveyor of luxury laments the victory of quantity over quality. For Marcus, the secret of a life well lived is clearly in the details: a white goose down pillow, a well-planned cruise, a glass of aged Madeira, a Charles Eames chair. But the man whose tireless pursuit of excellence opened the way for books like this is anything but a snob. Pragmatic, wise and delightfully irreverent, he turns his nose up only once. When a fresh-faced waiter presents the dessert list with a little too much ceremony, Marcus gently refuses it, asking instead for a fresh pink grapefruit. A few minutes later the waiter presents a modest ball of juice, flesh, sunshine. Marcus tucks in. At the table beside us a woman looks up from her crepes suzettes.

"It's hard to believe," says the man who brought Europe to America, "but outside Texas, you will not find a better grapefruit."

Lone Stars

By Michael Slimmer and Michelle Collotta

ASH Back in the 1960s, Mary Kay Ash was enjoying a successful career in sales. Then she retired. Four weeks and $5000 later she launched Mary Kay Cosmetics. With the aid of her 20-year-old son, Richard and a bit of good ole' Texas know-how, the company has become the largest direct seller of skin care products in the United States. This brilliant entrepreneur has provided millions of women with the opportunity to gain financial and personal success, selling make-up and skin care products in 29 markets worldwide. Her goal today, as always, is to help women and men everywhere achieve their full potential.

BASS When Sid Bass was given control of the family oil empire by his father in 1968, the eldest of the four Bass brothers was only 25 years old. Bass joined forces with brother Lee and fellow Texan Richard Rainwater to buy large stakes in Texaco, Disney and RJR Nabisco. The Harvard alumnus has also become a driving force in the on-line investment game, buying a 40% stake in the Houston on-line brokerage and software firm TradeCast. Sid, Lee and brothers Bob and Ed own more of Fort Worth than any sole person or group — 38-square-blocks in total. Their property line begins in the center of downtown, Sundance Square, and spreads out from there. Along with his second wife, Bass contributes quite a bit ot time and his $1.3 billion fortune to local charities and projects in Fort Worth. He recently donated $20 million to Yale University.

BUTT "One of the biggest pitfalls in business is under-estimating the competition," says Charles Butt, Chairman and CEO of HEB supermarkets. With over 265 stores HEB has become one of the largest private chains in the United States. The San Antonio based billionaire claims that Texas optimism helped him to create his fortune. Butt recently told *Texas Monthly* magazine that the Lone Star state is the sort of place "where people can start something small and watch it grow." With over 50,000 employees, Butt (who has an estimated net worth in excess of $1.2 billion) attributes his success to "finding the right folks" to become a part of his team. The much celebrated art collector and sailor stands behind the motto which hangs on his office wall: "Keep your eyes on things you can't see."

CRONKITE As a young student at the University of Texas at Austin, Walter Leland Cronkite, Jr. was bitten by the journalism bug while working for his college paper. Enjoying the life of a newshound so much, Cronkite dropped out of college in 1935 and took a full-time job at *The Houston Post*. 'Uncle Walty' joined CBS News in 1950, where he became co-creator and head-anchor for the *CBS Evening News* until his retirement in 1981. That trademark deep and gravelly voice provided the nation with a collected narration of historic events like the Vietnam War and the Apollo moon landing. In fact, it was Cronkite (emotions laid bare for all to see) who broke the dire news of President Kennedy's assassination to the vast majority of grieving Americans. The "most trusted man in America" recently told reporters that he visits Austin "as often as I can but not often enough." And that's the way it is.

CUBAN "The key to keeping wealth is never thinking you're smart. Many people think they're so smart that they know things other people don't. You have to stay humble," Mark Cuban told journalists last year. The boyish 41 year old bachelor, who recently bought the Dallas Mavericks, is adored by both players and fans for his modest approach to the game and indeed, life. Cuban made his fortune when Broadcast.com, the company he co-founded, was bought by Yahoo! for $5.7 billion.

DEDMAN In his entertaining memoir, *King of Clubs*, philanthropist Robert Dedman concludes: "I've lived an extraordinary life for an ordinary guy." That is no mere boast. At the age of 18, he decided to make $50 million and begin giving away $1 million a year by the age of 50. Five years later he was a partner in a major Dallas law firm. At 31 he founded ClubCorp International and quit practicing law seven years later. Dedman built his first country club (north of Dallas) in 1957 and now owns more than 230 golf and resort properties in thirteen countries – including Pinehurst, the venue for the 1999 U.S Open. Dedman chose education as the primary beneficiary of his philanthropy, which includes a $56 million endowment for Southern Methodist University and funds for 800 merit scholars at the University of Texas at Austin. After donating $1 million to UNT, the self-made billionaire told reporters: "The more I give, the more I have left." The 74 year old is worth $1.2 billion.

HARRELSON

Woody Harrelson plunged into the country's consciousness in the role of simpleton bartender Woody on the television sitcom *Cheers*, where he won an Emmy for best supporting actor. Work in films like *Natural Born Killers* and *Indecent Proposal* helped to shed his nice guy image, but it was in the controversial *The People vs. Larry Flynt* that he was finally taken seriously. Harrelson's portrayal of "filth king" Flynt led to a much deserved Oscar nomination. Today, along with his many film projects, Harrelson is an active environmental activist and promotes the use of industrial hemp in the manufacturing of clothing and paper. Harrelson married his longtime sweetheart Laura Louie in 1992. They have two daughters.

DELL At the tender age of 34, Michael Dell just happens to be the richest man in Texas. With wife Susan and their four children, the Dells live on what has been called "the campus," a 'home' more than twice the size of any other in Austin. The 33,000 square foot house was designed by the modernist firm of Gwathmey Siegel Dell's parents, a doctor and stockbroker, moved the family from New York to Texas when Dell was a young boy. In high school the budding entrepreneur famously bought himself a BMW with the money he made selling subscriptions to *The Houston Chronicle*. Today, the 15 year old Dell Computer company has annual sales in excess of $18 billion, with over 24,000 employees.

GOODMAN The polo playing tycoon, John Goodman and his wife, Carroll – daughter of Isla and Tommy Recking – are popular figures in Houston, where they throw lavish parties in an impressive River oaks mansion. In the summer of 1998, Goodman brought his polo team to England to represent the US in the Westchester Cup Competition. Goodman's team, the Isla Carroll, beat others from all over the world to capture the trophy, which was presented by Queen Elizabeth II. The Chairman of Goodman Manufacturing, America's largest privately held maker of air conditioning, heating and home appliances, also publishes *Cowboys and Indians*, a celebration of the west..

ELLERBEE Texan Linda Ellerbee is a correspondent, news anchor, producer, director, author, public advocate, motivational speaker, wife and mother. Early in her career, this forthright broadcaster worked as a writer for *The Associated Press*, before securing a coveted spot as co-anchor of *NBC News Overnight*. But shortly after the publication of her critically praised tome, *And So It Goes – Adventures in Television*, NBC fired the bespeckled anchor, claiming 'artistic differences.' Ellerbee fought back, accusing the network of letting her go because she didn't fit the 'image' of the blonde, blue-eyed, talking-head. "We call them twinkies. You've seen them on television acting the news, modeling and fracturing the news while you wonder whether they've read the news or if they've blown dried their brains, too." In 1987, Ellerbee started Lucky Duck Productions with companion Rolfe Tessem, producing programs for the cable network Nickelodeon. When everything was really starting to come together again – two Emmys, three Peabody Awards – Ellerbee was informed by doctors that she had breast cancer. Typically, she chose an aggressive and experimental attack and in true Ellerbee fashion, she won.

HINES Gerald D. Hines founded his namesake company in 1957. It has today become one of the most successful real estate firms in the world. Former Chairman of the Federal Reserve Bank of Dallas, this modest Houstonian (who describes his family as his greatest achievement) is credited with setting new industry standards for quality in real estate and management. His portfolio includes more than 500 properties, valued in excess of $9 billion. He has covered 125 million square feet worldwide and specializes in site selection, rezoning, design, construction bidding and purchasing. While Hines' home office is located in Austin, the company also holds sister offices in Aspen, Atlanta, Chicago, Mexico, New York and San Francisco. These days his son, Jeff, runs the day to day operations of the company.

HUNT "If you're in the hospitality business, you have to love being a host," says Caroline Rose Hunt, quintessential Texan lady. "Over 20 years ago, my children and I decided to prevent an old Dallas mansion from being torn down. We saw great possibilities in making this building something very special." Today it is a world-class hotel and restaurant called The Mansion on Turtle Creek. Thus began the story of Rosewood, a luxury hotel collection that boasts the extraordinary Mrs. Hunt as its Honorary Chairman. She also co-owns a Dallas-based retailer of extravagant antiques and gift items.

JONES Tommy Lee Jones, an eighth generation Texan, fell in love with acting as a student at the prestigious Dallas prep school, St. Mark's. Described by school officials as "sullen, morose and belligerent," he broke out of his shell while performing in a student production of *The Caine Mutiny Court Martial*. A football scholarship led him to Harvard, where he shared a dormitory with Al Gore. Although Jones dreamed of playing for his home team, the Dallas Cowboys, hopes were dashed due to his slight, lanky build. He moved to New York after graduation and won a role on Broadway just ten days after arriving. Jones brought home an Academy Award for his work on the 1993 film *The Fugitive*. Jones often returns to his roots, a 4000 acre ranch in San Saba, Texas, the town of his birth.

LAY Kenneth Lay is the founder and CEO of Enron, North America's largest buyer and seller of natural gas. Lay has also expanded Enron into a water company by buying companies in the U.K., Mexico and Argentina. A true corporate chieftain, he originally worked as an economist at Exxon, then joined the Navy and from there worked at the Pentagon. Lay later held positions at the Federal Energy Regulatory Commission and the Department of the Interior while teaching economics at George Washington University. Currently worth some $70 million, Kenneth Lay lives in Houston.

MANDRELL While on a trip one night, to The Grand Ole Opry, young Barbara Mandrell whispered in her father's ear: "Daddy, I wasn't meant to be in the audience." Raised in a family of musical enthusiasts, her mother, Mary, was a music teacher and before Mandrell could speak she was reading music and playing the accordion. Launched into superstardom when she was asked to sing on a concert tour featuring country legends Johnny Cash and Patsy Cline, Mandrell recently put singing on the back burner to pursue acting.

FOREMAN In 1994, two months shy of his 46th birthday, George Foreman knocked out Thomas Moorer, becoming the oldest man to win the heavyweight title in boxing – and recapturing the belt he lost to Muhammad Ali, 20 years earlier. It was the comeback story of all time from one of boxing's most colorful characters. Born in Marshall, Texas, Foreman first won the title at the age of 24, taking out Joe Frazier after only two rounds. A year later, it was off to Zaire for the the legendary 'Rumble in the Jungle.' "All I had was overconfidence and I paid big time," Foreman said after the painful loss to Ali. The fighter with a heart of gold now spends his time at the youth center and church he founded. To relax, Foreman and his family like to hang out on their Texas ranch, playing with their pet lions and tigers.

McLANE

The best type of leader, according to Drayton McLane, is someone who encourages people, gives them hope, and tells them there's always tomorrow. McLane is Chairman of the Houston Astros – which he bought for $115 million – and the McLane Group, the grocery distribution company originally founded by his grandfather. In 1990, McLane's company merged with Wal-Mart, the firm owned by his lifelong friend Sam Walton, for cash and $5.6 million in shares. Along with his wife Elizabeth, the affable philanthropist is a member of the First Baptist Church of Temple, where he teaches Sunday school, serves as a Deacon and is a past Chairman of the Board. Drayton McLane lives in Cameron with his wife. He is worth upwards of $1.1 billion.

McMURTRY

The novels of Larry McMurtry have redefined the myths with which the west is associated. From his first novel, *Horseman Pass By*, a glimpse into the world of a modern day cowboy, to the mother/daughter saga of *Terms of Endearment*, McMurtry's poignant character depictions have garnered him awards from the Pulitzer (*Lonesome Dove*) to the Oscar (*The Last Picture Show*). Born in Wichita Falls, McMurtry received his BA from North Texas State College and his Masters from Rice University. Nearly 40 years after the publication of his first book McMurtry is continuing to shine. His latest work, *Duane's Depressed*, focuses on the characters who populated *Picture Show* and *Texasville*. Besides teaching gigs at American University, Texas Christian University and his alma mater, Rice, the man from "the falls" also owns bookstores in both Washington and Dallas.

McNAIR

Bob McNair's Cogen Technologies is the largest privately held power company in the nation. McNair is bringing an NFL team to Houston and has offered to aid in financing stadium construction. He has also owned several world-class racehorses, including Touch Gold, which won the Belmont Stakes in 1997. McNair's advice on how to become a millionaire is "Take risks, stay liquid, and create value, not wealth." Bob McNair is worth $1.1 billion. McNair and his wife Janice live in Houston.

Photo: George Lange

JAMAIL

Joe Jamail's lucrative career as an attorney began in the Texas District Attorney's office. The longhorn litigator went on to specialize in personal injury law, where a fortune in the billions was made (in a suit against oil giant Texaco, he received an estimated $345 million.) Jamail's 'small firm' usually rings up $100 million a year in settlements. The self-made billionaire invests in stocks and municipal bonds and prides himself on his ability to "understand people." A graduate of the University of Texas, Jamail annually donates vast sums to his alma mater, although he continues to hunger for the big-money cases. The 74 year old has said "It's hard to quit. There's still some loose money out there."

NELSON

Long-haired rocker and eulogist for the heart, Willie Nelson has spent his life weaving lyrics and music, creating a country blanket as wide as Texas itself. Born in Abbot in 1933, he began playing guitar when he was six and writing heartbreak songs at seven. He made Patsy Cline a star when he wrote her smash hit 'Crazy' and put Billy Walker on the hit-single map with 'Funny How Time Slips Away.' Since then, Nelson has produced literally hundreds of hits. An enduring success, Willie Nelson remains one of the finest singer/songwriters in the world.

PEROT

Ross Perot has lived in and served Texas for all of his life. In 1962, his wife Margot loaned him $1000 to start a one man data processing company. Today, Electronic Data Systems is a multibillion dollar corporation employing more than 70,000 people. The one-time Presidential candidate has actively fought to improve the quality of life in his home state – leading, for instance, the War on Drugs committee, which made Texas the least desirable state to be caught for illegal drug operations in the US. To date, this tiny titan has donated over $100 million to various worthy causes.

RAINWATER

Financier Richard Rainwater grew up in a Lebanese community in Fort Worth and attended Stanford University with Sid Bass, heir to the Bass Oil Fortune. After graduation, he went to work for the Bass family as a financial advisor, famously helping to turn $15 million into a $5 billion fortune by investing heavily in companies like RJR Nabisco, Texaco and Walt Disney. Rainwater's relationship with George W. Bush has been the subject of considerable scrutiny for some time. Indeed, it could be argued that Bush would never have gone into politics if he hadn't met Rainwater, who orchestrated the Texas Rangers stadium deal which netted Bush more than $15 million. One of the most powerful corporate dealmakers in the country, Richard Rainwater's net worth exceeds $1.1 billion.

SAROFIM
One of the most highly respected financial minds in the world, Fayez Sarofim specializes in investing in household name companies like Coca-Cola and Procter & Gamble. Born in Egypt, 'The Sphinx' relocated with his family to the United States as a child and received his MBA at Harvard Business School. In 1958, Sarofim began his own investment and money management firm with a $100,000 inheritance from his father. In 1982, he founded Sarofim Realtor Advisors with major investments in General Motors, Stanford University and E.I. du Pont de Nemours – crediting Sarofim with well over $50 billion. In 1998, *Barrons* crowned him "Brand Champion" for his tried-and-true methodology of investing in blue chip companies. Although he famously avoids publicity, Fayez Sarofim remains a popular figure on the Houston social circuit.

LOVETT
Born in Klein, a small town named after his great-grandfather, singer/songwriter Lyle Lovett was raised on the family ranch, where his audiences consisted mainly of horses. Later he played at local folk festivals and clubs during his college days at Texas A&M University. After years of playing the circuit, Lovett was launched into stardom in the early 1980s when he appeared in a made for television movie. After hearing Lovett sing, Nanci Griffith recorded his song "If I Were the Woman You Wanted" and invited him to sing on her album. True superstardom came through his surprise marriage to actress Julia Roberts. Although the relationship ended, Lovett continues to shine. He has crossed over from country crooner to big band belter, with an almost cult-like following of fans and critics (among them directors like Robert Altman, who has cast the unlikely actor in his films).

McCONAUGHEY
Uvalde native Matthew McConaughey and those Lone Star size dimples are more than enough to get you noticed in Hollywood – add a bunch of talent and an eye for a good script and you have something approaching a perfect formula. After studying film at the University of Texas at Austin, McConaughey landed a role as attorney Jack Brigance in *A Time To Kill*. McConaughey's performance brought him to the attention of Steven Spielberg, who cast him in *Amistad*. A man of great stamina and a strong affinity for the ridiculous, Matthew McConaughey has been described by friend Sandra Bullock as "The Mayor of Good Times."

SIDHU

Sanjiv Sidhu partly attributes his success to the location of Texas in the United States. Last year he told reporters that it is easier to do business in Texas "because you can do business on the East Coast, the West Coast and in between. If you're based in New York, it's tougher to do business with California and Japan." Sidhu founded i2 Technologies in his apartment little more than a decade ago. His mission was to bring human intelligence to the web. i2 is now one of the leading supply chain management companies in the world. Headquartered in Irving, Texas, Sidhu has approximately 2200 employees and maintains offices around the world. His blue-chip client list includes 3M, Dell Computer, Motorola and Texas Instruments. The 42 year old is estimated to be worth more than $1.1 billion.

WYLY

Sam Wyly has amassed an estimated $1 billion fortune in a diverse array of ventures, ranging from Steak Houses to arts-and-crafts stores. An emphatic environmentalist, his latest venture is GreenMountain.com, a website dedicated to selling alternative energy sources like wind and solar power. The company has successfully lobbied lawmakers in California, Texas and New Jersey to deregulate energy markets by requiring that three percent of the states' electricity pool come from nontraditional sources. Wyly's Maverick Capital, which was founded in 1990 with his son, Evan, manages more than $4 billion in assets from 700 institutions, including university funds. The 65-year-old Dallas investor is the founder of "Republicans for Clean Air" and, along with his brother Charles, was a major supporter of George W. Bush's presidential campaign.

RATHER

Dan Rather got into the 'headline' business hawking newspapers as a kid. That was a long time ago. The anchor of the *CBS Evening News* and host of the magazine format *48 Hours* is, at the age of 69, at the top of his game. A native of the Houston suburb, Heights Annex, Rather began his illustrious career working at the Huntsville branch of *The Associated Press* before signing with CBS in 1961. Three years after beginning his tenure at 'Black Rock,' the young Rather was appointed as the network's White House correspondent. Future stints as a reporter for CBS and as co-editor of the renowned *60 Minutes* led to Rather taking over the coveted chair held for so long by his colleague and fellow Texan, Walter Cronkite. Big shoes to fill, but Rather made the *Evening News* his own.

McCOMBS

Billie Joe McCombs has attributed his success to a paper route that he had when he was ten years old. "I had to throw the paper to the customer, I had to create new customers and I had to collect each week. It made an impression on what I've done with the rest of my life." An auto mechanic's son, McCombs dropped out of law school to sell Fords on commission. He later founded Clear Channel Communications, a global leader in the advertising industry with television and radio stations in 32 countries. Clear Channel operates 830 radio and 19 television stations and has interests in 240 international radio stations. McCombs, who also owns the Minnesota Vikings, lives in San Antonio with his wife and three children. His estimated worth is $2.1 billion. Ⓐ

When Luxury is a Necessity.

Exquisite fabrics, accessories and clothing.

New York - 821 Madison Avenue, tel. 212 980-7961 Aspen - 316 South Galena Street, tel 970 544-0502
Milano, Venezia, Firenze, Roma, Udine, Malpensa
Capri, Ischia, Porto Cervo, Santa Margherita, Forte Dei Marmi
also available at Nieman Marcus, Bergdorf Goodman, Wilkes Bashford,
Mario's, Mitchell's, Halls and other fine specialty stores.

PAR EXCELLENCE

By Curt Sampson

*Single malt scotch, naked men and Cadillac golf carts - just some of the
treats awaiting those lucky enough to play a round on America's most
exclusive golf courses. Curt Sampson reveals all.*

Golf came to America in the Gilded Age, a period marked by relentless capitalism, vulgar taste and ostentatious displays of wealth. Early American golfers built huge buildings to shelter the bar, the lockers, and the dining room, and that made golf a rich man's sport, quite the opposite of the game's humble roots. Although the game became much more democratic by mid-century, lots of delicious decadence survives.

When an English golfing society visited friends here a few years ago, I always made a point to trail behind them as we entered another clubhouse. Mouths always dropped open as we entered the building, as if their owners had had a sudden attack of adenoids. The high-ceilinged, chandeliered opulence, so unlike the more modest structures back home, dazzled and disoriented them. So did the weather.

After a few days in the Texas heat, and following many assurances that such informality would give no offense, about half of the twelve-man Searchers Golfing Society started wearing shorts. But none of them looked comfortable. Their dark socks and blinding white legs gave them the look of men startled from bed by a fire alarm. They were strangers in a strange land. We played the best courses, often for free, because we Americans like the sound of an English, Irish or Scottish accent around our clubs; perhaps it links us to a royal and ancient tradition we've never had but still vaguely miss.

After a competition against a home team, the 24 new friends would eat, drink and tell stories. "You can't believe the day I had at Gleneagles yesterday," said Mike Vaughn, an accountant from Birmingham. He referred to the Gleneagles in Plano, Texas, not the one in central Scotland. "My opponent's a bloke named Win Holmes. He's 72 and he's just had a triple by-pass operation. Nicest guy in the world. Before we start, he takes me in the pro shop and buys me six balls and a hat. Then he says 'I've got you dicked.' Then he beats me like a drum. 'Don't feel bad,' he says. 'I've beat plenty of people in my time.' All of this would be very rude in England. But I took no offense. It's just America - or Texas, rather."

The Searchers gaped at Colonial, where a local lad named Ben Hogan allowed the display of his trophies and medals in two glass cases on the second floor of the mammoth white clubhouse. They gasped at the perfection of the architecture at Brook Hollow and at stories of Byron Nelson's feats when he played there regularly 30 years ago. But Preston Trail could not be topped. At "The Trail," as insiders know it, bowls of cashews, not mere peanuts, grace the tabletops in the bar and locker room. Professional golfers and local residents Lee Trevino, Lanny Wadkins, David Graham and David Frost are members and use the club frequently. And when the Searchers concluded their friendly competition with

Page 39: *Deadly Sandtraps at Pebble Beach Golf Links, CA.*
Above: *Jack Nicklaus tees off at Spy Glass Hill, CA.*
Page 43: *The National Pro-Am Competition - Pebble Beach.*

Preston Trail, and the setting sun streaked the sky in pink, three waiters paraded solemnly into the dining room carrying trays of glasses. In each of the glasses sloshed a dram-and-a-half of golden brown single malt Scotch whisky, out of the bottle for the first time in fifteen years. As Mr. Woody Thames of the host club concluded a toast to the fellowship the great game allows, and then we drank, a piper in full Highland dress entered, droning a martial tune. He marched slowly around the big room and all of us, red-faced and exhilarated, marched along behind him.

A misspent young adulthood as a sullen and unsuccessful golf professional afforded me many hours at various private golf courses in the United States. Long did I ponder the society and style at the clubs where I was a mere guest, or a merer employee. Who were these people, how did they get in, and how could they afford the lavish expenditure of time and money? In a happier decade as a writer, the ruminations continued to boil. A publisher's curiosity about Augusta National Golf Club matched my own, and I was commissioned to write a book about the place.

During a year's research for *The Masters: Golf, Money, and Power* in Augusta, Georgia I learned that the simplest path to the tiny, secret society is to be a physician living in Augusta. There are perhaps six members with such a profile. The pioneer was the local medical doctor who, many years ago, treated Augusta National's co-founder and chairman Clifford Roberts' prostate problem with such apparent skill that he received a letter inviting him to join, and join he did. To qualify for the national part of the Augusta National membership is more daunting. You must be wealthy, you must have been a guest before so that the incumbents can evaluate your personal style, and you must consider yourself and be considered a guardian of the traditions of the game. The latter attribute is important because Augusta National, founded by an uncompromising aristocrat named Bobby Jones and run by the unyielding autocrat Roberts, hosts one of golf's four major championships every year. Both Jones and Roberts are dead now, of course, but their ideals may live forever at the club they created. The members I met explained - off the record, of course - the joy and the terrible burden of belonging to Bobby Jones's home course. The joy part is obvious. The course is a masterpiece, the dues are modest, the prestige is incalculable and the history of the home of the Masters is intoxicating. But the poor member inevitably becomes an object of desire, like the only man in the pub with money for another round. Upon his elevation to the tiny society, dimly known and seldom seen relatives and friends - and their relatives and friends, and their former fraternity brothers - suddenly make ingratiating and suspicious contact. "So how are you, Billy?" they ask. "Playin' any golf?"

Articulating the desire to play or to join, I learned, is the biggest gaffe you can make. One does not apply to Augusta National; one is selected from the almost limitless supply of those who would cherish a locker and the club's uniform, a green sports jacket. But no one told Bill Gates about the importance of discretion. In 1998, the computer billionaire spoke too publicly about his heart's desire, *The Wall Street Journal* splashed a story about his wish on its front page, and now America's richest man may never be a member of Augusta National. While I wanted just one round on the course so badly it embarrassed me, I kept my mouth shut and didn't repeat Mr. Gates' mistake. Silence and luck succeeded. The invitation finally came, through the father-in-law of a friend of a friend. "Slow down please," I begged my benefactor as we glided down Magnolia Lane toward the clubhouse. Ripples of weak November sunlight and shade played on the long hood of his dark blue Cadillac. My book would not be printed for another three months, and I knew they weren't going to like it at Augusta National; I'd never get to do this again.

It was a revelation. On a cold and soggy autumn day, the course played monstrously long from the back tees: two drivers got me on the first green, a par four that the pros play with a drive and an eight iron in April. Despite recent rain, the greens putted as fast and true as snooker tables—snooker tables with voluptuous hills and hollows, like Pamela Anderson in a green dress. My promising round ran aground at the 14th, which I knew from my research to be the site of dozens of Masters disasters, and having the most difficult green on the course. Simply because I feared I would, I four-putted from twenty feet. I shot 83, if you must know. Trying to look casual as I pocketed a few books of matches in the clubhouse afterward, I circumnavigated the dining room and looked at the walls. Jones' clubs hung in a case on a wall. A series of remember-when photos brought a thoughtful smile: Sam Snead with hair, Arnold Palmer with a cigarette and a variety of Augusta National holes in the days when the pine trees were merely saplingss and not the looming giants they are today.

Like the golf course itself, the club building exuded museum quality dignity and presence. The bill for the day - nine holes at the par-three course, 18 more at the "big course," a caddie, two Diet Cokes and a package of crackers – came to $228, payable a few weeks later to my host. Even with the $20 tip my caddie literally begged for during the final three holes, the tariff for the day seemed entirely reasonable. As they say at Augusta National, it's not about the money.

A silver-sided motor coach disgorged 40 golfers on the driveway in front of the Pebble Beach Golf Links. Like a formation of geese, the golfers glided into the beautifully appointed professional's shop to purchase been there-played that golf shirts and to pay $400 each in green fees. While its sublime golf course has aptly been compared to the Sistine Chapel, Pebble Beach prints too much money, too publicly, to achieve the aura of its neighbor, Cypress Point. No tour buses block the view at Alastair MacKenzie's masterpiece above the rock bound Pacific coast and the first tee seems always to be free. Five foursomes jammed Augusta National the day I played there; three groups went out in reasonable weather my morning at Cypress Point; and on the lucky day I played San Francisco Golf Club, which is next door to the Olympic Club and is just as good a golf course, I'll be damned if I saw another group all day. Solitude and the availability of caddies is the hallmark of a truly great American golf course, just as crowds and swarming golf carts define the lesser lights.

No one at all teed off during my two hours at Seminole. I visited that shrine to North Palm Beach society in 1993, while researching a chapter on clubhouses for the USGA's centennial book, *Golf, The Greatest Game*. Before and after my examination of Seminole's famous cathedral-like locker room, I observed to the golf professional that no one seemed to be playing golf that day, and that my clubs and spiked shoes were idle in the back seat of my rental car. His amused smile indicated they would remain unswung and unfilled as long as I remained on the grounds. But to be rejected at Seminole is no disgrace. For this is the club which discouraged the membership applications of two local lads, Jack Nicklaus and Greg Norman. Reportedly, their money is too new.

One of the myths about the private golf club in the United States is that the bankers and moguls therein discuss high finance between shots. There's actually very little of that. The game is too absorbing, even for them. Jokes like what the bartender said when a horse walked into his bar —"why the long face?"— are far more common than speculation on stock splits. But while the conversation is nothing special, there's always something a little different about the elite American golf club. Perhaps, like Merion, you have hosted US Opens and are quite happy to have all that behind you. Perhaps you have made a fetish of your exclusivity, like the New York club that would not invite a college football star named Cosmo Yacocozza to join. "We would never have a member whose name was so hard to spell," sniffed one of the gatekeepers. Some clubs are equally persnickety about appearance. When professional basketball coach George Karl appeared for his day of golf at Balturol wearing shorts, his shocked host shooed him right back into his car to change into long pants. Money and celebrity can bring an instant buzz, as at Trump International, a new club in Florida, which

Below Left to Right: PGA Champs David Graham,
Jack Nicklaus and Greg Norman.

charged a $300,000 initiation fee to each of its 250 members. "Yes, he plays here every weekend, Saturday and Sunday, when he's in town," says Bruce Zabriskie, the Director of Golf, speaking of the club's founder, flamboyant real estate tycoon Donald Trump. "He's pretty good. He breaks eighty sometimes. But Mr. Trump never practices; he likes to play."

No one attribute defines the cosseted, thick-carpeted private course in the United States. But sometimes the essence of a thing is in its extremes. And for that we must return to Preston Trail Golf Club in Dallas, Texas, a peculiarly American golf club. The Trail is for men only, and many or most of its members made their millions by guessing correctly where to drill. Oil men are wild and crazy. The golf course is exquisite; for 14 years, it hosted the Byron Nelson Classic on the PGA Tour. When big name entertainers, astronauts or politicians visit Dallas, they play at the Trail. There's a bit of tartan plaid on the locker room rug, but that's where the royal and ancient ends. They drive their carts on the greens. "Our rule on that was 'don't drive your cart within gimme distance,'" recalls Gene Shields, once the pro there. "It was just a very relaxed atmosphere, a place to let your hair down." There are no limits on the number of players per match, so groups of five to ten are not unusual. One Christmas Day, the only day of the year the club is closed, a member just back from drilling in Australia desired to play but found the place locked up. No problem, except that like most Texans, he wouldn't countenance carrying his clubs. So he propped his big golf bag on the back seat of his Cadillac with the clubheads sticking out the window, and that was his golf cart. No report that he drove on the greens that day.

As a men-only club, golfers might stroll about the clubhouse unencumbered by clothing. Once I was looking at shirts in the pro shop when I noticed a naked man examining putters. It was Mickey Mantle, who was to baseball what Bobby Charlton was to soccer. But the middle-aged man without a stitch was, in his way, not that underdressed. Fully outfitted for golf, The Mick wore only a pair of golf shoes - no socks - and a pair of shorts - no underpants. His tan lines confirmed it. A gregarious character, Mantle died of liver disease a few years ago. This may explain why someone challenged him to play nine holes in the nude one warm day at Preston Trail. He accepted the wager - won - and evened out his tan. While other American clubs and clubmen trace a straighter line to the traditions of the ancient game, Mickey Mantle's performance confirms that something happened to golf when we colonists got a hold of it. ◑

THE FEW PRECIOUS DROPS THAT MANAGED TO ESCAPE NAPOLÉON'S LIPS.

With L'Esprit de Courvoisier, you will share an experience that Napoléon Bonaparte savored almost 200 years ago. For within this most rare cognac, the House of Courvoisier has blended the finest vintages in history. Indeed, it includes Courvoisier's most precious cognac, dating back to 1802 and the golden age of empires. From the private stock of royalty to you, we proudly offer our most splendid treasure. To sip L'Esprit de Courvoisier is truly to relive history.

For more information or to reserve a bottle, please call 1-800-336-3783.

COURVOISIER.

EUROPE IN AMERICA

By Trevor White

Europe's top talent has always been attracted to the United States
to live and work in the world's most exciting economy.
We examine the influence of Europeans on life in America.

The Statue of Liberty was presented to the United States in the summer of 1885. This monumental gesture of friendship was designed by Frédéric-Auguste Bartholdi and paid for by the people of France. But when it arrived in America, no-one could find the money to hoist the statue into its present position on Liberty Island. The colossal edifice lay in sections on the streets of New York, where visitors paid 50 cents to climb a ladder up the 30-foot arm.

In an act of supreme ingratitude, many Americans questioned why Liberty's pedestal should cost as much as the statue itself. Congress rejected a bill to allocate funds for its construction. Finally, Joseph Pulitzer, owner of the *New York World*, appealed to the general public to raise funds. $100,000 was donated in five months. Five months, no doubt, in which some people wondered whether France had ever done anything for them.

The truth, of course, is that the French have given much to America. Without their assistance – arms, ships, money – the American Colonies may never have won independence from the British. And their "huddled masses" helped to build this country. In October 1886, when President Grover Cleveland finally dedicated the Statue of Liberty, 100,000 people who were born in France were living in America. Today the figure is closer to a million.

The new world has always beckoned Europeans. Dazzling, delighting and disturbing, America is Rome to Europe's Greece, a precocious child in search of counsel and the self-styled savior of the universe. It is More's Utopia, Thoreau's Walden Pond and Thompson's Las Vegas.

My own people, the Irish, were among the first immigrants to arrive in great numbers. Nearly four million came between 1820 and 1880. Armed with fast tongues and a well-worn fear of God, they built railroads, canals and skyscrapers. Some of them prospered quickly: many years before the Statue of Liberty arrived in the city, an Irish-American called Mrs. Richard Caton was the toast of New York Society. She had three daughters, who became the Duchess of Leeds, the Marchioness of Wellesley and the Baroness Stafford.

The Irish have not exactly gone away. Look for them on the streets of Los Angeles, running around like the cast and crew of an epic drama. Starring Liam Neeson and Gabriel Byrne, directed by Neil Jordan, with a soundtrack by U2. You can almost hear the schmaltzy narration by Frank McCourt: "Persecution, Famine and Michael Flatley. The Irish have endured them all. So for hundreds of years we've said sod all that and set sail for unknown futures."

When Mrs. Caton infiltrated the British aristocracy, she could hardly have imagined that Empire and all its dubious trappings would soon come crashing down. In America today, obscure European titles are all very well, but liberty lies in a lucrative I.P.O.

"When I first moved to New York in 1995," says the Hon. Toby Young, an English journalist, "I thought society hostesses would be falling over themselves to invite me to parties." Young has returned to London with a stern warning: "Aristocratic or not, Europeans have been rumbled. As far as most New Yorkers are concerned, you're just another freeloading parasite."

Toby Young's sentiments are echoed by Countess Vanessa von Bismarck, a German aristocrat who owns her own public relations company in New York. "Having a distinguished European name hasn't been much help to me. On the contrary, I find myself having to work twice as hard because people are so suspicious of the Germans."

This sort of candor is refreshing but many recent immigrants have a more optimistic, or doggedly naïve, tale to tell. Besides, Americans and Europeans have long had a warm regard for each other. One might even describe it as a mutual obsession: back in the nineteenth century, when Mrs. Caton was welcoming society to her Fifth Avenue mansion, Henry James heroines were scouring *les magasins de Paris* for the finest silk underwear. Today, a Yankees baseball cap – its subtext less than subtle: "you had to be there" – has as much cultural resonance in Europe as a Fendi baguette has in America.

Page 47: Clockwise from top left –
Tina Brown, *the British Editor of Talk Magazine. Spanish heart-throb* **Antonio Banderas**, **Donatella Versace**, *the Italian beau monde fashion designer, and* **Jean Georges Vongerichten**, *who brought haute cuisine to a hungry new audience.*
Page 48: Bemused Americans flock to inspect the Statue of Liberty on its arrival in the United States – June 1885.
Above: Ellis Island, where many European immigrants arrived in the United States.

Europe's influence on life in the United States is particularly evident on the country's great shopping streets - Rodeo Drive, Michigan Avenue, Union Square, Worth Avenue and Madison Avenue. These temples of retailing are home to a who's who of European purveyors of luxury. And the invasion shows no sign of abating. Companies like Giorgio Armani, Prada, Bulgari, Christian Dior and Versace are all expanding their U.S. operations.

In the last eighteen months, Hermés has opened new stores at the Bellagio in Las Vegas, in Atlanta and at South Coast Plaza in Costa Mesa. The 163-year-old French luxury house has just opened a 20,000 square foot flagship store on New York's Madison Avenue.

Even a punitive 21% import tariff on clothing has not deterred smaller outfits like Bottega Veneta and Helmut Lang from venturing into the American market at a time of unprecedented prosperity. "I think that Europe is here to stay," says Umberto Angeloni, the Chairman of Brioni, an Italian menswear firm beloved of corporate chieftains. "Americans are more conscious of quality than ever before. That's why so many of the old European fashion houses are expanding into the huge American market."

In some cases, European firms have bolstered American fashion by investing in local heroes. For instance, LVMH, the giant luxury goods conglomerate, recently bought a one-third stake in Michael Kors. In a comment which illustrates the benefit of such marriages, Kors predicted that the investment would take him from "American designer" to "global brand."

With the exception of Tiffany and a handful of other Elite 1000 members, few American firms are equipped to compete with ancient purveyors of luxury like Hermés and Louis Vuitton. As Pier Guerci, CEO of Loro Piana, puts it, "I don't see the horizon for luxury brands expanding overnight. The market will continue to be dominated by a limited group of players, devoted to serving the most demanding group of people who live on the planet."

Nicola Bulgari, Vice-Chairman of Bulgari, the Italian jeweler, supports Guerci's claim: "when it comes to producing a product that is practically a work of art, Europeans have the advantage of being able to dip into a cultural and historical patrimony that is unparalleled."

Nadja Swarovski, an elegant young ambassador for Swarovski, the Austrian crystal company, is more optimistic about the prospects for American luxury goods companies, although she emphasizes the significance of positioning: "Really creative marketing and advertising is essential. For example, Coach, which is more or less a mass marketed product, is perceived to be of a higher calibre than its competitors' products, due to its revamped marketing strategy. This increases people's willingness to pay a higher price for the product, which in turn allows Coach to create higher quality products."

Yves Saint Laurent has arguably had a greater influence on fashion than anyone working in the industry today. The French designer has long been drawn to America, both for business and inspiration. When he visited New York last year (to accept a lifetime achievement award from the Council of Fashion Designers of America) Saint Laurent admitted "When I design a collection, I have two places in mind – Paris and New York – because they are the two capitals of fashion." A few months later he appointed a new Creative Director: Tom Ford, the American who has already revitalized the ailing fortunes of Gucci. Like Rose Marie Bravo, the former CEO of Saks Fifth Avenue who is now at the helm of Burberry, Tom Ford represents a new wave of Americans, whose energy and creativity are transforming European fashion houses. At last, the traffic is beginning to flow two ways.

Above: Clockwise from top –
Rodeo Drive *offers shoppers a delightful taste of European style.*
Nicola Bulgari *and* **Nadja Swarovski** *consistently produce immaculate treasures for American consumers.*
Page 51: Clockwise from top left –
Big European retailers like **Louis Vuitton**, **Gianni Versace**,
Giorgio Armani *and* **Bulgari** *have a major presence in America, from New York's Madison Avenue to Rodeo Drive in Los Angeles.*

According to former European Union Commissioner Sir Leon Brittan, "politically, Europe and America share common instincts, values and interests. But above and beyond that, at the level of strategy, we are usually partners." I prefer the conclusion of writer Michael Mosettig, who merely suggests that the relationship is "characterized by increasing candor." One can almost see the diplomats, quietly murdering each other at lunch. Followed, of course, by afternoon tea. Bearhugs on the croquet lawn.

Writing in *Time* magazine recently, Charles Krauthammer put European respect for America in a totally different light, when he noted that the world is not multipolar but unipolar. According to Krauthammer, the reason why nobody emerges to challenge American hegemony is because America is largely benign: "It does not extract tribute. It does not seek military occupation. It is not interested in acquiring territory - indeed, it specializes in giving it up." Acknowledging the quibbles of people like the French Minister for

Culture who described Disneyland Paris as a cultural Chernobyl, Krauthammer goes on to predict that Europe may well emerge as America's greatest adversary. For the moment, however, that seems improbable – as unlikely, perhaps, as the end of the *ancien régime* must have seemed to Britons at the dawn of the twentieth century.

Today, millions of Europeans live and work in America. Some of them enjoy very public success. Look, for instance, at French chefs Daniel Boulud and Jean Georges Vongerichten, who are reinventing *haute cuisine* for a hungry new audience, or actors Arnold Schwarzenegger and Jean Claude Van Damme, who lend an exotic twist to American machismo. Of course, the vast majority of Europeans in America are busy doing things which rarely trouble the gossip columnists. They are waiting on tables, erecting buildings, saving lives, trading futures, selling condominiums and teaching yoga. They come from Norway and Portugal, Greece and Finland, Switzerland and Denmark, Sweden and the Czech Republic. And they live and work all over the United States.

– In Texas a property developer called Giorgio Borlenghi gives Donald Trump a run for his money. His burgeoning empire is born of a wish "to recreate something of the old world in downtown Houston." A skeptical banker once asked the proud Italian how long his family had been in business. Borlenghi was hurt, but did not hesitate: "Since the Quattrocento."

– In Los Angeles a Yorkshireman called Frank Bowling calls the shots at the Bel-Air Hotel. The Carlyle, its New York twin (which is also managed by a charismatic Brit, James Sherwin) is America's answer to Claridges. But this bastion of old Hollywood is better compared to Le Prieuré. Staying at the Bel-Air is like watching a daytime soap opera, starring ravenous blondes, toupéed billionaires and Europeans desperate for a glimpse of either. Frank Bowling produces this colorful show every day of the year.

– Diane von Furstenberg's mother spent much of the Second World War in a concentration camp. Born in Belgium of Russian heritage and educated in Britain, the designer of the wrap dress used exotic roots and good old fashioned chutzpah to win over royalty and rabble alike, in a life which reads like airport fiction. And her son, Alexandre, is married to a modern-day Miss Caton: Alexandra Miller, one of duty-free tycoon Robert Miller's three daughters. In a recent *Vanity Fair* profile, von Furstenberg said "The one thread I've always had – always, always, always – is that I've never wanted to compromise my freedom. Maybe that goes back to my mother being a prisoner of war."

— Thierry Despont has designed homes for many of America's more prominent titans, including Bill Gates and Calvin Klein. Born in Limoges, he graduated from the école des Beaux-Arts in Paris before studying urban planning at Harvard in the early 1970s. A consummate showman, Despont ignores quips that his buildings are vulgar anachronisms (a recent profile compared him to "a tutor for wealthy philistines"). As one of the most successful architects working in America today, Thierry Despont is too busy building lavish homes to care about his critics' carping.

What do these Europeans have in common? Initiative and intelligence. Were they destined for success, wherever they ended up in the 50 year aftermath of the bloodiest battle in history? That seems unlikely. Open access to capital is the lynch pin of America's hugely successful economy, while social freedoms promote a culture of personal industry. And opportunism is encouraged in a land which foreigners have always been quick to call their own.

However, as a recent arrival, I do suggest that Europeans also bring certain resources to the new world; that we are, if you will, here to help, with all the mischief and vagueness that word implies. The worst of us cling to old-world delusions about class — and those handsome Spanish keep stealing all your women — but I have to believe that Europeans have something (besides sex) to offer America. Consider, if you will, the automobile, the television, the jet aircraft and the computer. They weren't all created in Europe. But none were invented in America.

I temper this impudence with the concession that *right here right now* I have to adapt. I live on Manhattan, a global island. One of the more common words in my vocabulary is *dannabad*, thank you in Bengali, for Bangladeshi taxi drivers. A city like New York demands this self serving flexibility. Without it newcomers would perish.

At the beginning of the twentieth century, the Irish dramatist George Bernard Shaw argued that patriotism is "the conviction that a country is superior to all others, because you were born in it." Two world wars later, borders seem more irrelevant than ever, and patriotism is often dismissed as a dangerous clarion-call. Yet there is still a place for national pride, though I do not mean the triumphalist breast-beating which passes for patriotism in middle America. European immigrants know that one or two generations down the line, their kin will have lost most traces of native accent, language and lore. In respecting the traditions and customs of their homeland, while acknowledging that success requires an open mind, they make America a richer place.

There's a flip side to this, of course. Last Christmas I divested the local pharmacy of two dozen toothbrushes ($4.99 apiece) as Christmas presents for friends and family back home in Ireland. What better illustration, I reasoned, of American ingenuity and industry than a disposable electric toothbrush? Everyone loved them, except the begrudgers, who murmured "what a country!" To which I responded, with a proud grin: "I know. I live there." The veteran English journalist Harry Evans went a few steps further when he sat down to write *The American Century*, his brilliant history of life in the country from 1889 to the present. As he said in a recent interview, "I felt there was an impertinence in analysing the history of a country and criticizing aspects of it as a foreigner." So the lifelong Mancunian became an American citizen.

Like his book, Mr. Evans' new passport is an expression of respect and affection for a country in which men like John Kluge (German), George Soros (Hungarian) and Michel Fribourg (Belgian) needed neither titles nor friends in high places to make their billions. They relied instead on good ideas and access to capital.

Ambitious young men and women will follow in their footsteps. In fact, Europeans will always flock to this giant of commerce and culture. Intoxicated by that first glimpse of Liberty, they will cherish the freedom that she represents. And if, like me, they're Irish, they will quietly wonder how so many people from so many places can live in something approaching peace. Ⓐ

Page 52: Clockwise from top left —
Vogue Editor **Anna Wintour** *reigns supreme as the British queen of American fashion. With Angela's Ashes,* **Frank McCourt** *gave wild geese a glimpse of impoverished Ireland — and a generous dollop of melodrama. Thankfully, times have changed. Frenchman* **Patrick Demarchelier** *is one of the world's most celebrated fashion photographers. Finally,* **Anthony Hopkins** *may be the sexiest Welshman alive (after Tom Jones, of course).*
Above: **Isabella Rossellini***, the Italian actress and model who blends old world elegance with new world ambition.*

MIRACLES.

LA MER®

Neiman Marcus

AMERICA'S ELITE 1000

The best Luxury Goods, Shops and Services
in the United States of America.

AARON BASHA
Jewelry and Watches

To the world's most fashionable moms, from Melanie Griffith to Demi Moore to Hillary Rodham Clinton, the name Aaron Basha is synonymous with exquisitely enameled baby shoes. While Basha's "Mary Janes" are famous, this third-generation jeweler (who is a father of four) also boasts a significant and varied collection of sought-after treasures. His showcases are filled with European jewelry designs in 18-karat white and yellow gold. Whether set with dazzling diamonds, brilliant colored stones or overlaid with layers of vibrant French enamel, each piece has been hand-selected or custom-designed under the supervision of Aaron Basha himself.

680 Madison Avenue
New York, NY 10021
Tel: 212-935-1960
Fax: 212-759-8294

ABACUS
Restaurants

"I want everyone who experiences Abacus to feel as if they are a guest in my home," chef Kent Rathburn recently told reporters. Rathburn was chosen as one of seven American chefs to cook at the James Beard Foundation's 1995 fund-raising Gala and he often caters for Tim Mondavi, Managing Director of the Robert Mondavi winery, at his home. Whether you sit in the elegant bar, the art-filled dining room or the kitchen-centered chef's table, Rathburn's global eclectic cuisine (with an emphasis on the flavors of the Pacific Rim) is bound to please.

4511 McKinney Avenue
Dallas, TX 75205
Tel: 214-654-0402

ABC CARPET & HOME
Specialty Shops

ABC is a grand tour of continents and cultures on ten floors. Opened in the 19th century solely to sell carpets, the firm has since grown to become a collection center, offering everything from antiques to modern Chinese cabinets. ABC has reclaimed the ethos of a time when objects were lovingly made by hand. It isn't unusual for customers to leave with a Windsor chair, leather-bound Tibetan trunk and Moroccan tiled table all in the same day. Equally popular is the entire floor dedicated to bolts of every fabric imaginable: Kasmiri silks, brocades, velvets and chinoiserie.

888 Broadway
New York, NY 10003
Tel: 212-473-3000
Fax: 212-674-1150

L'ABSINTHE
Restaurants

Paris has Lipp, La Coupole, Bofinger, and Brasserie Flo: New York has L'Absinthe. Nestled in the Upper East Side of Manhattan, close to Christie's and Sotheby's, Chef Jean-Michel Bergougnoux's acclaimed restaurant continues to lead the brasserie revival trend. The Frenchman is determined to offer New Yorkers the most authentic Parisian brasserie experience in the city.

227 East 67th Street
New York, NY 10021
Tel: 212-794-4950
Fax: 212-794-1589

THE ACADEMY AWARDS
Events

Oscar can make or break a career, turn a box-office turkey into a soaring eagle, take an unknown ingénue and send her on the super highway to stardom. What about the night itself? You've seen it all before – like billions of people in 149 other countries. But the real fun starts after the winners and losers vacate the Dorothy Chandler Pavilion and move on to the post-Academy Awards parties. The *Vanity Fair* soirée, hosted by Graydon Carter, is the hottest ticket in town – usually better than the Governor's Ball. Then there's Elton John's benefit and the Miramax bash. This is where the real show *business* gets done.

8949 Wilshire Boulevard
Beverly Hills, CA 90211
Tel: 310-247-3000
Fax: 310-271-3395

ACQUAVELLA GALLERIES
Art Dealers

The exclusive worldwide agent for Lucien Freud since 1993, Acquavella is one of the leading art galleries in the world. Founded in 1921 by connoisseur Nicholas M. Acquavella, the gallery's original focus was on Old Master paintings, specializing in Italian Renaissance and Baroque works. Today, the extensive collection is almost exclusively made up of 19th and 20th century art, including impressionist, cubist and surrealist masterworks. Important exhibits of Monet, Redon, Léger, Picasso, Viola and Johns have helped the gallery rise to superstar status; Steve Wynn turned to Acquavella when he was looking to amass a collection to rival the great museums.
18 East 79th Street
New York, NY 10021
Tel: 212-734-6300   Fax: 212-794-9394

ADMIRAL LIMOUSINE SERVICE
Chauffeur Services

This 32 year-old firm serves a select corporate clientele with a fleet of 50 limousines. The only service recommended by the Four Seasons Hotel, Admiral drivers are multilingual, polished and knowledgeable. Before pick-up, they leaf through client files, greeting them with their favorite newspaper and, for instance, offering a herbal tea if a client prefers not to have caffeine. Renowned for going the distance, both literally and metaphorically, Admiral once drove a couple from Washington to Minnesota.
1243 First Street SE
Washington, DC 20013
Tel: 202-554-1000   Fax: 202-863-0775

AEGIS
Wealth Management

Thomas Layng Guerriero's innovative wealth management division offers expertise and investment advice for private clients and institutions. Aegis provides long-term strategies and asset management while seeking to achieve superior returns and minimize risks. This year, Aegis launched netbroker.com, a website that offers clients on-line assistance with portfolio confirmation, investment and insurance resources, financial planning and proprietary equity research. The firm's latest venture is the creation of a Biotech and Large Cap mutual fund.
230 Westcott, Suite 1
Houston, TX 77007
Tel: 713-863-7000   Fax: 713-863-7037

HOTEL ADOLPHUS
Hotels

The Adolphus holds virtually every architectural, interior design and hospitality award in the industry. A Dallas landmark for more than 80 years, it is a unique creation of fortune and flamboyance from an extravagant age. Beer baron Adolphus Busch spared no expense in erecting what generous critics have called "the most beautiful building west of Venice." In 1981, an $80 million renovation completely restored the building. This Noble House flagship, which is ably managed by John Dodson, now features 435 guest rooms, including 20 suites, with 31 different floor plans. The Lobby Living Room plays host to a million dollar art collection, which spills over to guests' rooms and suites. This American landmark has hosted Queen Elizabeth II, President Bill Clinton and Estée Lauder.
1321 Commerce Street
Dallas, TX 75202
Tel: 214-742-8200   Fax: 214-651-3588

ALEXANDRA LIND

Fashion   *Rising Star*

If Alexandra Lind hadn't become a designer, she would have committed herself to studying art history. Not surprising, since her *demi-couture*, ready-to-wear evening gowns are an aesthete's dream. The 28-year-old designer combines traditional and modern elements to create distinctive looks for only 100 private clients. Aside from personal consultation, Lind offers pieces from her collection at Henri Bendel, Bergdorf Goodman and on Fashion500.com.

240 West 35th Street, Suite 800A
New York, NY 10001
Tel: 212-594-0988   Fax: 212-594-0774

ALAN FLUSSER

Fashion

Inspired by icons like Fred Astaire and Gary Cooper, Alan Flusser is one of America's best upmarket menswear designers. Serving a diverse array of celebrities and CEOs since 1980, the firm has produced made to measure suits, bespoke suits, neckwear, hosiery, suspenders, shoes and handkerchiefs for well dressed luminaries like Bob Costas. When a client wanted something to wear for a dinner party that wasn't a tuxedo, suit or sport jacket, Flusser custom made a corduroy, cashmere and cotton smoking jacket with satin lapels. Flusser is the author of *Style and the Man*, the definitive record of the best menswear outlets in America.

Saks Fifth Avenue, 611 Fifth Avenue, 6th Floor
New York, NY 10022
Tel: 212-888-7100   Fax: 212-940-4849

AIDA THIBIANT
EUROPEAN DAY SPA

Spas and Clinics

For over 27 years Aida Thibiant's philosophy has remained the same: a calm spirit and the correct, consistent skin care régime will give you a healthy glow and maintain a youthful look. Time spent in this relaxed, yet sophisticated spa is an investment in the future of your beauty and well-being. To continue the pampering at home, don't leave without a bottle of the Thibiant Calming Tonique.

449 North Canon Drive
Beverly Hills, CA 90210
Tel: 310-278-7565   Fax: 818-709-9827

AKIN, GUMP, STRAUSS, HAUER & FELD

Law Firms

The 10th-largest law firm in the United States, with over 850 lawyers, Akin, Gump, Strauss, Hauer and Feld have been five of the most trusted names in America since 1945. The firm has a diversified practice and represents regional, national and international clients in a wide range of areas, including corporate, intellectual property, legislative, litigation, real estate and tax.

1333 New Hampshire Avenue, NW
Washington, DC 20036
Tel: 202-887-4000   Fax: 202-887-4288

ALGABAR

Specialty Shops

Showcasing the finest furniture, bath, bedding and decorative accessories, Gail Baral's store feels like a cross between a Parisian *atelier* and a Balinese boutique. The collection includes bamboo accessories for the home by Dutch designer Joanett van Whetten and modern, streamlined furniture in dark oak wood by Edouard Rambaud of Paris. Algabar is a key destination for interior designers, celebrities and discerning world shoppers.

920 North La Cienega Boulevard
Los Angeles, CA 90069
Tel: 310-360-3500   Fax: 310-360-3505

ALAIN DUCASSE

Restaurants   *Rising Star*

Every once in a while, the restaurant world gets its knickers in a twist over the arrival of some uber-chef to these shores. More often than not, the reality fails to live up to the hype. But with this newcomer, it seems safe to say that the brouhaha will be entirely justified. Arguably France's greatest chef, at one point Alain Ducasse owned and operated two Michelin three-star restaurants – a Herculean feat, as any foodie will confirm. Although it has yet to open at the time of writing, we predict that his miniscule (60 seat) restaurant will give fellow Europeans Jean Georges Vongerichten and Daniel Boulud a run for their money. What are you waiting for?

Central Park South
New York, NY 10019
Tel: 212-265-7300

ALBERT HAJE   *Best Kept Secret*

Architects and Interior Designers

As a young(er) man, Albert Haje traveled the world as a personal assistant to a Saudi Prince. On returning to New York he decided to become an interior decorator – and soon snagged a job revamping the Walter Chrysler Estate. Asked if he was surprised to land such a prestigious gig without formal experience, the charismatic New Yorker graciously explains "I've been lucky – very lucky." Since then, Haje has worked on many illustrious projects, including the restoration of *Overlook*, George Mason's first house, and the interiors of mansions for Mrs. Walter Annenberg, Mr. & Mrs. Arthur Altschul Sr. and a penthouse apartment for Prince Bandar bin Sultan.

201 East 69th Street, Suite 8-0
New York, NY 10021
Tel: 212-734-3472

THE ALBUQUERQUE MUSEUM
OF ART & HISTORY

Museums

An exquisite repository of Southwestern art, this venerable instaition proudly displays work by Georgia O'Keeffe, Bert Phillips and other renowned artists who were inspired by New Mexico's majesty. Plan your visit around their *Empire of the Sultans* exhibit (October 29, 2000 – January 2001) which will include gold leaf books, pottery, tiles, woven works and other Ottoman treasures hoarded by a private collector. End your visit by relaxing and reflecting in their charming sculpture garden.

2000 Mountain Road NW
Albuquerque, NM 87104
Tel: 505-243-7255   Fax: 505-764-6546

ALEXIS HOTEL
Hotels

In 1995, the Sultan of Brunei stayed in this quirky hotel, and enjoyed his stay so much that he wanted to buy it from Bill Kimpton – right there on the spot. Of course, the answer was a firm no, but the Sultan was invited to decorate one suite and one room to his liking. Located in the heart of Seattle, the hotel rooms are huge; light, airy decor complements an unusual collection of antiques. Stay in the John Lennon Suite, where the walls are lined with lithographs of lyric sheets by the man himself. Or, if you're a jazz lover, stay in the Miles Davis suite, which boasts Davis' own unique artwork. Attend evening wine tastings or enjoy chef Tim Kelly's delicious vegetable-based menu in the Painted Table Restaurant.

1007 First Avenue
Seattle, WA 98104
Tel: 206-624-4844   Fax: 206-621-9009

ALFRED BULLARD
Antiques

Alfred Bullard founded his namesake business in 1924 and handed it over to William Bertolet in 1964. A former art history post-graduate student, Bertolet has brought the firm an international reputation of knowledge and good taste. Located two blocks from Rittenhouse Square, the collection boasts 18th and 19th century English furniture and decorative arts. Representing the hard-to-find, the firm offers 18th century looking glasses, and George I walnut bureaus. The showroom is open by appointment only.

1604 Pine Street
Philadelphia, PA 19103
Tel: 215-735-1879   Fax: 215-735-4820

ALONG CAME MARY!
Party Organizers and Caterers

Mary Micucci began her party organizing firm in the mid-seventies, from the back of a Volkswagen Bug. Now known as the "Queen of Catering," Micucci dominates the Hollywood entertainment and movie premiere scene, throwing Barbra Streisand's wedding bash, as well as the spectacular after party for *Titanic*. A full-scale production company, the firm is staffed with master chefs, award-winning art directors, floral designers and a research department that works to ensure authentic reproductions for creations that necessitate historical accuracy, like a medieval garden party or a 19th century Southern plantation ball.

5265 West Pico Boulevard
Los Angeles, CA 90019
Tel: 323-931-9082   Fax: 323-936-8249

TINA ALSTER, M.D.
Cosmetic Surgeons

The Washington Institute of Dermatologic Laser Surgery was the first comprehensive laser surgery and skin care facility of its kind in North America. Dr. Tina Alster, President and Director, is a world renowned lecturer on cosmetic laser surgery and is also the author of numerous medical articles and textbooks, including *Cosmetic Laser Surgery*, *The Essential Guide to Cosmetic Laser Surgery* and *Manual of Cutaneous Laser Techniques*. She serves on several professional boards and is a consultant to skin care companies, having developed and patented a successful skin care line and other ancillary products. Dr. Alster and the Institute have been featured in dozens of articles, news reports and television and radio programs, explaining her superior techniques in various cosmetic procedures and dermatologic laser surgery. Highly recommended.

2311 M Street NW, Suite 200
Washington, DC 20037
Tel: 202-785-8855   Fax: 202-785-8858

ALPHA GALLERY
Art Dealers

Located on a gallery and restaurant-dense expanse of Newbury Street, Joanna Fink's exquisite contemporary art gallery represents the estate of Milton Avery and specializes in paintings, sculptures and works on paper by Modern Masters like Pablo Picasso.

14 Newbury Street
Boston, MA 02116
Tel: 617-536-4465   Fax: 617-536-5695

Antonio's Antiques

Fine Period Furniture

AMERICAN MUSEUM OF NATURAL HISTORY
Museums

For 125 years, the American Museum of Natural History has been one of the world's pre-eminent science and research institutions, illuminating millions of years of the earth's evolution. Occupying 23 buildings, the museum houses a huge collection of anthropological artifacts, ranging from a full-size dinosaur's skeleton to Cro-Magnon paintings. Permanent exhibits include Oceanic Birds, African Mammals, Eskimos and Meteorites. The Naturemax Theater is an IMAX theater with superior sound and an enormous screen.

79th Street & Central Park West
New York, NY 10024
Tel: 212-769-5000

AMARYLLIS, A FLOWER SHOP
Florists

This floral design studio, which is owned by Elena King, has a client roster that includes many of Washington DC's governmental, cultural and retail institutions, including the Supreme Court, the Corcoran Gallery and Chanel. Chief Designer Richard Davis will travel anywhere, town or country, to provide his breathtaking arrangements and decor for your special event or private function. Davis' eclectic work, ranging from classical to European, is a favorite among the Capitol's most discerning corporate and governmental event planners.

303 H Street, NW
Washington, DC 20001
Tel: 202-289-8535   Fax: 202-289-8537

AMANGANI
Hotels

Earlier this year, Amangani's deluxe suite was awarded "Best View in the World" by *Hideaway* magazine. With a heavenly panoramic view of the Grand Teton mountain range, the celebrated suite is as comfortable as it is breathtaking. With his and her sunken tubs, pacific redwood walls, Oklahoma sandstone accents and black slate bathrooms, one feels wonderfully close to nature here. General Manager Monty Brown customizes services for "Amanjunkies" – offering hiking tours, ski guides or game-viewing safaris. For a reservation during summer months, book your suite at least two months in advance.

1535 North East Butte Road
Jackson, WY 83001
Tel: 877-734-7333   Fax: 307-734-7332

AMERICAN ANTIQUES
Antiques

As a third generation folk art and antiques dealer, Austin Miller has been immersed in the business all his life. For a generation of baby-boomer collectors of American decorative arts and painted furniture, Miller is the man to go to for cigar store indians, pilot house eagles and ships' figureheads. While much of his business is conducted via catalogs and the internet, if you walked into his store, you might find a collection of folk art paintings or a very unusual 19th century American William Tell weather vane.

1631 Northwest Professional Plaza
Columbus, OH 43220
Tel: 614-451-7293
Fax: 614-459-2080

THE AMERICAN HOTEL
Hotels

It has been said that there are two types of guests who frequent the American Hotel: those who get it and those who don't. Those who do can live without fax hookups, complimentary cellphones and giant-screen televisions. Of the eight bedrooms, the best are room 15 (the largest) and "The Apartment", a two floor duplex with a fireplace and waterfront view. Summer week-end reservations are notoriously difficult to secure without four to six months notice. For those who can't get a room, owner Ted Conklin offers a cozy bar and widely acclaimed restaurant. Every wine producing country in the world is represented on the 80 page wine list.

Main Street
Sag Harbor, NY 11963
Tel: 631-725-3535
Fax: 631-725-3573

THE AMERICAN ORIENT EXPRESS
Travel Consultants

North America's premier luxury train preserves the relaxed, romantic feel of legendary trains from America's past on nine routes throughout the United States and Canada. Vintage cars from the '40s and '50s—the golden age of railroads—have been restored to their glistening, polished mahogany-and-brass best. The dining cars boast tables set with fine china, linens and silver, while the sleeper cars complete the historic picture in all their time-honored glory.

5100 Main Street, Suite 300
Downers Grove, IL 60515
Tel: 630-663-4550
Fax: 630-663-1595

AMERICAN SAFARI CRUISES
Powerboats & Yachts

American Safari specializes in intimate, active, deluxe cruises in Alaska and the Californian wine country on two mega-yachts: the 21-passenger, 120 foot *Safari Quest* and the 12-passenger, 105 foot *Safari Spirit*. Itineraries focus on close-up viewing of wildlife, fine dining, kayaking, fishing and exploration by Zodiac inflatables. In 1999, the firm completed major refitting and interior redesign, adding staterooms on both yachts, investing $1 million per vessel.

19101 36th Avenue West, Suite 201
Lynnwood, WA 98036
Tel: 888-862-8881   Fax: 425-776-8889

AMERICAN CLUB
Hotels

This venerable 236 bedroom resort offers guests everything from a top-notch spa to a full service French cooking school. Amenities include four different golf courses, two of which were used to house the 1998 US Women's Open and the 2000 PGA Championship Tour. Also offered are a hunting preserve, hunting and fishing club, trap shooting, and fly fishing on Lake Michigan.

Highland Drive
Kohler, WI 53044
Tel: 920-457-8000   Fax: 920-457-0299

ANDRA GABRIELLE
Fashion

Redefining the term handmade, Andra Gabrielle's designs include styles for day, evening and a lingerie collection. Her client list includes international celebrities, artists and models. Kristin Scott Thomas, Michelle Pfeiffer, Susan Sarandon and Annette Bening have all worn her limited edition garments, many adorned in antique beads and delicate silks. The beading is a hand technique: each bead is threaded, one at a time, in the Chelsea gallery.

305 West 21st Street
New York, NY 10011
Tel: 212-366-9624   Fax: 212-691-9565

ANDREA ROSEN GALLERY
Art Dealers

An unusually committed gallery owner, Andrea Rosen believes that in choosing to make art, the artist and dealer take on a responsibility to the public. Her dedication to nurturing artists is evident in a roster of emerging and established names, including Rita Ackermann, Miguel Calderon, and Harmony Korine. The gallery also represents the estate of Felix Gonzales-Torres, mounting occasional shows of the Cuban artist's complex work.

525 West 24th Street
New York, NY 10011
Tel: 212-627-6000   Fax: 212-627-5450

ANDREW DORNENBURG PRIVATE DINING
Party Organizers and Caterers

Formerly a chef at Boston's Biba and New York's Judson Grill, Andrew Dornenburg now provides catering for discriminating individuals. When a client mentioned that she loved the lobster served at a certain restaurant, Dornenburg went there to get it; on the occasion of a client's move to San Francisco, he whipped up a meal made of Bay area specialties.

527 Third Avenue
New York, NY 10016
Tel: 212-642-5870   Fax: 212-682-5868

ANDREW L. TERNER
Art Consultants   Best Kept Secret

At the forefront of contemporary art consultants, Andrew Terner's client list includes celebrated captains of industry, entertainers and entrepreneurs. An immensely charming figure, Turner has bought and sold 20th century masters like Picasso, Miró, Matisse and Warhol.

28 East 10th Street
New York, NY 10003
Tel: 212-505-8521   Fax: 212-979-9140

ANTHONY'S
Restaurants

Executive chef Russell Cody received a degree from Texas A&M University in Microbiology and then went on to culinary school at the impressive New England Culinary Institute in Vermont. For the past three years, Cody has been filling the walls of Anthony's with various awards and accolades. Entrees include whole hearth roasted duckling with Mahogany cracked skin, accompanied by Minnesota wild rice and fresh mango-apricot sauce. For dessert, the made-to-order soufflés are most popular. A separate bar area is a cozy favorite for an afternoon cocktail or a late-night dessert.

4007 Westheimer Street
Houston, TX 77027
Tel: 713-961-0552

ANDOVER SHOP
Fashion

Owner Charlie Davidson is a real old-fashioned character, brimming with wit, wisdom and genuine enthusiasm for the art of creating made-to-measure suits. Inspired by the dignity and grace of a bygone era – he cites Bobby Short as an exemplar of style – Davidson has spent the past 50 years producing classic styles and traditionally elegant suits for some of the most discerning men in the world. Described as "people who are in love with clothing," Andover's clients are a remarkably loyal bunch - many have been customers for over thirty years.

22 Holyoke Street
Cambridge, MA 02138
Tel: 617-876-4900   Fax: 617-876-3789

ANTONIO'S ANTIQUES

Antiques

Just north of Silicon Valley lies a sybarite's haven – a 40,000 square feet cache of 17th, 18th and 19th century furniture, tapestries, paintings and decorative accessories. Founded in 1960 by a young Antonio Mariani, who left his home in Taranto, Italy with but an inherited knowledge of antiques and an overwhelming ambition to create a great antiques business in America. Today, discerning visitors from around the world descend upon Antonio's huge Bryant Street warehouse and Sansome Street showroom (located in historic Jackson Square) for one of the largest selections of English, French and

Italian furniture in the country. 18th century northern Italian commodes, French armoires and Tuscan trestle tables are just some of the riches offered. In light of the new difficulties involved in exporting rare pieces from Europe, Antonio's Antiques offers a convenient, hassle-free way of bypassing all the red tape.

701 Bryant Street
San Francisco, CA 94107
Tel: 415-781-1737   Fax: 415-243-9227

ANTHONY A.P. STUEMPFIG

Antiques

Son of the famous American landscape painter, Walter Stuempfig Jr., Anthony Stuempfig has been in the antiques and fine arts business since 1963. By 1970, he began to specialize in early 19th century American classical and Empire furniture. He also handles high-end decorative arts from Europe as well as a small quantity of paintings, drawings, sculptures and watercolors. Clients include major museums and private collectors.

2213 St. James Street
Philadelphia, PA 19103
Tel: 215-561-7191

ANTINE ASSOCIATES

Architects and Interior Designers

Anthony Antine has developed a signature style as an interior designer for a discerning clientele. He trained as a couturier at New York's Fashion Institute of Technology. - dressing women like Barbra Streisand - but for the past 18 years, Antine has used luxurious fabrics and rich colors to design interiors for customers around the globe. Recent projects include a private residence for Robert Redford, an Adirondack-style house in the hills of Atami, Japan, and a beach house in Malibu.

750 Park Avenue
New York, NY 10021
Tel: 212-988-4096

L'ANTIQUAIRE & THE CONNOISSEUR

Antiques

From magnificent mosaics of the Ancient Roman and Byzantine Empires to Italian ceramic bowls, L'Antiquaire & The Connoisseur features an abundance of European curiosities. The firm specializes in Italian and French furniture from the 16th to 18th centuries but also carries decorative arts of Spanish and German origin. The Manhattan treasure trove is led by Helen Fioratti, a true connoisseur, who will gladly confirm a pieces' provenance. Fioratti's collection includes textiles, works on paper, paintings and sculpture.

36 East 73rd Street
New York, NY 10021
Tel: 212-517-9176   Fax: 212-988-5674

DARRICK E. ANTELL, MD

Cosmetic Surgeons

Saudi Arabian princesses, *Sports Illustrated* swimsuit models and individuals from across the globe have flocked to the private plastic surgery practice of Dr. Darrick E. Antell. Renowned for his studies on aging, Antell specializes in facelifts, facial rejuvenation, body contouring and breast augmentation. In fact, an Antell facelift has become a status symbol among his veritable "Who's Who" list of patients. The always discreet physician is a perfectionist with a keen eye for detail and aesthetics, earning him the role of spokesman for the American Society of Plastic Surgery and garnering him a regular position on the *Best Doctor* lists – as well as the invite lists of many of his society clients. Though the wait for an appointment can be lengthy, it's well worth it. When asked how long one of his facelifts lasts, Dr. Antell confidently replies: "forever." It doesn't get any better than this.

850 Park Avenue
New York, NY 10021
Tel: 212-988-4040   Fax: 212-988-0527

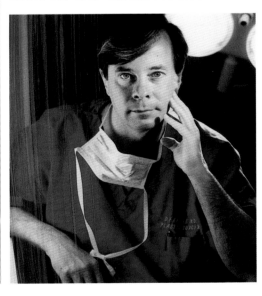

ANTONY TODD
Florists

Antony Todd knows how to create a scene. When the Queen of Jordan wanted to throw an intimate tea party, she called on Todd, who personally chose all the fabrics, linens, tabletop accessories and flowers. The self-taught designer is revered by the likes of Hugh Hefner, the New York City Opera and *Harper's Bazaar's* Kate Betts. After reading about Todd in a newspaper, a Connecticut couple commissioned the Australian to completely redesign their home. From understated floating gardenias to elaborate nuptial events, Antony Todd is a master of modern style.

307 Seventh Avenue
New York, NY 10001
Tel: 212-367-7363   Fax: 212-367-7359

ARAUJO
Winemakers

Winemaker Bart Araujo produces about 25,000 bottles of sublime Cabernet Sauvignon each year from the Eisele Vineyard. He and his co-owner/wife Daphne happily reward loyal mail order members but if you're on the waiting list (or the waiting list *for* the waiting list), you should probably think about hitting the auctions. Araujo's Cabernet has a predominant currant flavor with chocolate and cedar tones, though it promises a cigar-box aroma after time.

2155 Pickett Road
Calistoga, CA 94515
Tel: 707-942-6061
Fax: 707-942-6471

ARCHITECTURAL ACCENTS
Specialty Shops

Some of the best architects, builders and designers in America, as well as homeowners, have been flocking to this 30,000 square foot showroom in Buckhead since it first opened its doors in 1983. Owner and architectural designer, Charles Nevinson stocks the building with a world class 18th and 19th century collection of antique mantels, doors, columns, pilasters, chandeliers, stained glass, mirrors, plumbing fixtures, statuary, tiles, ironwork and hardware. All of these are then restored and refurbished for reinstallation into new or renovated buildings. In addition, Architectural Accents represents an impressive list of European lantern and hardware manufacturers, as well as carrying its own line of cast stone, carved wood and marble mantels.

2711 Piedmont Road
Atlanta, GA 30305
Tel: 404-266-8700   Fax: 404-266-0074

ARCHIVIA
Specialty Shops

Joan Gers and Cynthia Conigliaro offer a vast selection of books in the fields of architecture, the decorative arts, gardening and interior design. The award winning Madison Avenue space is organized into five major categories: European architecture and furniture, American architecture and furniture, Gardening, Interior Decorating, and Applied arts, including gold, silver, textiles, ceramics and modern design. Gers and Conigliaro have 25 years of expertise between them. Joan Gers was a partner at the legendary 999 Bookshop on Madison Avenue and Cynthia Conigliaro received her Masters Degree in Architecture from Columbia University in 1987.

944 Madison Avenue
New York, NY 10021
Tel: 212-439-9194

ARMFIELD, MILLER & RIPLEY
Property Consultants

An affiliate of Sotheby's, this Virginia-based company has managed many prestigious sales and boasts the expert guidance of realtors who have worked in the luxury-homes sector for more than 20 years. Consistently cited as the firm to trust in northern Virginia, they handled the sale of Senator John Warner's home and the estate of the late Pamela Harriman, the American Ambassador to France.

P.O. Box 1500
Middleburg, VA 20118
Tel: 540-687-6395   Fax: 540-687-5195

The Garden Court at the Asia Society

ART LUNA SALON
Hair and Beauty

In business for more than 20 years, Art Luna is acutely aware of events in the ever changing world of style and beauty, and he has set his own trend by refusing to follow the fickle winds of fashion. Art Luna has created a civilized and calm environment in which he and his stylists can attend to the color and cutting needs of their discerning clients. Many enjoy getting 'snipped' while relaxing in the peaceful garden. Just ask the likes of Anjelica Huston, Dermot Mulroney, Melanie Griffith, Don Johnson and Ellen DeGeneres, to name a few.

8930 Keith Avenue
West Hollywood, CA 90069
Tel: 310 247-1383   Fax: 310-247-8672

ARTESIA
Restaurants

When he's not hunting, fishing or playing with his children, Executive Chef John Besh is busy incorporating local ingredients (from fresh shrimp to thyme pulled straight from the ground) on Artesia's award winning menu. Located in an historic, two-story Creole mansion, forty minutes out of New Orleans, this French country dining retreat is frequented by a discerning local crowd, as well as by celebrities passing through town, hungry for one of Besh's hand-rolled potato dumplings. Ask Nanette to reserve table 10 for you – beside the fireplace, it offers a commanding view of the dining room.

21516 Highway 36
Abita Springs, LA 70420
Tel: 504-892-1662   Fax: 504-871-9952

ART OF EATING
Party Organizers and Caterers

Cheryl Stair and John Kowalenko's "last minute checks" are legendary – visiting an event site five or six times after it's chosen, studying every feature, like cracks in the slate or roots grown up over the soil. These husband and wife perfectionists cater to clients like Billy Joel and Martha Stewart (they cater her annual summer "crab pick"). Art of Eating cooks everything on premises and is able to produce any type of cuisine from around the world, from Cuban to Pacific Rim. This charming couple are VIPs in their own right; for big events call six to nine months in advance.

P.O. Box 3232
East Hampton, NY 11937
Tel: 631-267-2411
Fax: 631-267-2435

ART OF FITNESS
Fitness

Husband and wife team Art and Patricia Clyde, who own Art of Fitness, have been in the fitness business for 15 years. Their small, private facility occupies the fifth and sixth floors of a penthouse – the sixth floor atrium is great for yoga. Seven trainers specialize in yoga, kickboxing and weight management. A former New Jersey State Trooper, Art uses resistance equipment, cardiovascular and abdominal training either at the facility or in members' homes. Art's *Workout on the Go* (described by Patricia as "a suitcase book") is a great way to bring a training regimen on vacation.

39 West 56th Street, 5th Floor
New York, NY 10019
Tel: 212-262-4040

ASHFORD.COM
Websites

Although primarily known for flawless diamonds, this acclaimed new website offers everything from writing accessories to fragrances. Top tier brands include Lambertson Truex, Bettina Duncan, Roni Brunn and Vacheron et Constantin. The jewelry department is stocked with fresh creations by 23 innovators, including award winners Chris Correia and Tina Segal. Grammy winner Faith Hill wore the flawless 15 carat Ashford diamond while singing the national anthem at Super Bowl XXXIV.

3800 Buffalo Speedway, Suite 400
Houston, TX 77098
Tel: 713-369-1300
Fax: 713-623-0444

THE ASIA SOCIETY
Museums

The Asia Society is dedicated to fostering an understanding of Asian culture. A nonprofit, nonpartisan educational institution, the museum presents a wide range of programs including major art exhibitions, performances and international corporate conferences. Founded in 1956 by John D. Rockefeller III, it includes an auditorium, a bookstore, and a small but well-stocked gift shop. Exhibits include an impressive collection of Japanese calligraphy.

725 Park Avenue
New York, NY 10022
Tel: 212-517-ASIA

ASANTI FINE JEWELERS
Jewelry and Watches

An authorized Fabergé dealer, Nelson Holdo is more of a connoisseur than a proprietor. With over 20 years of experience, Holdo offers one of the strongest collections of colored gems in the country. Renowned for exceptional custom design and an impressive array of emeralds, rubies and sapphires, Holdo also carries a large selection of Cartier and Bulgari watches.

2640 Mission Street
San Marino, CA 91108
Tel: 626-403-0033

THE ASPEN CLUB & SPA
Fitness

This Colorado club more than fulfills its pound-shedding and pampering promises – from sport-specific training to Bindi herbal body therapy. The buffet of services is somewhat bewildering; clients usually set daily "recipes", scheduling hourly treatments, so that they don't aerobicize through their three o'clock meeting. Entrepreneur Michael Fox ensures that personal trainers are up to the minute on the latest in physiology breakthroughs. Aspen Club also houses racquetball, squash and tennis courts.

1450 Crystal Lake Road
Aspen, CO 81611
Tel: 970-925-8900   Fax: 970-925-9543

AUGUSTA NATIONAL GOLF CLUB
Golf Clubs
Golf writer Lorne Rubenstein notes that, with its "ample and lovely grounds," Augusta promotes the "feeling that golf should be a good walk enhanced." This esteemed home to The Masters offers a legendary expanse of perfect grass and some of the best golf worldwide. The Augusta course was laid out in 1934 by architects Bobby Jones and Alister Mackenzie on what had been a Georgian fruit tree nursery.

P.O. Box 2806
Augusta, GA 30903
Tel: 706-667-6000   Fax: 706-736-2321

ASPEN MUSIC FESTIVAL
Events
The music festival was founded in 1949, during a two-week gathering in Aspen to celebrate the 200th anniversary of the birth of the German writer and philosopher Goethe. In the aftermath of World War II, it was an optimistic dream — an international convocation and music festival in a dormant mountain town. Wealthy industrialist Walter Paepcke pulled it off, bringing together Albert Schweitzer, José Ortega y Gasset, violinist Nathan Milstein and American novelist Thornton Wilder to begin the tradition of the music festival. Now internationally acclaimed, the annual celebration commemorates Goethe's tradition of fueling the mind, body and spirit by offering fellowships to aspiring musicians through its music school.

2 Music School Road
Aspen, CO 81611
Tel: 970-925-1940   Fax: 970-920-1173

ASSETS PROTECTION SYSTEMS
Security Consultants
Ray Chambers, former Army Deputy Chief of Staff, has had some very bizarre requests. Once, a frantic man called, requesting that a personal tracking system be created for his father-in-law, a target for assassination. Today, Chambers' company specializes in corporate security consulting. Currently writing a book on liability avoidance, Chambers can turn your home into a veritable Fort Knox.

11113 Bella Loma Drive
Largo, FL 33774
Tel: 727-596-9650
Fax: 727-596-8486

～

SHERRELL ASTON, M.D.
Cosmetic Surgeons
In the topsy-turvy world of the New York social scene, it's not always who you know but also who you were "cut" by. If your face or eye lift was done by Sherrell Aston, you are in good company. Dr. Aston is well know for his rejuvenation work on former American Ambassador to France, Pamela Harriman, along with many other leading ladies — and men. The chairman of the plastic surgery department at Manhattan's Eye, Ear & Throat Hospital, Aston is married to Muffie Potter; together they are one of Manhattan's smartest couples.

728 Park Avenue
New York, NY 10021
Tel: 212-249-6000

HOTEL ASTOR
Hotels
In 1996 Lebanese-born, Paris-educated, investment banker Karim Masri bought a delapidated Art Deco gem, turning it into one of the hippest hotels in the country. Refreshingly low key, rooms are drenched in a sand-beige color scheme, chairs are slip covered in the finest Belgian linen and the timber joinery is by leading French cabinet makers Chantiers Baudet (also responsible for Barneys New York). The hotel restaurant, an Art Deco-inspired atrium, features Johnny Vinczencz's 'New Floridian' cuisine.

956 Washington Avenue
Miami Beach, FL 33139
Tel: 305-531-8081
Fax: 305-531-3193

～

AT HOME
Specialty Shops
At Home offers the finest in specialty tabletop, fine crafts and gifts. Antique tables and cabinets overflow with antique Wedgewood, Leeds Creamware and authentic English Delftware. The firm also offers accomplished modern works — substantive, glazed porcelain dinnerware and the finest in hand blown glassware and dishes. Antique or new, every item is handcrafted and chosen with a discerning eye. Paul Garzotto keeps the shop growing, filling it with unique treasures from around the world.

4445 Travis Street
Dallas, TX 75205
Tel: 214-528-0400
Fax: 214-528-0492

～

AUBERGE DU SOLEIL
Hotels
Auberge du Soleil was founded 15 years ago as a California-French restaurant under the direction of Claude Rouas, the quintessential Frenchman-turned-Californian. Discreetly tucked away on top of Rutherford Hill, overlooking a 33-acre olive grove, the Mediterranean-style villa and cottages boast elegant furnishings, terracotta tiles, fluffy pillows on luxurious king-sized beds with Frette linens and fireplaces for the cool evening air. If dining on the terrace with the sun setting isn't reason enough to sojourn here there are many activities to consider: hot air ballooning, horseback riding, tennis, mineral spas and wine tasting in any of the hinterland's 200 wineries.

180 Rutherford Hill Road
Rutherford, CA 94573
Tel: 707-963-1211
Fax: 707-963-8764

AUREOLE NEW YORK

Restaurants

Charlie Palmer is a leading exponent of Progressive American cuisine. Critics rave about his bold flavors and dramatic presentations. Try the sublime foie gras escalope with crisp fig tart. Warm ambiance, impeccable service, superlative food – no wonder this elegant restaurant is routinely rated a favorite among discerning New Yorkers.

34 East 61st Street
New York, NY 10021
Tel: 212-319-1660   Fax: 212-750-8613

AU BON CLIMAT WINERIES

Winemakers

Jim Clendener left his native Acron, Ohio after graduating college and literally traveled the world, tasting wine, studying the growth pattern of grapes and observing the best climates under which to grow them. Au Bon Climat was founded in 1982 on just 50 acres. The winery produces 23,000 cases of Pinot Noir and Chardonnay; smaller quantities lead to extra attention and ultimately, varietals that rival those from the best French vineyards. The Isabelle Pinot Noir is outstanding.

P.O. Box 113
Los Olivos, CA 93441
Tel: 805-937-9801

AUBRY

Portrait Painters and Photographers

This Paris-born photographer's work ranges from hospitality and resort photography to architecture, interior design and travel. Producer of four photobooks and contributor to the best-selling photobook of all time, *A Day in the Life of America*, he regularly shoots for *Architectural Digest* and exhibits around the globe. Creator of the Bio.Graph, a compilation of photos, documents and computer technology to tell the story of a person's life, Aubry's innovation has made him one of the most popular photographers in New York.

100 West 23rd Street
New York, NY 10011
Tel: 212-414-0014   Fax: 212-414-0013

AULDRIDGE MEAD

Hotels

Auldridge Mead Bed and Breakfast Country Inn was established in 1992 by owner Craig Mattoli. Mattoli, who was a mathematical physicist in the 1970s and a Wall Street takeover specialist in the 1980s, bought this historic treasure in 1989 to restore it and to begin a new career designing hand carved furniture from beautiful and exotic woods. Situated in a nook of upper Bucks County that has attracted the Guggenheims and the Heinzs, the Inn has been host to Senators, super models, actors, rock stars and visitors from around the world.

523 Geigel Hill Road
Ottsville, PA 18942
Tel: 610-847-5842   Fax: 610-847-5664

AXIS TWENTY

Specialty Shops

Renée Gaston owns and runs this contemporary classic design shop where she stocks furniture and designs by luminaries like Le Corbusier and Mies van der Rohe. Gaston recently downsized her business in order to cater more exclusively to the needs of individuals, offering full service interior and architectural design consultation for the discriminating client.

200 Peachtree Hills Avenue, NE
Atlanta, GA 30305
Tel: 404-261-4022

THE AVON CENTRE

Spas and Clinics

Time was when the name Avon conjured up images of a woman knocking at your door with a sampling of oddly packaged products. Today, the Avon staff are still as skilled and courteous as in years gone by – but of course they now offer the latest treatments and services. The company's flagship boutique on Fifth Avenue offers a complete range of health and beauty treatments to pamper and soothe the body and soul.

725 Fifth Avenue
New York, NY 10022
Tel: 212-755-2866   Fax: 212-310-6350

AZZURA POINT

Restaurants

James Boyce spent six years working with Daniel Boulud at New York's Le Cirque. His California-Mediterranean cuisine includes carefully crafted delicacies like a Maine Lobster risotto, served with Porcini and white truffle essence. Be sure to sit near a window and enjoy views of the sunset, Point Loma Lighthouse and the lights of downtown San Diego.

4000 Corronado Bay Road
Corronado, CA 92118
Tel: 619-424-4477

AUJOURD'HUI

Restaurants

Formerly of the White Barn Inn, Executive Chef Ed Gannon prepares a menu of original American food with French influences. While the selections change daily, favorites include crisp veal sweetbreads with crawfish, artichoke and green mustard, and a roasted Maine lobster with crab meat wontons and pineapple compote. Cozy corner tables overlook the Boston Public Garden and the two private dining rooms each seat 16. Patrons choose from a 25 page wine list, boasting a Chateau Lafite Rothschild for $1500.

200 Boylston Street
Boston, MA 02116
Tel: 617-351-2072   Fax: 617-351-2293

IF YOU THINK THIS ISN'T THE YEAR FOR DIAMONDS YOU'RE IN FOR A LONG MILLENNIUM

THE THREE-STONE ANNIVERSARY RING

DE BEERS

A DIAMOND IS FOREVER

BADGLEY-MISCHKA

Fashion

Mark Badgley and James Mischka are that rare breed of designers in the often frenetic and tumultuous fashion world. Their hand-beaded gowns and cocktail dresses cater to a young, modern couture customer, yet they do not forsake women of any age. Their timeless designs appeal to many a leading lady – Mira Sorvino, Catherine Zeta Jones and Cameron Diaz among them. "Our style harks back to the glamorous Hollywood of the Forties," state the designers. But don't be fooled. Simplicity is still key. "One zip and you're dressed," they say, adding "It's fabulous if you can spend hours getting ready, but a woman should also be able to bring a dress to work and change there for an evening out."

525 Seventh Avenue
New York, NY 10018
Tel: 212-921-1585   Fax: 212-921-1585

B & B INTERNATIONAL

Antiques

B&B International Gallery and Boylan Studios is a 15,000 square feet complex in Chelsea's landmark Starrett Lehigh Building. Owned by sisters Nuala and Anne Boylan, it houses a variety of vital and complementary entities. These include an antiques division crowded with rare objects from a host of countries (a portion of the proceeds returned to local charities in that country), an art gallery which has a reputation for exhibiting emerging artists, and a professionally equipped photo studio which attracts world renowned photographers. In this light and airy industrial loft, Nuala Boylan and her team, Kristen Eikenberry and Tracy Harrison-Peixoto, have recently launched B+B Home, a line of home accessories. The premier collection, Coconuts and Cream, represents a marriage of delightful contradictions. The simplicity of natural materials in their organic state is combined with the richness of refined details – like the signature piece, a hollowed coconut with a sterling silver base. "Our philosophy," says Boylan, "is to pair the sleekness of contemporary home furnishings with more traditional and ornate designs. We believe that it is modern to be eclectic."

601 West 26th Street
New York, NY 10001
Tel: 212-243-0840   Fax: 212-645-5029

BACCHANALIA

Restaurants

Owners and chefs Ann Quatrano and Clifford Harrison prepare contemporary American cuisine at this Victorian cottage in Georgia's capital. Recently transplanted to Howellmill Road, Bacchanalia now seats 75. Rated the most romantic restaurant in the city by *Atlanta* Magazine, it hosts many anniversaries and other special celebrations. Ask Anne's sister Frances Quatrano to reserve the chef's table for you. It seats up to eight and is positioned in the center of the dining room. Dinner and lunch are served Tuesday through Saturday.

1198 Howellmill Road
Atlanta, GA 30318
Tel: 404-365-0410

BARBARA GLADSTONE GALLERY

Art Dealers

Representing 22 artists who work in photography, video, film, installation, painting and sculpture, this Chelsea gallery has recently showcased James Turrell's light and space installations, Matthew Barney's films and the photography of Jean-Luc Mylayne. Barbara Gladstone is a cutting-edge alternative to many of the city's more predictable institutions. The renowned British sculptor Anish Kapoor, a former winner of the Turner Prize, Kcho, Gary Hill and Lari Pittman have all drawn in serious crowds this year.

515 West 24th Street
New York, NY 10001
Tel: 212-206-9300
Fax: 212-206-9301

BALDWIN GALLERY
Art Dealers

The Baldwin Gallery in Aspen has set a new standard for galleries in the American West to rival its New York or European counterparts. Housed in a historic Victorian building, the gallery has a 7,500 square foot space which it uses to showcase the leading contemporary artists it represents. The artists represented include Donald Baechler, Jennifer Bartlett, Christo and Jeanne-Claude, Eric Fischl, Robert Mapplethorpe, Louise Nevelson, James Rosenquist and Donald Sultan. In addition to an exciting exhibition schedule, the gallery has extensive holdings of work by gallery and other artists. Harley Baldwin and Richard Edwards are partners in the gallery – an important cultural institution in a town that includes the Aspen Music Festival, the Aspen Art Museum and the Aspen Film Festival.

209 South Galena Street
Aspen, CO 81611
Tel: 970-920-9797

BARBARA ISRAEL GARDEN ANTIQUES
Antiques

From wrought-iron French gates to a pair of marble German shepherds, Barbara Israel is essential for the sophisticated, elegant garden. Located in a 19th century country farmhouse in Katonah, her firm boasts a vast array of curiosities: fountains, figural and finial statues, architectural forms and accessories for the garden. Ranging from the 16th to 20th century, the pieces originate from America, England, France and Italy. Adding drama to an outdoor garden becomes easier with Israel's acclaimed book, *Antique Garden Ornament – Two Centuries of American Taste*.

296 Mt. Holly Road
Katonah, NY 10536
Tel: 914-232-4271

BARBARA KRAKOW GALLERY
Art Dealers

To contemporary art aficionados, Barbara Krakow's name is synonymous with cutting-edge, quality art. A walking encyclopedia of aesthetics and good taste, Krakow recently told reporters: "I have a commitment to a range of work that I firmly believe in because it touches me emotionally, it's what I care about most." Artists represented include Kevin Raney, Kiki Smith, Roy Lichtenstein and Michael Mazur.

10 Newbury Street
Boston, MA 02116
Tel: 617-262-4490
Fax: 617-262-8971

BARBERA BROOKS FINE FLOWERS
Florists

"Flowers speak volumes about human behavior, its values, its fashion," writes Barbera Brooks in her guide, *Fine Flowers by Phone*. From a simple nosegay of lily-of-the-valley to a 'handful' of tiny narcissus, Brooks' creations tend to be elegant and understated – like the clients she represents. Born and raised on a farm outside of Memphis, Tennessee, the former horticulturist, botanist and stockbroker brings her affinity for the simple country life into all of her arrangements, big and small. Warmly recommended.

2288 Union Street
San Francisco, CA 94123
Tel: 888-346-3356   Fax: 415-674-5590

BARBARA LOCKHART
Architects and Interior Designers

It is hard to ignore Barbara Lockhart. This delightful woman is one of America's preeminent architectural interior designers. Commercial projects of note include the new Chasen's Restaurant in Beverly Hills, Le Dome Restaurant in Los Angeles and the View Restaurant in Washington, D.C., while her impressive residential résumé includes the William Randolph Hearst/Marion Davies estate and a private residence designed with the Frank Lloyd Wright Foundation. Her projects are worldwide. Lockhart's philosophy centers on her belief that it is important to research the roots and history of a project and then create harmony with her client's needs – something that does not always come quickly, but is always noticeable.

The unparalleled designer has been graced with the most coveted awards in her field, such as the S.M. Hexter Most Outstanding Interior Designer in America Award, the Beverly Hills Architectural Achievement Award and the American Society of Interior Designer's Lifetime Achievement Award for Design Excellence. Lockhart was recently highlighted by Christie's as one of 20 innovators of 20th century style. Equally, Lockhart has been the honoree of many charitable organizations for the same care and acumen that she brings to her work.

710 North Bedford Drive
Beverly Hills, CA 90210
Tel: 310-276-8228   Fax: 310-271-0256

BARRY FRIEDMAN
Art Dealers
For over 25 years, Barry Friedman has been exhibiting and dealing European decorative arts, avant-garde paintings from the 20s and 30s, works on paper, sculptures, vintage and contemporary photography. Within the past few years, Friedman has also moved into the field of contemporary decorative arts, with exhibitions featuring studio glass, art furniture, ceramics and wood objects.

32 East 67th Street
New York, NY 10021
Tel: 212-794-8950   Fax: 212-794-8889

BARTRAM & BRAKENHOFF
Powerboats & Yachts
Specializing in the marketing, sale and charter of high quality yachts, David Lacz also assists in crew placement and custom designs. The Delta Tri-Deck fiberglass motor yacht is an excellent example of his firm's superior inventory. The 124 foot yacht includes an on-deck owner's stateroom, three guest cabins, a gym, a beautifully appointed saloon and dining area with a large sky lounge.

2 Marina Plaza - Goat Island
Newport, RI 02840
Tel: 401-846-7355   Fax: 401-847-6329

BATH & TENNIS CLUB
Private Clubs
The name says it all at this historic Palm Beach Club, which offers members two pools and eight clay tennis courts. Tennis pro Patrick Cramer keeps the members in good form on the courts, and they can cool down at the strictly casual clubhouse, an historic landmark. The Bath & Tennis Club was founded in 1926, incorporated in 1938 and currently has "a rather extensive" waiting list.

1170 South Ocean Boulevard
Palm Beach, FL 33480
Tel: 561-832-4271

BAUMAN RARE BOOKS
Specialty Shops   Best Kept Secret
Like a painting, a good book can double in value within a few years. Specializing in landmark books in all fields, Bauman has three outlets. Its largest shop, located on Madison Avenue, is home to thousands of rare books, covering the 15th to the 20th centuries: Americana, literature, travel and exploration, history, sciences, art and illustrated books, fine sets and children's classics. Bauman is also located on the elegant lobby level of the Waldorf-Astoria hotel on Park Avenue. The third branch of the firm is on Locust Street in Philadelphia.

535 Madison Avenue
New York, NY 10022
Tel: 212-751-0011

BAREFOOT ELEGANCE
Architects and Interior Designers
Barefoot Elegance, the interior design company founded by Dot Spikings and Jennifer Castle, caters to a clientele who desire furniture, linens, dinnerware, accessories or exotic imports which add luxurious touches to their homes. "Our approach to style is encapsulated in the name of our company," Castle states. "The foremost thought behind our designs is to create an environment which is elegant, but at the same time is one in which you can kick off your shoes and relax. Elegance does not have to be foreboding." Their work has been featured in leading publications and numerous collectors' coffee table books, such as *Great Escapes* and *The Essence of White*.

801 Paseo Nuevo
Santa Barbara, CA 93101
Tel: 800-834-8146   Fax: 805-499-3288

BARNARD COLLEGE
Colleges
Barnard may be the single most inspiring lesson in the continuing vitality of the women's liberal arts college. When its neighbor and historic partner, Columbia, offered to absorb the college in the early 1980s, Barnard faculty resisted. Columbia subsequently backed off and simply accepted women on its own. A death knell for its sister? Hardly. The alma mater of Margaret Meade, Zora Neale Hurston and Jeanne Kirkpatrick is drawing its best applicants ever and continues to thrive as a distinctive part of the larger university community on the Upper West Side of Manhattan.

3009 Broadway
New York, NY 10027
Tel: 212-854-2037
Fax: 212-854-7491

BAY HILL CLUB & LODGE
Golf Clubs

Arnold Palmer's Bay Hill Club spans 270 acres along the shores of the picturesque Butler chain of lakes. Featuring 27 holes, the course is known as one of the toughest on the PGA tour, but eminently fair. Members of the club and guests at the cozy 64-room lodge enjoy fine dining, golf, a full service salon & spa, swimming and a business center. Golf greats Dow Finsterwald and Scott Hoch are both members. Beware of the eighteenth – it is the trickiest, most-feared hole on the course.

9000 Bay Hill Boulevard
Orlando, FL 32819
Tel: 407-876-2429   Fax: 407-876-8054

BAYVIEW LIMOUSINE
Chauffeur Services

As synonymous with Washington as the apple, Bayview Limousine is the largest chauffeur service in the state. What began as a single car business in 1990 is now a 25 car expert service. Limousines feature a wide range of amenities, like full leather seats as standard, sophisticated audio-visual equipment and freshly stocked bars – not to mention their competent and discreet drivers, who always put the client first. Computers track incoming flights to ensure that a car is waiting curbside, no matter how late or early the client arrives. In 1999, Bayview was named *Chauffeur service of the year* by the National Limousine Association.

22001 Pacific Highway South
Seattle, WA 98198
Tel: 206-223-6200   Fax: 206-824-9884

BARNEYS NEW YORK
Fashion

When Barneys moved from downtown Seventh to uptown Madison, many of its fans booed and hissed, claiming that it would never retain its originality and wit. Less than ten years after the move the nay-sayers have definitely been proven wrong. With Simon Doonan still at the creative helm, this fashion-world mecca continues to attract lovers of fashion and fantasy. While classic designers like Lauren, Yamamoto and Gaultier can still be found, Barneys continues to showcase the latest collections from today's hottest young designers.

660 Madison Avenue
New York, NY 10021
Tel: 212-826-8900   Fax: 212-450-8489

LE BEC-FIN
Restaurants

Originally from Lyon, France, Georges Perrier began his culinary career when he was 14 years old. Studying alongside French masters Michel Lorrain and Jacques Picard, he soon became recognized as one of the best chefs in France. His Philadelphia jewel-box offers a superlative six course menu, focusing on delivering a lighter menu – Perrier actually blows air into some of his sauces. His latest culinary breakthrough is the "lobster press," squeezing unnecessary juice to harness the essence. *Condé Nast Traveler* Editor Tom Wallace refers to Perrier as a "living monument."

1523 Walnut Street
Philadelphia, PA 19102
Tel: 215-567-1000   Fax: 215-568-1151

BEACH BISTRO
Restaurants

Life is full of hidden opportunities: after graduating law school in Canada, the only way that Sean Murphy could make money was waiting tables. As luck would have it, he fell in love with the restaurant business and soon opened Beach Bistro, located on the pristine sands of Anna Maria Island. Today, his comfortable, stylish restaurant seats 55 people (try to snag one of the five window tables which overlook the ocean). The wine room, which seats four, is an oenophile's delight, offering a magnificent tasting menu and the intimacy which memorable soirées demand. Chef Andrea Goyette's specialties include a rack of domestic lamb and Gulf Coast Bouillabaise. Hollywood luminaries like Anne Bancroft, Mel Brooks and Robert DeNiro have all enjoyed dinner here. Warmly recommended.

6600 Gulf Drive
Holmes Beach, FL 32417
Tel: 941-778-6444
Fax: 941-779-2308

BERGDORF GOODMAN
Fashion

Battle of the sexes or just good positioning? Either way Bergdorf Goodman and its brother across the way, Bergdorf Goodman Men, are considerable powers among New York's plethora of department stores. Both house an infinite array of the finest collections by big-name designers like Calvin Klein, Badgley-Mischka, Gucci et al.; but they also carry some of the more interesting and unusual gift items available. The only problem? Trying to dodge Fifth Avenue traffic to get that Loro Piana scarf you forgot.

754 Fifth Avenue
New York, NY 10019
Tel: 212-753-7300

BEACON HILL NANNIES
Employment Agencies

When stockbrokers Julie Pellatt, Paula Chiungos and Katherine Robinson left Kidder, Peabody & Co. to start their own domestic help business, their colleagues scoffed. That fall, the stock market crashed, appropriately, and the trio founded Beacon Hill. The firm is different from its competitors in that the nannies are upscale, college-educated women. The firm urges clients to be choosy – offering dozens of interviews with each nanny. All candidates undergo psychological and physical evaluation prior to registration with the firm.

825 Beacon Street
Newton, MA 02459
Tel: 800-736-3880   Fax: 617-630-9398

BEAUVAIS CARPETS
Specialty Shops

Recognized as a world class dealer in museum quality antique carpets and tapestries, Beauvais also provides decorative carpets for the design industry. Its roster of clients includes premier interior designers as well as top collectors and museums. With one of the largest selections of European and Oriental carpets and tapestries in the nation, Beauvais shows regularly at the International Fine Arts and Antique Dealers show in New York and the Palm Beach International Art and Antique Fair.

201 East 57th Street
New York, NY 10022
Tel: 212-688-2265   Fax: 212-688-2384

BEL-AIR COUNTRY CLUB
Private Clubs

The Bel-Air Country Club was one of the first private clubs in the Los Angeles area. Primarily a golf club, there are also tennis courts and member events are hosted throughout the year. Located in the country's entertainment capital, the club's membership is eclectic; celebrities and movie executives rub shoulders with professionals from many other fields.

10768 Bellagio Road
Los Angeles, CA 90077
Tel: 310-472-9563
Fax: 310-472-5843

HOTEL BEL-AIR
Hotels

Oil millionaire turned real-estate developer Alphonzo E. Bell built this Mission style hotel for his planning and sales offices in 1922. Considered by many to be Los Angeles's best kept secret, the retreat is stretched over 12 acres, dazzled with pink primrose, miniature yellow daffodils, red azaleas, white roses and flowering peach and apricot trees. 92 rooms and suites offer quiet and anonymity – hardly surprising, then, that the hotel has always been popular with stars. Grace Kelly often stayed in suite 160 with its king-size canopy bed, wood-burning fireplace and French doors, opening to a terrace and Jacuzzi. General Manager Frank Bowling makes a point of making sure every guest feels at home.

701 Stone Canyon Road
Los Angeles, CA 90077
Tel: 310-472-1211   Fax: 310-476-5890

BEL-AIR INVESTMENT ADVISORS
Wealth Management

You know you're in good hands when your investment firm has developed a "sleep-well quotient," a baseline for formulating an asset allocation plan that won't keep you up at night worrying. Senior managing director Todd Morgan answers his own telephone, is available all the time and spends many hours asking questions about a family's long-term goals. A potential client of Bel Air has at least $10 million to invest; the client roster includes diva Barbra Streisand, Geraldo Rivera, Lee Iacocca, Donna Karan and Hollywood producer Jon Peters.

1999 Avenue Of The Stars
Los Angeles, CA 90067
Tel: 310-229-1500
Fax: 310-229-1535

BELL'OCCHIO
Specialty Shops

If there were awards for the finest curiosity shops in America, Bell'Ochio would be a perennial winner. Reinterpreting the atmosphere of a little Parisian shop, Claudia Schwartz and Toby Hanson seek out refined products from Europe's historic ateliers, hand picking French and Italian ribbons, handmade silk flowers, antique linens, handmade horn combs, toiletries, Parisian face powders and elegant boxes to entice the discerning shopper from around the world. This year, Bell'Occhio introduced its collection of 18th century French antiques.

8 Brady Street
San Francisco, CA 94103
Tel: 415-864-4048
Fax: 415-864-2626

BELLAGIO

Hotels

Like a true empire builder, Steve Wynn has come up trumps again with his latest addition to the Strip. From the hand blown Venetian glass floral display in the lobby, the theme of all-things-Italian continues right through to Sirio Maccioni's menu at Le Cirque. Pass through the indoor garden and view the multi-million dollar art collection, with works by masters such as Picasso, van Gogh and Miró. With beautiful rooms, extensive gaming opportunities and dancing water fountains out front, there is little more a Las Vegas hotel could offer. At least this year.

3600 Las Vegas Boulevard South
Las Vegas, NV 89109
Tel: 702-693-7111

LE BERNARDIN

Restaurants

The combined talents of chef Eric Ripert and owner Maguy LeCoze ensure that dining at this vaulted ceilinged, teak-lined, French seafood restaurant is never short of inspiring. Ripert, whose style is firmly rooted in French haute cuisine, serves a lively, herb-accented menu which includes clever combinations like black bass ceviche topped with mint, coriander and chilies, and a seafood broth, enriched with lobster, truffles and foie gras. LeCoze is the perfect hostess, running a flawless dining room accented with fresh, stylish bouquets. At lunch the food is just as robust and the dining room is a bit quieter.

155 West 51st Street
New York, NY 10019
Tel: 212-489-1515
Fax: 212-265-1615

BERRY-HILL GALLERIES

Art Dealers

In the 1980s James Berry—Hill served two terms on President Reagan's Cultural Property Advisement Committee, and he has been a member of the Cornell University Museum Advisory Board. One of the nation's leading collectors of American Art, he offers a discreet and confidential alternative to private collectors, estates and museums looking to purchase fine 18th, 19th and 20th century American paintings and sculpture. Berry-Hill Galleries also boasts a significant collection of Modern European and Old Master paintings.

11 East 70th Street
New York, NY 10021
Tel: 212-744-2300
Fax: 212-744-2838

BERINGER WINE ESTATES

Winemakers

Beringer produce a full range of premium varietal wines from six award-winning wineries. The company controls more than 10,300 acres of vineyard land in the coastal regions of California, part of its key strategy of maintaining high quality and reliable grape supplies. Beringer boasts a trio of leading Cabernet Sauvignons: Private Reserve, Knights Valley and Chabot Vineyard. The Private Reserve Napa Valley Chardonnay is also particularly good.

600 Air Park
Napa, CA 94558
Tel: 707-963-7115

BERNARD & S. DEAN LEVY

Antiques

After studying art history in college, Dean Levy enthusiastically took his place in the family business — one of the most prominent antique firms in America. Founded in 1901, the five story showroom contains only American antiques, particularly Philadelphia pieces. Every room is designed in period style, offering the feel of a museum display. The Levy family has figured prominently in creating the collections of The Metropolitan, San Francisco, Houston and Minneapolis Museums of Art.

24 East 84th Street
New York, NY 10028
Tel: 212-628-7088   Fax: 212-628-7489

BEST DOMESTIC SERVICES

Employment Agencies

For those who prefer a proper English maid, a robust French chef or a nanny who can teach their children German, Best Domestic Services is the quality answer to long-term domestic needs. Each nanny, maid, butler, chef, housekeeper and chauffeur is rigorously trained, tested and screened before manager Don Williams offers their portfolio for client consideration. For those who prefer a short-term basis, the firm offers a 24 hour, seven days a week emergency nanny care, chefs, maids, and butlers — doesn't it feel good to relax?

9107 Wilshire Boulevard, #675
Beverly Hills, CA 90210
Tel: 310-205-3100
Fax: 310-205-3109

BESSEMER TRUST
Wealth Management

Bessemer Trust manages $20 billion for just over a thousand clients. Established in 1907 by the heirs of steel tycoon Henry Phipps, it was originally a family office, but has served "outsiders" since 1974. The typical account size is about $20 million. Through its nationwide offices, Bessemer boasts access to top venture capital, private equity, and real estate managers — and one of the highest staff-to-client ratios in the business.

630 Fifth Avenue
New York, NY 10111
Tel: 212-708 9100   Fax: 212-265-5826

BESTSELECTIONS.COM
Websites

When you are looking for a Bhutanese geometric Box, a doggie travel kit, a pair of exotic wood sunglasses and a few ounces of Beluga caviar, you wouldn't expect to find them all in one place. In the "real" world of retail, it would be highly unlikely to find them even at close proximity to each other, which is why BestSelections.com will surprise and delight even the most discerning online shopper. This sophisticated international galleria stocks the very best goods in each of its 175 categories.

350 Seventh Avenue
New York, NY 10001
Tel: 212-465-9797   Fax: 212-465-9444

THE BEVERLY HILLS HOTEL
Hotels

Glamour, wealth, and romance, anyone? They're all here at the historic Beverly Hills Hotel. Built before there even was a place called Beverly Hills, its bungalows have been a playground for the stars — from silent era starlets to the Beatles to Howard Hughes, who considered number 4 to be his home away from home (sometimes, Hughes would venture into the Sunset Room lounge and have a drink with Humphrey Bogart and Marlene Dietrich, who broke the no-slacks-for-ladies rule). Bungalow five has a private swimming pool which was added at the request of business magnate Walter Annenberg.

9641 Sunset Boulevard
Beverly Hills, CA 90210
Tel: 310-281-2958
Fax: 310-281-2989

BIJAN
Fashion

With clients like Steven Spielberg, Warren Beatty, Larry King, David Geffen, Elton John and Tommy Hilfiger, Bijan is one of the more expensive and exclusive men's salons — the custom-made clothing is produced in a numbered series to ensure individuality. In one visit, a client could walk away with a diamond, platinum and yellow-gold watch and a cashmere coat lined in Russian sable. While the boutique is usually reserved for fitting the rich and powerful in fine couture, Bijan's designers once outfitted the interior of a train car for a client who refused to travel by plane. As the charismatic designer puts it, "If the mountain does not come to Mohammed, Mohammed goes to the mountain."

421 North Rodeo Drive
Beverly Hills, CA 90210
Tel: 310-271-1122
Fax: 310-271-2988

BILL WALKER CLOTHIER
Fashion

Outfitters to Houston's best dressed gentlemen for the past 30 years — including local tycoons like Bob McNair and Rodney Martin — Bill Walker specializes in fine menswear and bespoke custom tailoring. Blending classic sophistication and strict attention to detail, Walker's new shop in the Uptown Park luxury shopping village offers an elaborate international line, including Hickey-Freeman, Giorgeo Carreli and Barry Bricken.

1141-01 Uptown Park Boulevard
Houston, TX 77056
Tel: 713-871-9811
Fax: 713-871-9449

LAWRENCE BIRNBAUM, M.D.
Cosmetic Surgeons

Dr. Lawrence Birnbaum conducts his practice in the midst of the universally accepted mecca of plastic surgery — Beverly Hills. Not only has his practice included a disproportionately large number of celebrities and the like, but often when a cosmetic surgeon desires plastic surgery for themselves they will seek his skills. For over 20 years the physician has devoted his practice to ethical excellence. His hallmark — a natural-look despite the improvement sought. In this land of ever-questioning media, Birnbaum's surgical skills have fooled some of the keenest of scrutinizing

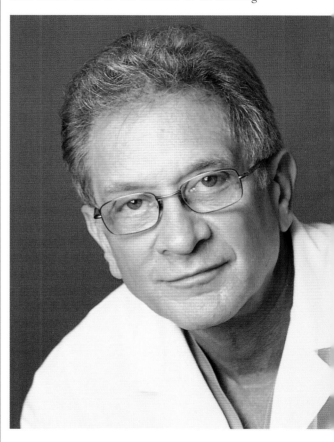

eyes. This has been especially true of his male patients who do not possess the hair or will to use makeup to cover obvious scars that are often so prevalent with many of the more conventional techniques. Whether it is in facial improvements or in working to make the patient's hands look as young as their face, or in any area in between, this famed surgeon has set new standards, just as he did in breast reconstruction following mastectomies a number of years ago. Birnbaum's consultations alone are worthwhile, if only to come away with sufficient knowledge to make an informed decision about any surgery being pondered.

153 South Lasky Drive, Suite 1
Beverly Hills, CA 90212
Tel: 310-556-5663   Fax: 310-556-8013

THE BISHOP'S LODGE

Hotels   *Best Kept Secret*

Nestled in its own private valley in the colorful foothills of the Sangre de Cristo Mountains, the Bishop's Lodge is the kind of picture-perfect hideaway one sees on the silver screen. Spanish Colonial and Native American styles dominate your accommodations, while canyons, prairies and streams surround you. Horse riding, skeet shooting, tennis and the like are easy distractions from the scenery – if you've lost the use of your senses, that is. As a gateway, the resort is near Santa Fe's galleries, museums and shops.

Bishop's Lodge Road
Santa Fe, NM 87504
Tel: 505-983-6377   Fax: 505-989-8739

BIBA

Restaurants

Executive chef Lydia Shire, in conjunction with partner Susan Regis, prepares a menu of American eclectic cuisine, culled from her travels and studies around the world. The Szechuan spiced duck with purple aubergine was inspired by Shire's trip to China, while the 'Seoul' full short ribs are reminiscent of her trip to Korea. The dining room, designed by Adam Tihany, accommodates 150 guests in an elegant, casual setting. Sit beside the windows, which offer a serene view of the Boston Public Garden, or stop by the downstairs lounge for an appetizer.

272 Boylston Street
Boston, MA 02116
Tel: 617-426-5684

BLACK DIAMOND RANCH

Golf Clubs

In the rolling countryside of Florida's Nature Coast, Black Diamond offers 1240 acres of privacy reserved for fewer than 800 families, hosting 36 holes of championship golf. The members-only equity club has amenities ranging from tennis and swimming to dining and relaxed socializing, all within a very private residential community. Thousands of live oaks, dogwoods, myrtles, magnolias and azaleas enhance the already stunning landscape. The golf club includes two golf courses, Ranch and Quarry, designed by Tom Fazio, who returned in 1997 to add nine more holes to the ranch course. The club hosts the Dodge Shoot-out celebrity tournament every June.

2600 West Black Diamond Circle
Lecanto, FL 34461
Tel: 352-746-7400

BLACK PEARL ANTIQUES & FINE ARTS

Antiques

In 1990, Richard LeBlanc's passion for Renaissance art and ancient Chinese antiquities drove him out of the advertising field and right into his gallery. The collection, housed in a historical landmark, is divided into four sections: fine arts, ancient Chinese antiquities, sculpture and period furniture. A treat for personal collectors, most of the inventory is extremely rare – at the time of writing, LeBlanc had a Connecticut cherry Queen Anne highboy, kept in the same family since 1730, and a spectacular collection of Chinese tomb pieces.

2217 Main Street
Glastonbury, CT 06033
Tel: 860-659-3601   Fax: 860-659-2387

BLISS

Spas and Clinics

Unlike her model and movie star clients, owner Marcia Kilgore's skin has always been a bit on the wild side. In desperation, she enrolled in a skincare treatment program one summer, practicing her newfound treatments on her friends. In no time, Kilgore couldn't get her friends out of her living room. Today, fully-loaded facials and hot milk-and-almond pedicure are among the profusion of services available to those in need of high-quality pampering. In 1999, Bliss opened its second outpost on 57th Street in the new LVMH Tower. Plans are in the works for a spa on the west coast, as well as a new line of bath and body products.

568 Broadway, 2nd Floor
New York, NY 10012
Tel: 212-931-6370   Fax: 212-965-1433

BLOOM

Florists

Leaving a thriving career on Wall Street in 1993, Lesly Zamor fell in love with the idea of flower-selling and soon Bloom was up and running. His floral and event designs reflect the modern sensibility of New Yorkers in their simple yet sophisticated designs. By grouping together a variety of flowers according to a common color, Zamor crafts exquisitely monochromatic creations, focusing exclusively on the flowers without relying on filler. He offers a variety of custom services, including weddings, corporate events, film sets and other off site locations, supervising every aspect, from renting space, hiring entertainment, designing interiors around a theme to, of course, furnishing the flowers. A new store will open in Fall 2000 at the prestigious W Hotel, with 2000 square feet of simple, elegant and beautiful flowers.

16 West 21st Street
New York, NY 10010
Tel: 212-620-5666   Fax: 212-620-0973

BLUE ANGEL

Restaurants   *Rising Star*

Philadelphia restaurateur Stephen Starr opened Blue Angel (his fourth eatery in the city) on Halloween, 1999. Local hero Peter Dunmire presides over the kitchen, serving traditional French bistro food in a chic setting. The dining room was originally the Quaker City Bank, dating back to 1900 – the original stained glass ceiling and mini-tile floor have been restored. A French hat rack gives the dimly lit, romantic room the feel of a true Paris Bistro. The peppered duck served with caramelized celery root is particularly good and the cheese plates are a must. Enthusiasts include Bruce Willis and local symphony musicians.

706 Chestnut Street
Philadelphia, PA 19106
Tel: 215-925-6889

THE BOULDERS

Hotels

Nestled among the dramatic boulders of the high Sonoran desert foothills, north of Scottsdale, The Boulders offers outstanding guest services, fine dining and two 18-hole Jay Morrison-designed golf courses that have each received the Gold Medal Award from *Golf* Magazine. The resort's private country club features eight tennis courts, a lap pool, and a spa and fitness center, overlooking panoramic desert vistas. With five dramatically different restaurants, the Boulders can match any mood from the romantic elegance of The Latilla to the casual informality of Cantina del Pedegral, with its festive Mexican favorites.

34631 North Tom Darlington Drive
Carefree, AZ 85377
Tel: 480-488-9009
Fax: 480-488-9428

BLUMKA GALLERY

Art Dealers

Anthony Blumka specializes in Medieval and Renaissance works of art, sculpture and furniture. Catering to private collectors and leading galleries, he shows by appointment only. Located on the Upper East Side of Manhattan, Blumka's gallery is cool and sophisticated, drawing in visitors from around the world. The gallery is a member of the Appraisers Association of America, the Art and Antique Dealers League of America and the National Antique and Art Dealers Association of America.

101 East 81st Street
New York, NY 10021
Tel: 212-734-3222
Fax: 212-249-1087

BLACKBERRY FARM

Hotels

Opened in the early 1930s by the socialite couple Florida and Dave Lasier, Blackberry Farm is a delightful bastion of Southern style and charm tucked away at the foot of the Great Smoky Mountains. A true retreat in every sense, 44 rooms offer king-sized beds, fireplaces, refrigerators, whirlpools and private porches. Decorated in fine English and French antiques, hand chosen by owners Kreis and Sandy Beall, the rooms are difficult to leave. Luckily the Tennessee treasure offers smart activities, including wildflower hikes, fly fishing, mountain biking, tennis and swimming. Try to secure a room in autumn; the foliage is breathtaking.

1471 West Millers Cove Road
Walland, TN 37886
Tel: 865-984-8166   Fax: 865-983-5708

CYNTHIA A. BOXRUD, M.D.

Cosmetic Surgeons

Raised on a farm in Minnesota, Cynthia Boxrud trained as a conductor. After spending a few harried years leading an orchestra, she realized that life on the road was not as she'd imagined. Boxrud quickly enrolled in medical school. A firm believer in the idea that "facelifts are a thing of the past," she uses Botox injections to smooth wrinkles rather than disrupt the rest of the face. Boxrud flies to New York several times a year to join forces with Dr. Patricia Wexler, another specialist in Botox treatment.

152 South Lasky Drive, Suite 1
Beverly Hills, CA 90212
Tel: 310-282-0777   Fax: 310-282-0744

BRASSERIE PERRIER

Restaurants

George Perrier's upscale casual bistro offers a relaxed atmosphere and the culinary talents of Chef Chris Scarduzio. Specialties include the steamed clams, Chinese eggplant and black bean sauce, and a delectable roasted lamb sirloin, served with haricot vert salad. The low-lit, intimate dining room seats 100. If you value seclusion, ask General Manager Joe Amrani to seat you in the private dining room, which seats only 18.

619 Walnut Street
Philadelphia, PA 19103
Tel: 215-568-3000

BROWN-DAVIS INTERIORS

Architects and Interior Designers

Robert Sidney Brown and Todd Dyer Davis joined forces in 1994 to create Brown-Davis Interiors, which has rapidly garnered a reputation as one of the premier residential and commercial interior design and interior architecture firms in the country. Their work spans from contemporary to traditional, while maintaining a unique and original style. Both have been significantly influenced by their upbringing and heritage. Brown has an English aesthetic (his family moved to the States just before his birth) and Davis, a native of Southern California, is inspired by the contemporary architecture and design of his home state. Among their most elaborate projects are the British Embassy in Washington, D.C., a 26,000 square foot custom-built residence in Maryland, and the apartment of a Manhattan heiress who has one of the world's finest private art collections. Their work has been featured in a plethora of interior design publications and television programs. Brown-Davis Interiors recently launched a custom furnishing line and this year promises the introduction of a wide range of new products. If the tasteful duo were not busy creating interior and furniture designs for others, they would probably become elaborate fixer-uppers — as they enjoy buying, redesigning, renovating and reselling properties. Davis would also spend considerably more time restoring classic automobiles. But their many satisfied clients (such as British Ambassador, Sir Christopher Meyer and his wife Lady Catherine Meyer) would be sorely disappointed.

1617 29th Street NW
Washington, DC 20007
Tel: 202-333-5883
Fax: 202-333-9748

THE BREAKERS
Hotels

One of the last great hotel resorts in Florida, The Breakers was built in 1926 by the heirs of Henry Flagler to replace the original Breakers Hotel, which burnt to the ground in 1925. The building, with its twin towers and grand loggia facing the ocean, was influenced by the Villa Medici in Rome. The public rooms are opulent, with marble floors and hand-painted murals on the ceilings and walls. Rooms and suites overlook a sunken central courtyard with fountains and a large, reflecting pool or the Atlantic Ocean. The property boasts two 18-hole golf courses, tennis courts and comprehensive spa services. Snag a shingle-style cottage — large, two-story houses, originally built for the hotel's wealthier guests, who needed extra room for domestic help.

One South County Road
Palm Beach, FL 33480
Tel: 561-655-6611   Fax: 561-653-6312

BREEDERS' CUP
Events

A pinnacle of the sporting calendar, the Breeders' Cup is the ultimate test for talent and ability in thoroughbred racing. The annual event is a day of champions; not just for the horses, but also for their owners, trainers, breeders and jockeys, who compete for over $13 million in purse money (and the bronze horse trophy). Since the inaugural event in 1994, prominent North American and European horsemen have enthusiastically participated by sending their top horses to compete for the Cup.

2525 Harrodsburg Road
Lexington, KY 40504
Tel: 606-223-5444   Fax: 606-223-3945

BRIDGEHAMPTON POLO CLUB
Polo Clubs

Matches are a major social event here, attracting many of New York's society and fashion gangs to the grounds of Two Trees Farm in Bridgehampton. Founded in 1995 by Neil Hirsch and Peter Brant, the Mercedes-Benz Polo Challenge and The Hamptons Cup are battled out over six consecutive weekends during July and August. Sponsors include Moet et Chandon, Dolce & Gabbana and *Leading Hotels of the World*. This is high-goal polo at its most glamorous, with a slew of international players and bystanders like Ron Perelman, Kim Basinger, Sean "Puffy" Combs and Cindy Crawford.

40 East 52rd Street, Floor 23
New York, NY 10022
Tel: 212-421-1367
Fax: 212-906-9096

BRANDEIS UNIVERSITY
Colleges

Brandeis is a research university that manages to feel like a liberal arts college. So when one marvels at excellence across an array of master's and doctoral programs, and a world-class graduate school for Economics and Finance, it is critical to remember that the university retains its undergraduate-friendly nine-to-one student-to-faculty ratio and a median class size of just 17. And there's something about the atmosphere of the place: Brandeis has always maintained a culture of intellectual seriousness that distinguishes it from its clubbier Ivy peers.

P.O. Box 9110
Waltham, MA 02254
Tel: 781-736-2000   Fax: 781-736-8699

THE BROADMOOR
Hotels

Located at the foot of Cheyenne Mountain, Broadmoor is one of America's premier resorts and the longest holder of the prestigious Mobil Five Star and AAA Five Diamond awards. The 3000-acre property has 700 rooms and suites, a world-class amenity spa and fitness center, plus more than 110,000 square feet of meeting space. Other amenities include 11 restaurants and lounges, a cigar bar and nightclub, three championship 18-hole golf courses, 12 tennis courts, three swimming pools, hot air ballooning and access to the Cheyenne Mountain Zoo.

One Lake Avenue
Colorado Springs, CO 80906
Tel: 800-634-7711
Fax: 719-577-5700

THE BROOK
Private Clubs

One of the most exclusive gentleman's clubs in the United States, The Brook's priority is social over business; briefcases are checked at the door and conversation is supposed to focus on more lofty subjects than the day's Dow Jones. Members include international heavy hitters as well as a long list of powerful Americans: this was FDR's club of choice. Meals are served at common tables and the food is exceptionally good, especially for a club.

111 East 54th Street
New York, NY 10022
Tel: 212-753-7020   Fax: 212-644-6111

BROWN BROTHERS HARRIMAN
Wealth Management

Brown Brothers Harriman is an owner-managed partnership that provides financial services in eight key areas: commercial banking, currency consulting, securities brokerage and research, mergers and acquisitions, private equity, foreign exchange, investment management and global custody. For 175 years it has maintained offices around the world, with clients ranging from multinational institutions to individual investors. Known for going to extraordinary lengths to please the customer, the firm once arranged for one of its managers to help a client put up his Christmas tree. Incidentally, President Bush's father was a partner in BBH.

50 Milk Street
Boston, MA 02109
Tel: 617-742-1818

BROWN UNIVERSITY
Colleges

Ah, the life on Providence's fabled College Hill: Against the handsome backdrop of an historic New England port, Brown conspires (along with the Rhode Island School of Design) to create an idyll of tony intellectualism. No wonder, then, that Brown, with its world-class resources, innovative curriculum and dedicated alumni – Ted Turner and the late John F. Kennedy Jr. among them – has become a crossroads for some of the brightest and most privileged students from around the world.

P.O. Box 1920
Providence, RI 02912
Tel: 401-863-1000   Fax: 401-863-3700

BROWNS
Specialty Shops

Lois Von Morganroth's Los Angeles firm specializes in the cleaning of beaded gowns and retailoring where necessary to clean separate garment parts. Demi Moore, Michelle Pfeiffer and Madonna frequent the premises, as do clients from around the world – many ship their treasures via Federal Express from Paris, London and Hong Kong. Possibly America's most exclusive hand dry-cleaning service.

1223 Montana Avenue
Santa Monica, CA 90403
Tel: 310-451-8531

BROOKLYN MUSEUM OF ART
Museums

Recently home to the controversial British import, *Sensation*, this museum, located in a city which boasts the Met and MOMA, stands its own ground. Housed in a Beaux-Arts building designed in 1893 by McKim, Mead and White, virtually the whole history of art, from the early Egyptians to contemporary American painters, is represented here – the permanent collection includes more than one and a half million objects. 2001 exhibits include *Masterpieces of Fashion* and *Scythian Gold in the Ukraine*.

200 Eastern Parkway
Brooklyn, NY 11238
Tel: 718-638-5000   Fax: 718-638-5931

Courtesy of the Brooklyn Museum of Art: The Doge's Palace at Venice, by Claude Monet

BRYAN CAVE
Law Firms

One of the 25 largest law firms in the United States, Bryan Cave is built on 125 years of solid performance and offers legal counsel and advice in virtually every area of interest to business and entrepreneurial clients. 550 lawyers practice in a wide range of disciplines at 17 domestic and international offices, from Kansas City to Abu Dhabi. Lawyers practice in client service groups, which target either an area of law (e.g. intellectual property) or an industry group (e.g. health care).

One Metropolitan Square
11 North Broadway, Suite 3600
St. Louis, MO 63102
Tel: 314-259-2000   Fax: 314-259-2020

BRYN MAWR COLLEGE
Colleges

Katharine Hepburn went to Bryn Mawr and in many ways, she's still a workable emblem for the place and its virtues. The college of 1200 female undergraduates (and 500 grad students of both genders) is on, but perhaps not of, Philadelphia's venerable Main Line. That is to say, like its distinguished alumna, Bryn Mawr builds on its fine lineage while never being confined by it. That sense of utter correctness one gets is not a lack of imagination or curiosity, but a rigorous attention to detail and an insistence on getting things right. No wonder, then, that Bryn Mawr sends a greater percentage of its students to doctoral programs than any other institution in the United States.

101 North Merion Avenue
Bryn Mawr, PA 19010
Tel: 610-526-5000   Fax: 610-526-5138

BUNNY WILLIAMS
Architects and Interior Designers

Like her predecessor Nancy Lancaster, who influenced generations of decorators in Britain as the doyenne of Colefax & Fowler, Bunny Williams's strong tradition of gracious southern living, coupled with a knowledge of English antique furniture, has helped the soft-spoken Virginian to carve out a remarkable career. A member of the Interior Design Hall of Fame, her elegant work is regularly featured in *Architectural Digest*, *House and Garden*, *House Beautiful* and *Elle Décor*. Williams has had design projects in New York, California, Texas, Florida, Maine and even the South of France, with homes varying from a penthouse to a ranch. A partner in Treillage, a garden furniture shop in Manhattan, Williams is the author of the book *On Garden Style*, which won the 1999 "Quill and Trowel" Award.

306 East 61st Street, 5th Floor
New York, NY 10021
Tel: 212-207-4040
Fax: 212-207-4353

BURGUNDY WINE COMPANY
Wine Merchants

This exceptional wine merchant only carries the wines of Burgundy and the Rhone Valley and the same grape varieties (Pinot Noir, Syrah and Chardonnay) as found in California and Oregon. All wines are hand selected by Albert Hotchkin and Geraldine Tashjian, who visit the cellars of every producer they carry at least once a year. They follow the wines from harvest to bottle to ensure that only those wines which genuinely impress them are stocked in the shop. Their cellars contain over 100,000 bottles, from fabled Grand Crus to delicious, hand-crafted wines for everyday drinking. All wines, regardless of cost, are kept under impeccable temperature controlled conditions of 53 to 55 degrees. Every effort is made to ensure their clients receive bottles as if they just came out of the finest Burgundian cellars. Burgundy Wine Company publishes a monthly client newsletter which includes vintage information, background on producers, as well as totally objective tasting notes – not the opinions or scores of assorted "experts." People interested in receiving this free newsletter have only to contact the company. Warmly recommended.

323 West 11th Street
New York, NY 10014
Tel: 212-691-9092   Fax: 212-691-9244

C & M ARTS
Art Dealers

Specializing in postwar American art, C & M regularly shows works by Willem de Kooning, Jackson Pollock, Arshile Gorky and Andy Warhol. The gallery won Best Art Gallery Show (nominated by the International Association of Art Critics) for its recent exhibition of Picasso's portraits of his lover Dora Maar, alongside de Kooning representations of women. Meanwhile, *Women of Warhol: Marilyn, Liz and Jackie* was widely acclaimed as one of the best shows last year.

45 East 78th Street
New York, NY 10021
Tel: 212-861-0020   Fax: 212-861-7858

CAFÉ ANNIE
Restaurants

Café Annie has long been at the forefront of southwestern dining. Managed by the charming Lonnie Schiller, the Café seduces tony diners with its lofty ceilings, black and white limestone floors and leather banquettes. Executive chef Robert Del Grande has a Ph.D. in biochemistry, which may explain why he's so good at pairing colors and flavors. Specialties include rabbit enchiladas with red chile mole, beef breaded in roasted coffee beans and a delectable goat cheese crepe.

1728 Post Oak Boulevard
Houston, TX 77056
Tel: 713-840-1111   Fax: 713-840-1558

CAFÉ ALLEGRO
Restaurants

Offering an ethnically diverse menu, this enchanting restaurant is simple and elegant. Chefs Ted Habiger and Curtis Carter change their menu frequently. Favorites include a veal tenderloin wrapped in Italian pancetta, which is grilled over pecan logs, sliced and arranged with wood toasted polenta, sautéed garlic, broccolini and a zinfandel veal sauce. A 40 page wine list showcases top French clarets.

1815 West 38th Street
Kansas City, MO 64111
Tel: 816-561-3663
Fax: 816-756-3265

CAFÉ DES AMIS
Restaurants

Brothers Gary and Dennis Baker's intimate country bistro has just 13 tables; there is no best table here and, conversely, no Siberia. In an equally democratic (or merely eccentric?) vein, there is never a guaranteed menu. On Monday, there could be three entrees and on Tuesday, 12. But the restaurant remains a local favorite, particularly among Portland's young (and not so young) lovers. The small space is decorated in oak, dressed in blue and mahogany linens. Specialties include a fillet of beef with port garlic sauce and seared duck with blackberry sauce. Warmly recommended.

1987 Kearney Street NW
Portland, OR 97209
Tel: 503-295-6487

CAFÉ L'EUROPE
Restaurants

In their careers as restaurateurs – spanning five establishments and thirty years – Lidia and Norbert Goldner have always emphasized the significance of top flight service, outstanding cuisine and a warm, inviting ambiance. Lidia, a fabulous hostess with a nose for good wine, is ably assisted out front by Maitre d' Bruce Strickland, whose civility and competence are legendary. As executive chef, Norbert presides over a team who help to create his award-winning French-Continental cuisine. As for the elegant, flower strewn dining room, the Goldners have never hired an interior designer in their lives. You cannot teach good taste: some people, it seems, have got it in spades.

331 South County Road
Palm Beach, FL 33480
Tel: 561-655-4020
Fax: 561-659-6619

CAKEBREAD CELLARS
Winemakers

Jack Cakebread began his career as an auto mechanic and aspiring photographer. In 1973, he was commissioned by Nathan Chroman to take photographs for his *Treasury of American Wines*. Scouting for locations, Cakebread stumbled upon a run-down old ranch being offered for $2500. Today the charismatic connoisseur oversees 165 acres, producing multiple vintages, including the reserve line 'Three Sisters.' The family-owned operation includes sons Dennis, Steve and Bruce and wife Dolores, who is a master chef and gardener. Cakebread lives on New York time, heading down to the vineyards at 3:30 a.m. He explains that he works so hard because "If I can't sell the wine, I'll have to drink it, so it better be good."

8300 St. Helena Highway
Rutherford, CA 94573
Tel: 707-963-5221
Fax: 707-963-1067

CALDWELL SNYDER GALLERY
Art Dealers

In 1982, lifelong art lovers Oliver Caldwell and Susan Snyder founded their namesake gallery on San Francisco's famed Sutter Street. In the past 18 years, the duo have amassed a colossal collection of the finest in contemporary American art, including works by the likes of Cole, Morgan, Regina Saura, Mamel and Anaro. Director Kathryn Foave opens the two story space to the public seven days a week.

341 Sutter Street
San Francisco, CA 94108
Tel: 415-392-2299
Fax: 415-392-4609

CALIFORNIA CULINARY ACADEMY
Culinary Schools

Once an aspiring doctor, Keith Keogh was led to cooking by fate – he has been in the kitchen for 23 years. President of arguably the finest culinary institution on the west coast, his mantra boasts: "teach to the soul of a chef, not the technician." Limited class size and four student-run restaurants enable the Academy to remain on top – so far on top that culinary voyagers from around the world travel to San Francisco solely to enrole in Keogh's classes. The CCA is also highly regarded for their catering of weddings, garden parties and black-tie benefits.

625 Polk Street
San Francisco, CA 94102
Tel: 415-771-3500
Fax: 415-771-2194

CALLAHAN CATERING
Party Organizers and Caterers
For "the love of a good party," Peter Callahan quit the Wall Street grind and in 1985, opened his catering company, based in New York and Philadelphia. The caterer of choice for many Upper East Side socialites and celebrities, recent events include Asian dinners on the beach with pillows along low slung tables, and hip downtown parties with pu pu platters and fish and chips in artists palates. Chef Beth Parker had her hands full with cooking for three simultaneous parties thrown by Al Gore. There is a strong emphasis on design and concept – the influence of Callahan's fashion designer wife, Josephine Sasso, perhaps.
205 East 95th Street
New York, NY 10028
Tel: 212-327-1144   Fax: 212-327-1096

CALLIGRAPHY STUDIOS
Specialty Shops
Need business cards hand-printed in German? Linda Stein has been creating one-of-a-kind invitations, announcements, greeting and business cards since 1979. Specializing in designing personal monograms for stars like Quincy Jones and Victoria Principal, her staff include exhibiting artists who work in every style and language.
100 Reade Street
New York, NY 10013
Tel: 212-964-6007   Fax: 212-964-9170

CALVERT WOODLEY
Wine Merchants
Calvert Woodley specializes in Bordeaux wines and wine futures. The store holds an extensive inventory of virtually every classified American and Australian wine and rare French wines such as Romanée Conti. Customers enjoy personalized service offered by the store's small staff of seven, each of whom has worked in the industry for up to 25 years. These experts travel to the wine areas of the world in search of savory finds and hold wine tastings every week.
4339 Connecticut Avenue NW
Washington, DC 20008
Tel: 202-966-4400

CALVIN KLEIN
Fashion
Despite all the talk about selling this fashion institution to the highest bidder, the eponymous firm is, thankfully, going to remain under the leadership of the great Mr. Klein (for the moment at least). His sleek and modern designs, both in apparel as well as home furnishings, are as popular as ever. At the spring 2001 show in New York, photographers were tripping over themselves to snap admirers like Gwyneth Paltrow, Marina Rust, Aerin Lauder and Julia Roberts – proof that after all this time (and many tribulations) Klein is still on top.
654 Madison Avenue
New York, NY 10021
Tel: 212-719-2600   Fax: 212-292-9787

CAMBERLEY BROWN
Hotels
Reflecting the South at its comfortable best since 1928, this legendary hotel in Theater Square is the center of Louisville's social scene. A short stroll from Churchill Downs, home of the Kentucky Derby, its opulent ballrooms and lobby host some of the most gracious functions in the state. Camberley's arts and antiques gallery is located on the premises, along with a men's fine clothing store, barber shop and salon. Try the horseradish smoked salmon at the English Grill, the only four diamond restaurant in the state and home of the Hot Brown.
335 West Broadway
Louisville, KY 40203
Tel: 502-583-1234   Fax: 502-587-7006

THE CAMBRIDGE SCHOOL OF CULINARY ARTS
Culinary Schools
Roberta L. Dowling's love of cooking inspired her to give occasional cooking classes in her home. Response to the classes grew and grew, until she decided to find a better location. Today, that site is the renowned Cambridge School of Culinary Arts, which emphasizes the tenets of cooking established by Antoine Carême, a master of *haute cuisine*, and Auguste Escoffier, the father of classical cuisine. Mrs. Dowling has taught French and Italian cuisine to professional chefs and restaurateurs around the country, and has catered private parties for Princess Grace of Monaco, Julia Child and Senator Edward Kennedy, among many others.
2020 Massachusetts Avenue
Cambridge, MA 02140
Tel: 617-354-2020
Fax: 617-576-1963

CAMPAGNE
Restaurants
A former journalist, Peter Lewis left his job when he fell in love with the food, wine and culture of Southern France. Hardly surprising, then, that the menu at his smart Seattle restaurant is reminiscent of a French bistro. Chef Daisley Gordon is best known for his orange mille-feuille, served with poached rhubarb and crispy ginger, and a delectable foie gras pastry, served with orange braised shallots and turnips. The simple, elegant dining room seats only 40, so call at least a week in advance. Guests vie to sit at a window table that looks out over Pike Place Market and Elliot Bay.
87 Pine Street
Seattle, WA 98101
Tel: 206-728-2800   Fax: 206-448-7740

CAMPTON PLACE
Hotels
Rated as one of the top 10 hotels in America by *Condé Nast Traveler*, Campton Place is a quintessential boutique hotel in the heart of San Francisco, just yards from the edge of Union Square. Run with meticulous professionalism and genuine care for the well-being of guests, the hotel was obviously conceived by someone who knows well the perks of international travel, like Italian linens, English toiletries and a restaurant that makes every other eatery seem so far away. Add the most charming concierge service in America today, and you have something approaching the perfect city hotel.
340 Stockton Street
San Francisco, CA, 94108
Tel: 415-781-5555

CAMPANILE
Restaurants

Husband and wife owners Mark Peel & Nancy Silverton met in the kitchen of Wolfgang Puck's Spago. They opened Campanile & Le Brea Bakery in 1989. The Campanile itself was built by Charlie Chaplin in the 1920s, for his office; before it was completed he lost it in a divorce settlement to his first wife, Lita Grey. Serving Californian and Mediterranean fare in a chic venue, Campanile is consistently acclaimed as one of the best restaurants in L.A. Peel trained at two of France's greatest restaurants, La Tour d'Argents and Roger Vergé's Moulin de Mougins.

624 S. La Brea Avenue
Los Angeles, CA 90036
Tel: 323-938-1447
Fax: 323-938-5840

~

CAMPBELL, DETTMAN & PANTON
Property Consultants

Before establishing her own firm in 1992, Barbara Campbell was vice president of LCA, a major player in the Harbor Beach real estate market. A 40 year veteran of the industry, Campbell's clientele consists of celebrities, political figures and dot com entrepreneurs who simply explain what they are looking for — Campbell does all the leg work, offering homes with ocean views, private beaches, access to private marinas and 24-hour security.

2228 Southeast 17th Street
Fort Lauderdale, FL 33316
Tel: 954-525-2170
Fax: 954-527-1006

~

CANTERBURY HOTEL
Hotels

When a celebrity guest needed a specific brand of kitty litter and litter pan, general manager Letitia Moscrip found them. The only four star property in Indiana, the Canterbury Hotel is a historical landmark — so historical, in fact, that to add a freight elevator would be illegal. (Service people are kind enough to step out when guests step in). Guests used to being pampered will enjoy the presidential suite — equipped with two bedrooms and baths, a dining room that seats eight and a kitchen with a private service entrance. The acclaimed Restaurant at Canterbury is led by German chef Völker Rudolph, who has had a loyal, local following for the past 15 years.

123 S. Illinois Street
Indianapolis, IN 46225
Tel: 317-634-3000
Fax: 317-685-2519

CANNON/BULLOCK
INTERIOR DESIGN
Specialty Shops

Richard Cannon and Richard Bullock are interested in what makes a space a memorable experience, an interior landscape of value, depth and beauty. Joining their considerable talents in the 1980s, they formed Cannon/Bullock. With backgrounds in Architecture, Interior Design and Product Design they provide residential and corporate interior design. All their products and accessories are handmade, including furniture, wall coverings, rugs, window shades, lighting, tassels and trims, which are available through showrooms across the nation. They have recently introduced Suspensions, a resin laminate building product with handmade papers which can be used for everything from walls, furniture and case goods, to lighting fixtures and window treatments. Striving to blend the ancient and the new, once they have selected hand-made materials from around the world, Cannon/Bullock designers paint, sew and finish all products by hand, blending the ancient and the new to create a fresh customized design. Within the context of function, their mission is to create spaces that are both dramatic and memorable, whether traditional, period or contemporary and by mixing styles and periods, to create interiors which clients are only too happy to call their own.

4975 Valley Boulevard
Los Angeles, CA 90032
Tel: 323-221-9286   Fax: 323-221-9287

CANYON RANCH
Spas and Clinics

Rated best spa of 1999 by *Travel & Leisure*, Canyon Ranch is a 65,000 square-foot complex, spanning 70 acres in the foothills of the Santa Cruz mountains, one of the largest of its kind in North America. Staff include nutritionists, physicians, nurses, exercise physiologists, massage therapists and acupuncturists. There are 40 fitness classes per day, spiritual awareness classes, smoking cessation lectures and health consultations. A new 11,000 square-foot, $1.4 million Aquatic Center features three Watsu pools and two aqua therapy facilities.

8600 East Rockcliff Road
Tucson, AZ 85750
Tel: 520-749-9000   Fax: 520-749-1646

CANYON RANCH IN THE BERKSHIRES

Hotels

Marrying New England charm with modern luxuries, this 126 room health resort is within walking distance of the beautiful town of Lenox. 50 fitness classes are offered each day (everything from aerobics to t'ai chi) as well as creative arts classes, including painting and pottery. Doctors and nutritionists give daily lectures; low-fat, low-cholesterol meals are offered (alongside more sybaritic fare for the indulgent) and a full range of beautifying treatments are available.

165 Kemble Street
Lenox, MA 01240
Tel: 413-637-4100   Fax: 413-637-0057

CAREY INTERNATIONAL

Chauffeur Services

While meetings of world importance are being held, the chauffeurs of Carey International assure that everything is perfect—at least, to and from the airport. Political leaders, writers, sports players and CEOs rely on Carey International; the company's cars can be spotted at NFL games, the Grammys and other high-profile events. Operating in 420 cities in 65 countries, Carey always provides an English-speaking driver.

4530 Wisconsin Avenue NW
Washington, DC 20016
Tel: 202-895-1200   Fax: 202-895-1279

THE CARLYLE

Hotels

At the time of writing, the Carlyle Hotel is for sale. Despite fears that this wonderful institution could fall into the wrong hands, it remains one of the most impressive addresses in New York. The guest list reads like a who's who of world affairs, business and entertainment. Renowned among discerning Europeans as an exquisite retreat from the frenetic pace of life in the city, it is a legend among Manhattan hotels. Most of the lavishly appointed bedrooms and suites boast bathrooms with Jacuzzis and many have views of Central Park. Each room is individually designed, with delicate accessories such as chintz coverlets, antique satin boudoir chairs, or porcelain vases. The Carlyle Restaurant is one of the most comfortable dining rooms in New York. And after dinner, guests enjoy a drink in the elegant Bemelmans Bar or finish the night at the Café Carlyle, listening to the magical sounds of Bobby Short or Eartha Kitt.

35 East 76th Street
New York, NY 10021
Tel: 212-744-1600   Fax: 212-439-5878

CARIBOU CLUB

Private Clubs

The Caribou Club is not just the best place to be in Aspen. It is simply, says one New York newspaper, "the best private club in America." Wander down Caribou Alley. That's where you'll find the unmarked entrance of the club, which is located inside a 19th century architectural gem left over from silver boomtown days. Harley Baldwin – the king of Aspen – is sure to be there, presiding over the rich, famous and celebrated. Kevin Costner, Sally Field, Diana Ross, Don Johnson, Michael Douglas and Catherine Zeta-Jones are all members. In fact, on some nights it seems as if half of Hollywood is there along with the club's well-heeled locals, relaxing in the comfortable English-style surroundings and enjoying the great food and extraordinary cellar. Chef Miles Angelo, managing partner Louis Valasquez and sommelier to the spoiled, Oliver Jaderko, run the show. Dancing goes late. Actually, the only problem may be getting in. Ask a member to propose you. It should take about a year.

411 East Hopkins Avenue
Aspen, CO 81611
Tel: 970-925-2929

CARLYLE WINES

Wine Merchants

Pianist David Oei's hobby of collecting fine wines became rather serious in 1994, when he opened Carlyle, showcasing French, Italian and California vintages, brandies and spirits. The shop is a regular stomping ground for a very loyal but transient crowd, including Woody Allen, Sharon Stone and Kevin Bacon. Oei - who only drinks French burgundies - explains that although his customers summer elsewhere, winter elsewhere and travel for the holidays, they always come in to the store while in New York, and always stock up.

997 Madison Avenue
New York, NY 10021
Tel: 212-744-1028

CARLETON VARNEY DESIGN GROUP

Architects and Interior Designers

One of America's best-known interior designers, Carleton Varney heads Dorothy Draper & Co., the oldest established interior design firm in the United States. Varney's impressive roster of clients include superstars from the worlds of entertainment, fashion and business. The company is associated with the restoration and decoration of countless hotels, resorts, castles and private residences in Europe, the Caribbean, Asia and the U.S., including Dromoland and Ashford Castles in Ireland; The Grand on Mackinac Island; The Breakers, The Waldorf Towers and The Plaza Hotel in the U.S., as well as the Official Vice President's Residence in Washington D.C. and the U.S. Embassy in Tokyo. Varney was the White House design consultant to President and Mrs. Jimmy Carter. Varney's versatility in design can be seen in the wide range of products that bear his mark, ranging from dinnerware and crystal to furniture, light fixtures and linen designs. Varney and his sons, Nicholas and Sebastian, have recently designed a line of furniture (Varney & Sons) for Kindel of Grand Rapids.

60 East 56th Street
New York, NY 10022
Tel: 212-758-2810   Fax: 212-759-0739

CAROL DOPKIN REAL ESTATE

Property Consultants

With Carol Dopkin, clients meander along the Colorado countryside on horse-back, viewing executive estates, condominiums, land, commercial and investment properties. Dopkin, an Aspen resident, is so enthusiastic about the town that many clients contact her after purchasing a home to ask where the best French restaurant is or who the most reputable drycleaner is. Her team offers services that range from hiring household help to getting telephones installed to car service.

122 West Main Street
Aspen, CO 81611
Tel: 800-920-1186   Fax: 970-920-1976

CARROLL & CO.

Fashion

A publicist for Warner Brothers Studio, Richard Carroll was startled to find that in 1949 a man would have to travel across town to find a good suit. Inconvenienced and harried, Carroll was almost late for his brother's wedding because of traffic returning from a last minute alteration. He left the entertainment field to begin his custom-tailoring business on the then-sleepy Rodeo Drive. Now the premier source for men's fine clothing in Beverly Hills, Carroll & Company has a long tradition of quality, service and precise tailoring. With an inventory that includes Oxford, Savile Row and Hickey-Freeman, the firm carries the finest in updated traditional menswear.

425 North Canon Drive
Beverly Hills, CA 90210
Tel: 310-273-9060   Fax: 310-273-7974

CARSWELL RUSH BERLIN

Antiques   ***Best Kept Secret***

Carswell Rush Berlin grew up in a home steeped in American decorative arts and surrounded by fine examples of 18th century American furniture; his father had been a passionate collector. Today, he is a leader in bringing important examples of Sheraton, Directoire, Empire and French Restoration furniture to the market, focusing only on pieces from the finest designers and cabinet-makers in the world. Berlin offers dining tables, desks, armchairs, mirrors, sofas, stools and other pieces to private collectors by appointment only.

P.O. Box 0210, Planetarium Station
New York, NY 10024
Tel: 212-721-0330   Fax: 212-580-2095

CESSNA

Airplanes

When Clyde Cessna first took flight in his beloved Silver Wings in 1911, the die was cast. The eponymous company founded a few years later would embrace his legacy with an ongoing commitment to building the finest aircraft possible. Today, Cessna is the the only aircraft company in the world that designs, engineers and builds every model that carries its name. The three best-selling aircraft of all time are Cessnas and no wonder — from the Skyhawk to the Caravan to their newest Citation CJ2 — Cessna is the world leader in business jets.

One Cessna Boulevard
Wichita, KS 67215
Tel: 316-517-6000
Fax: 316-517-7812

CAROLINA HERRERA

Fashion

The late Diana Vreeland once called Carolina Herrera "la bombe." Herrera is intelligent, beautiful, radiant, like the matinée idols of yore — but with the tenacity and energy of today's stars. Her collection, like the lady herself, is the embodiment of elegance, luxury and sophistication. From her first show at New York's Metropolitan Club in 1980, the Venezuelan born designer has been a success — to put it mildly. In fact, of all the so-called "society" designers of her day, Herrera is the only one to survive. When you look at her lines, her colors, her cuts, you understand why — real style and class are eternal. "Business is very good right now," says Herrera, "But you always want to do more. That's the constant challenge."

954 Madison Avenue,
New York, NY 10021
Tel: 212-954-5757

CHAIKEN
Fashion

Once best known for their signature pants, Chaiken, under the direction of new designer Jeff Mahshie, has now expanded into everything from sportswear to eveningwear. Recently a design consultant for John Bartlett, Mahshie has taken Chaiken's classic image and broadened its scope – adding new divisions such as swimwear and a larger selection of the company's already exquisite knits. With details on a par with Savile Row, Chaiken caters to the woman who knows the meaning of true style.

580 Broadway, Suite 400
New York, NY 10012
Tel: 212-334-3501
Fax: 212-334-3504

CHARLES NOB HILL
Restaurants

A favorite among the critics, Charles Nob Hill stands out even in a city that loves food and has an abundance of restaurants to prove it. Chef Ron Siegel brings his experience at French Laundry and Restaurant Daniel to bear here in the landmark Clay-Jones building, preparing impressive French cuisine with a contemporary American flavor (try one of his signature dishes, such as Duck breast au poivre). Incidentally, Siegel was the first American chef ever to win the prestigious *Iron Chef* competition, a televised culinary battle in Japan.

1250 Jones Street
San Francisco, CA 94109
Tel: 415-771-5400   Fax: 415-771-3542

THE CASTLE AT TARRYTOWN
Hotels

Crowning the region's highest hilltop, the Castle At Tarrytown overlooks the picturesque Hudson River. Its stone facade, Gothic windows and Romanesque archways are more reminiscent of Medieval Britain than 21st century Hudson Valley, but the luxury, tranquility and service are not. This small deluxe hotel is the brainchild of Hanspeter and Steffi Walder, who bought The Castle, which was built over 100 years ago as a private residence. After scouring antiques shops in the U.S. and abroad, renovating extensively and redecorating, the Walders' realized their dream of offering guests a European hotel experience without going to Europe. Two short years later the hotel became a member of Relais & Chateaux. The year after opening they added more deluxe rooms and a fitness center. They continue to improve the hotel, with the addition this year of a tennis court and swimming pool. After a sumptuous dinner in the Equus Restaurant and drinks in the outdoor bar, overlooking the Hudson River, you could be forgiven for forgetting you are only 35 minutes from Manhattan.

400 Benedict Avenue
Tarrytown, NY 10591
Tel: 914-631-1980   Fax: 914-631-4612

CHALONE VINEYARD
Winemakers

Chalone is in John Steinbeck country, east of Salinas, some 2000 feet up in the rugged Gavilan Mountains. Around the turn of the century a Frenchman named Curtis Tamm ventured up there to plant vines in the limestone rich soil, but the winery as we know it did not come to fruition until Dick Graff and friends took over in the 1960s. Graff established strict Burgundian growing rules which remain in place today. Chalone mainly produces award-winning Chardonnay, but look out for their well priced, well made Pinot Noir.

P.O. Box 518
Soledad, CA 93960
Tel: 831-678-1717
Fax: 831-678-2742

CHARLESTON GRILL
Restaurants

Fusing low-country cooking and his own French-influenced technique, Chef Bob Waggoner creates contemporary southern haute cuisine using seasonal and regional ingredients. On an ordinary day, the California native dishes up pan seared lamb sweetbreads over truffled grits, local young zucchini blossoms stuffed with Maine Lobster and Smoky Mountain golden trout, served with crawfish tails. Winner of *Food and Wine*'s "Reader's Favorite Chef in North America" Award, Waggoner is a master with rabbit, oysters, crabmeat, fish, greens and grains. The Vintner's Room seats 40 – Sommelier Mark Ray offers over 16,385 vintages, representing 806 selections.

224 King Street
Charleston, SC 29401
Tel: 843-577-4522   Fax: 843-724-8405

CHARLIE TROTTER'S
Restaurants

One of the first American restaurants to feature a table in the kitchen, Charlie Trotter's has long been regarded as one of the finest restaurants in the country. After graduating college in 1982 with a degree in political science, Trotter embarked on an intense, four-year period of study and travel, including internships with celebrated chefs Norman Van Aken, Bradley Ogden and Gordon Sinclair. After reading every cookbook he could get his hands on and eating out incessantly, he developed a celebrated cooking style, rooted in the classic French tradition. Make reservations six weeks in advance.

816 W. Armitage Avenue
Chicago, IL 60614
Tel: 773-248-6228
Fax: 773-248-6088

CHARLOTTE MOSS INTERIOR DESIGN
Architects and Interior Designers

Charlotte Moss is an interior designer, lecturer and author. She spent a successful decade on Wall Street before launching a career in the world of interiors. Moss designs furniture and decorative accessories under license and produces her own home fragrance. She creates interiors that reflect the lifestyles of her clients by emphasizing the basic elements of comfort, practicality, and hospitality to produce surroundings that are at once elegant, distinctive, personal and functional.

16 East 65th Street
New York, NY 10021
Tel: 212-772-6244
Fax: 212-734-7250

CHASE INTERNATIONAL
Property Consultants

After visiting Lake Tahoe, Mark Twain wrote "Surely this is the fairest picture the whole earth affords." No-one is more conscious of this than Shari Chase, who recently sold a local property (Thunderbird Lodge, the Dreyfus Estate) for $60 million, the highest priced residential property in American history. Chase now has a London office, where she represents affluent Americans and Europeans in search of truly outstanding homes on both continents. Casino Developer Steve Wynn is a client.

195 Highway 50, Suite 201
Lake Tahoe, NV 89448
Tel: 775-588-6130
Fax: 775-588-1206

THE CHARLOTTE INN
Hotels

Located in the middle of Edgartown on a quiet side street, The Charlotte Inn is a refined collection of 18th and 19th century houses representing a bygone era. The guest rooms and common rooms have a distinctive Edwardian look with beautiful antique furnishings and artwork. Purposely 'behind the times,' the Inn strives to provide a peaceful, quiet atmosphere for guests to enjoy and unwind in, whether it be on the private terraces viewing the formal gardens, or relaxing in front of the fire in cooler months. L'Etoile, the Inn's exquisite restaurant, offers contemporary French cuisine in a conservatory feeling dining room, including an outdoor terrace in the season.

27 South Summer Street
Edgartown, MA 02539
Tel: 508-627-4751   Fax: 508-627-4652

CHASE MANHATTAN PRIVATE BANK
Wealth Management

Chase Manhattan offers private banking clients a broad range of sophisticated opportunities in alternate asset classes, such as hedge funds and investments in private equity and venture capital funds, while allowing clients (who have at least a million dollars) to make their own investment decisions. Chase managers offer up-to-the-minute expertise on financial solutions, tailored to clients' specific needs. Since the Rockefeller era, this bank has emphasized its "integrated approach to entrepreneurship and wealth management," and has long boasted a strong reputation within the industry.

205 Royal Palm Way
Palm Beach, FL 33480
Tel: 561-838-8700   Fax: 561-838-8778

CHATEAU DU SUREAU
Hotels

The closest thing to the French countryside near one of the most stunning destinations in North America – Yosemite National Park – Chateau du Sureau is a small, intimate hotel that reflects another time. The ten rooms in this Relais & Chateaux, five star, five diamond dream spot are each named after a different herb or flower to reflect their uniquely opulent and dramatic qualities, including canopy beds, wood-burning fireplaces, antique furnishings and views of the garden and the magnificent Sierra Nevada. In the estate's nature park, Villa Sureau, a luxurious two bedroom, turn-of-the-century style Parisian villa awaits the most discriminating guests.

48688 Victoria Lane, P.O. Box 577
Oakhurst, CA 93644
Tel: 559-683-6860
Fax: 559-683-0800

CHARLESTON PLACE
Hotels

Host to President Clinton, Bruce Willis and Mel Gibson, this elegant four star hotel is *the* place to stay while in South Carolina. Charleston Place's lobby is inspiring with its stunning marble floors and oversized chandeliers. Spa services include waxing, facials, massage and skin care consultations. Located in the heart of the downtown area, guests are only a block away from King Street, which offers the finest antiques and boutique shopping in South Carolina.

205 Meeting Street
Charleston, SC 29401
Tel: 843-722-4900
Fax: 843-724-7215

CHATEAU MONTELENA
Winemakers

The quest for great Cabernet Sauvignon has been the predominant goal of Chateau Montelena since day one. Jim Barrett bought the outfit in 1972, after 50 years of neglect, instilling a simple philosophy: "Make the best, period." In 1973, that philosophy (and a lot of hard work) paid off when the 1973 Chardonnay was rated above all other wines in a Paris tasting. Today, Jim's son Bo is the winemaker, offering sought-after vintages, including a complex 1996 Montelena Estate Cabernet Sauvignon, displaying intense varietal character of leather, briar, cassis and oak.

1429 Tubbs Lane
Calistoga CA 94515
Tel: 707-942-5105

CHEF ALLEN'S
Restaurants

Chef Allen Susser is one of the most innovative minds in the sunshine state. The culinary master trained at Bristol Hotel in Paris and the exclusive Turnberry Country Club in Florida before opening his signature eatery and developing "New World Cuisine," combining flavors only available in the surrounding areas of southern Florida and the Caribbean. Start with the Petrossian Beluga and move on to the Tribeca veal chop with almond-saffron risotto, wild mushroom ragout and double mustard sauce. Leave room for the chocolate strawberry macadamia soufflé – though if Pat Riley and the Miami Heat are in, you may want to order one ahead of time.

19088 Northeast 29th Avenue
Aventura, FL 33180
Tel: 305-935-2900
Fax: 305-935-9062

CHRISTOPHER WALLING
Jewelry and Watches

The only store of the internationally renowned jeweler, Christopher Walling, is located where else? – in Aspen, Colorado. You pass by it as you make your way down the Alley from Fendi and the Caribou Club. Described by Sotheby's as "undoubtedly one of the most exciting jewelry designers on the scene today," Walling's flower pins of abalone and freshwater pearl petals adorned with diamonds and rubies are rivaling his already famous X pearl earrings. Known in the jewelry world as a colorist for his exceptional stones, Walling's distinctive style is characterized by clear lines and unusual combinations. Aspenites wear Christopher Walling with gowns and they wear it playing polo or skiing. Princess Firyal of Jordan, Brooke Haywood and Elizabeth Taylor have all commissioned the Paris born, American designer to create one-of-a-kind pieces.

431 East Hopkins Avenue
Aspen, CO 81611
Tel: 970-925-1930   Fax: 970-925-1993

CHEF RETO'S RESTAURANT
Restaurants

In 1991, chef-owner Reto Demarmels opened his signature restaurant with his wife Lynne. A veteran of Four Seasons Hotels around the world, his "Geo-classical cuisine" is clearly a hit – the restaurant's 80 seat capacity is pushed to the limit almost every night. Try the walnut and garlic roasted clams or the outstanding rack of veal with sweet garlic sauce. This year, Demarmels launched Chef Reto's Catering, which can host anywhere from two to four hundred – at private homes or in ballrooms. The firm's clientele consists of corporate CEOs, *Fortune 500* executives and countless celebrities.

41 E. Palmetto Park Rd.
Boca Raton, FL 33432
Tel: 561-395-0633   Fax: 561-395-5074

CINDY GRIEM FINE JEWELS
Jewelry and Watches

Shopping at Cindy Griem's exquisite boutique-style jewelry salon is like looking through the jewelry collection of a friend with exceptionally good taste in a relaxed and informal surrounding. Designed using fine luxurious Fortuny fabrics — as well as silk Fortuny lamps of Venice, for which Cindy Griem is the exclusive dealer — the result is an intimate and inviting experience which caters to an international clientele. The salon is so inviting in fact, you will be hard-pressed not to spend a bundle. Griem's

creative selection of designers reflects the desires and needs of the modern savvy woman. The unparalleled pearl creations of Donna Vock meld luscious Tahitian and South Sea pearls with platinum, gold and diamonds to produce signature designs which complement the wearer. The works of Slane and Slane — strong lines of architecturally inspired gold and silver; Anne Pratt's award-winning collection of silver and gold crests and intaglios with pearls and precious stones; the platinum and gold creations of the house of Niessing — bold, detailed and strong; and Barbara Bagner, a long-featured designer, displays her one-of-a-kind works of art, created from 20-22 carat gold jewelry set with the most unique of stones. With such a fine array, even the most reluctant jewelry-shopper will certainly not want to leave Cindy Griem Fine Jewels empty handed.

112 South Mill Street
Aspen, CO 81611
Tel: 970-925-3800 Fax: 970-925-1800

CHISHOLM GALLERY
Art Dealers

Winner of a 1999 *Best of Palm Beach* Award, Chisholm Gallery houses a large collection of paintings, prints, sculpture, rare books and watercolors dedicated to polo. Based at the Palm Beach Polo and Country Club, Chisholm held Florida's first retrospective exhibition of rare equine memorabilia this year, organized by Cartier Jewelers.

The firm has served as Chisholm's largest supporter for the past 60 years. 100 rare objects were on display, including trophies, mallets, helmets, saddles and personal scrapbooks, loaned by polo's biggest superstars. The amicable Jeanne Chisholm is a tremendous resource for collectors and decorators.
13368 Polo Road West, La Quinta C-202
Wellington, FL 33414
Tel: 561-791-8607 Fax: 561-798-4582

CHEZ FRANCOIS
Restaurants

Executive Chef John D'Amico considers himself a contractor: "For 25 years, I have been building things with my hands." Located in an 1840s rustic, historical landmark building, the dining room is appropriately French, with brick walls and floors and dark, wooden beams. The outside patio seats only 40, so reservations are recommended. Specialties include *entrecôte au poivre* and a delectable *carré d'agneau au natural.*
555 Main Street
Vermilion, OH 44089
Tel: 440-967-0630

CHEZ PANISSE
Restaurants

Alice Waters *is* California cuisine. Since opening Chez Panisse in 1971, Waters has often been heralded as a seminal influence on contemporary American cooking. Her food is Southern French and Northern Italian inspired, and almost entirely seasonal and organic. Waters pairs only French, Spanish or Italian wines with her simple, "straightforward" cuisine, which is punctuated by olive oil, locally grown herbs, vegetables and grains.
1517 Shattuck Avenue
Berkeley, CA 94709
Tel: 510-548-5525 Fax: 510-548-0140

CHINESE PORCELAIN COMPANY
Antiques

Khalil Rizk and Conor Mahony offer a wide range of Chinese ceramics and works of art, Tibetan, Indian, Khmer and Vietnamese sculpture, as well as French furniture and decorations. Recent exhibitions have explored Khmer sculpture, Chinese enamels, 18th century Dutch decorative arts — and they recently mounted an acclaimed exhibition by contemporary Chinese painter, Liu Dan.
475 Park Avenue
New York, NY 10022
Tel: 212-838-7744 Fax: 212-838-4922

CHRISTIE'S GREAT ESTATES
Property Consultants

Christie's Great Estates, a subsidiary of Christie's plc, is a real estate marketing firm and leader in luxury residential sales. It operates through a network of more than 120 real estate firms, with over 500 offices and 14,000 agents in 13 countries. Affiliates have set record sales prices in locations as diverse as Mamaroneck, Paris, Sydney, Bermuda and Jupiter Island, Florida.
1850 Old Pecos Trail, Suite D
Santa Fe, NM 87505
Tel: 505-983-8733 Fax: 505-982-0348

CHUBB GROUP OF INSURANCE COMPANIES
Art Consultants

Running strong since 1882 on the principle "never compromise integrity," Chubb is a substantial insurance company with a long experience of appraising and insuring fine art, jewelry and furniture, offering itemized policies that cover even the largest, most valuable collections. The Masterpiece valuable articles program offers an international guarantee of your prized possessions either individually or under blanket coverage. Chubb offers residential, auto, excess liability and yacht insurance. Rest assured.

15 Mountain View Road
Warren, NJ 07059
Tel: 908-903-2000

CIBOLO CREEK RANCH
Hotels

Once the adobe fortress of outlaw Don Melitón, this extraordinary ranch still feels like the hiding spot it was in 1830, when Melitón, barely five feet tall, shot a man in a duel and fled the scene. Today, however, it is a good deal more comfortable. Home to celebrities enjoying a week of solitude, Houston socialites and European art cognoscenti, entrepreneur and historian John Poindexter's hideaway is also an important historical artifact (you won't see any 20th century amenities in the period setting). The 16 rooms, filled with antique Mexican and Spanish furnishings, are strikingly authentic (Is that an armoire? No, it's a bathroom entrance). As always, God is in the detail: guests are led to blazing bonfires after dinner, to gaze at shooting stars.

P.O. Box 44
Shafter, TX 79850
Tel: 915-229-3737   Fax: 915-229-3653

DENNIS CIRILLO, M.D
Cosmetic Surgeons

The Aspen Institute of Plastic and Reconstructive Surgery has gained an international reputation as a premier center for state-of-the-art cosmetic surgery in an exquisite alpine setting — a true spa environment where people can recuperate in comfort and anonymity. Director and founder Dennis Cirillo brought 20 years of experience to his Aspen practice; he was formerly the Chief of Plastic Surgery at Lutheran Medical Center in Manhattan. Known as one of the finest plastic surgeons in the country, Dr. Cirillo is a member of over fifteen national and professional societies and has published two books.

400 West Main Street, Suite 100
Aspen, CO 81611
Tel: 970-544-0500   Fax: 970-544-0566

CIRCLINE.COM
Websites

Circline, the premier dealer-driven marketplace for fine art and antiques, provides connoisseurs with an unparalleled selection of the highest quality pieces from hundreds of the world's most prestigious dealers. Collectors and design professionals can browse, research, or purchase from a "virtual inventory" with a market value in excess of $500 million. Circline is committed to quality and service:

each work is guaranteed for authenticity and accompanied by a photograph along with an in-depth description including history, country of origin, age and condition. To locate an item, visitors can search for a specific piece; browse the site looking for ideas; or even request that Circline staff find a particular item for them. Dealers, design professionals and collectors can take advantage of many other special services including an events calendar, and extensive online education. Over the past several years, Circline has established itself as the premier online destination for industry professionals and individual collectors seeking the world's finest art and antiques; like the 18th century French secretary and the 18th century Dutch hall bench, both above, courtesy of the Chinese Porcelain Company, a featured Circline dealer. For more information, visit www.circline.com.

One Park Avenue
New York, NY 10016
Tel: 212-817-9200

CITIBANK PRIVATE BANK
Wealth Management

With 100 offices in 58 cities and 31 countries, the Citibank Private Bank brings a global view to wealth management. Combining expertise, extraordinary service and personal attention, the firm's professionals bring a single-minded focus to help clients protect, grow and manage their wealth. Founded in 1998, it combined the banking, securities and insurance businesses of Citibank, Salomon Smith Barney and Travelers. Among the unique services of the firm is the Family Advisory Practice, counseling on business succession issues, inheritance, family governance and philanthropy. The minimum requirement for a private banking account is $3 million. Client business volumes rose to an all-time high of $140 billion in 1999, making Citibank Private Bank one of the largest private banks in the world.

153 East 53rd Street
New York, NY 10043
Tel: 212-627-3999

CLEVELAND MUSEUM OF ART

Museums

Set in the Fine Arts Garden, a 15-acre public landscaped park designed by the Olmsted Brothers, The Cleveland Museum of Art houses more than 30,000 works spanning 5000 years. From ancient Egyptian statues to Renaissance armor to van Gogh, the permanent collection boasts comprehensive Asian collections, medieval European art and pre-Colombian holdings. Recently, the museum has been active in acquiring 20th century art, adding important works by Warhol, Christo, Clemente, Richter and Close.

11150 East Boulevard
Cleveland, OH 44106
Tel: 216-421-7340   Fax: 216-229-5095

CLINTON HOWELL

Antiques

Specializing in antiques and fine art from the 18th and early 19th century, this gallery has enjoyed an enduring reputation, both for dealing in high quality objects and for Howell's scholarly approach to the business of selling antiques. Having studied antique furniture restoration in London, Howell returned to the US, where he opened a restoration workshop and began publishing the bimonthly, *Antique Furniture Newsletter*, which deals with connoisseurship, restoration, conservation and maintenance. Fusing the hands-on experience of a trained restorer with an extensive body of academic knowledge, his expertise and professionalism have contributed significantly to raising the profile of the antiques trade in New York.

19 East 74th Street
New York, NY 10021
Tel: 212-517-5879   Fax: 212-517-4826

CLODAGH

Architects and Interior Designers

Clodagh has no need for a last name, which implies a fame akin to Prince, Gwyneth and Hillary. Sadly not, but she is one of the best interior designers in America (ask Robert Redford). The Irishwoman's company pursues "total design," involving all the senses and all the elements. Renowned for an inventive and sensitive use of materials, her team of beautiful young assistants have a true understanding of their clients and a refreshingly quirky attitude— there may be talk of astrological signs or energy fields during a planning session. If you need a mantra (and some lost souls demand one) this is it: "contemplate, cleanse, clarify and then create."

670 Broadway, 4th Floor
New York, NY 10012
Tel: 212-780-5300
Fax: 212-780-5755

LE CIRQUE 2000

Restaurants

Feted by those who love great food and fun, Le Cirque is no mere New York restaurant – it is *the* New York restaurant. Housed in the landmark Villard Houses of the New York Palace Hotel, Sirio Maccioni's Madison Avenue gem is one very special eatery. Epicureans travel from around the globe to sample the distinctive creations of Chefs Sottha Khunn and Pierre Schaedelin, who add Asian touches to the menu, while ensuring that signature dishes like the Foie Gras Ravioli with Black Truffles stay true to their excellent form. Not to be upstaged, the daring interior by Adam Tihany combines classic elements of the century-old house with modern furnishings and colors; turning the rooms into a visual fantasy. And just in case you go out west, the Maccionis now have a branch of Le Cirque at the Bellagio in Las Vegas, so you will never need to run away to the circus.

455 Madison Avenue
New York, NY 10022
Tel: 212-303-7788   Fax: 212-303-7788

THE CLOISTER

Hotels

This luxurious retreat has lured visitors to Sea Island, Georgia since 1928. Amenities include private beaches, championship sports facilities, walkthrough gardens and a world-class, sea-side spa. Guests can also take part in walking tours of local historic sites, go horseback riding, play golf, or swim in two pools. A full orchestra accompanies evening dancing nightly. A popular getaway haven for honeymooners and couples celebrating anniversaries, the resort offers private cottage rentals.

100 Hudson Place
Sea Island, GA 31561
Tel: 912-638-3611   Fax: 912-638-5823

CLUB COLETTE

Restaurants

In just its second year of existence, Club Colette has already reaffirmed the reputation for excellence that Daniel Ponton first established with his private dinner club in Palm Beach in the early 1980s. Requests for membership quickly inundated his new Southampton dinner club, and the locale often attracted the "intimate" dinner parties of high-profile socialites during the summer season. Yet another reason to make the journey out to Long Island's eastern shores.

136 Main St.
Southampton, NY 11968
Tel: 631-283-1717

COEUR D'ALENE
Spas and Clinics

Duane Hegadone and Jerry Jaeger's pleasure palace, at the foot of the Idaho Rocky Mountains, is a self-contained, comprehensive service center, offering head to toe relief from facials to hot rock treatments. Herbal wraps, yoga and Shiatsu massage all complement the blissful view of the lakes from the lakefront meditation room. East meets west in this panoramic gem, enjoyed by John Travolta, Linda Hamilton and Pierce Brosnan, among many others. Incidentally, Coeur d'Alene also houses a luxury hotel and America's only floating golf green.

115 South Second Street
Coeur d'Alene, ID 83814
Tel: 208-765-4000
Fax: 208-664-7276

COFFIN & TROUT
Jewelry and Watches

Randy Coffin and David Trout's names often become a symbol for very special moments in someone's life. From wedding rings to fine watches, the operation, begun in 1984, offers an imaginative, distinctive collection of custom designed pieces as well as the work of Cédé, Judith Conway and Jaeger LeCoultre. The eye-catching settings of the Trigon and Bridges ring collections make maximum use of unusually colored gems and diamonds. Don't miss the impressive Mikimoto pearl collection nor the Rolex selection, including the Oyster Perpetual Lady-Datejust, set in 18 karat gold.

2442 East Camelback Road, Suite #18
Phoenix, AZ 85016
Tel: 602-956-1300
Fax: 602-956-8383

CLAREMONT RUG COMPANY
Specialty Shops

Antique rugs are clearly a passion for Jan David Winitz. When the President and Founder of the Claremont Rug Company talks about the rarely-found art-quality carpets he sells in his Bay Area galleries – using words like soul, inspiration and rapture – he could almost be mistaken for a hopeless romantic recalling the great love affair of his life. Of course, the extraordinary antique Persian rugs he carries, which range in price from $25,000 to well into the six figures, inspire awe in many people nowadays. Connoisseurs appreciate their great beauty, while savvy business people marvel at their value as an investment. First quality 19th century rugs have a double-digit increase annually, yet are only about one-tenth the price of similar quality paintings. The key is to find the rug that will both inspire your passion and be a wise investment, and that's where Winitz comes in. His clients rave about his keen eye for beauty and the first class service he offers, both of which are now available electronically for those who cannot make it to his gracious Oakland gallery complex.

6087 Claremont Avenue
Oakland, CA 94618
Tel: 510-654-0816   Fax: 510-654-8661

CLS TRANSPORTATION
Chauffeur Services

At CLS, the mission statement is simply: "To extend to our clients the highest degree of service possible, without intrusion." This blue-chip limousine company succeeds admirably, providing exceptional service, whether in a sedan, a stretch limousine, or a corporate aircraft. In addition, the company maintains a network of affiliates throughout the States and abroad to afford its clients great service literally anywhere in the world. From the unique demands of the famous, to the weary traveler looking forward to returning home, CLS consistently delivers a service beyond everyone's expectations.

6029 W. Slauson Avenue
Culver City, CA 90230
Tel: 800-266-2577   Fax: 310-397-1800

COLGIN
Winemakers

At a charity auction, an enthusiastic young couple asked Ann Colgin to autograph a bottle of her wine that they had just purchased. Colgin kissed the label, thus giving birth to the firm's official signature. The California native may well have the most exhausted lips on the west coast. More than 4000 people currently languish on her winery's waiting list. The 1994 Cabernet Sauvignon is rich and beefy, delivering currant, bay leaf, cherry and tar notes; unfortunately, only 400 cases were produced. With 1000 customers on Colgin's mailing list, everyone else must try their luck at auction, where fans are willing to pay up to 10 times the release price.

P.O. Box 491848
Los Angeles, CA 90049
Tel: 707-963-0999   Fax: 310-889-0085

CONGRESSIONAL COUNTRY CLUB
Golf Clubs

Ernie Els won his second U.S. Open on the Congressional Country Club's daunting Blue Course in 1997, edging out Colin Montgomerie by one stroke. The thrilling finale befitted a club with a 75 year history of championship golf. The work of original designer Devereaux Emmett on the Blue and Gold courses has been enhanced over the years by Donald Ross, Rees Jones, Robert Trent Jones Sr. and Tom Fazio. Featuring rigorous par fours and rolling hills, the Blue Course is the longest ever to host a U.S. Open.

8500 River Road
Bethesda, MD 20817
Tel: 301-469-2000
Fax: 301-469-2036

CONOVER REAL ESTATE
Property Consultants

Martha's Vineyard, with its preserved historical character and carefully protected natural environment, offers a perfect setting for romantic hideaways, vacations or wonderful year-round living. From rolling horse farms to fabulous beach front estates, Conover specializes in luxurious and distinctive properties, ranging from $500,000 to $12 million. Founded in 1988 by Gerret C. Conover and Thomas LeClair, the company, which has five sales associates and two real estate brokers, prides itself on giving clients personalized service — you might feel like the only one.

20 South Summer Street
Edgartown, MA 02539
Tel: 508-627-3757   Fax: 508-627-8617

CONTEMPORARY ART MUSEUM
Museums

Opened as Kunsthalle in October 1967, the Museum of Contemporary Art was created by a group of culturally concerned Chicagoans who recognized the need for an internationally oriented forum for contemporary art in Chicago. Today, the MCA collection includes more than 5300 works and features minimalism, post minimalism, conceptualism and surrealism. Artists represented in the collection include Francis Bacon, Ann Hamilton, Cindy Sherman and Andy Warhol. In 1996, MCA was renovated, extending the gallery to 45,000 square feet.

220 East Chicago Avenue
Chicago, IL 60611
Tel: 312-280-2660
Fax: 312-397-4095

MICHELLE COPELAND, M.D.
Cosmetic Surgeons

Some patients say that the best thing about Michelle Copeland's practice is that they never have to sit in a hospital waiting room, filling out annoying forms, exposed for the whole world to see. It's true that the practice has an on-site operating room and post-operative care center. A leading member of the American Society for Aesthetic Plastic Surgeons, Copeland is preferred by many New Yorkers for liposuction, face-lifts, breast augmentations and lifts and equally for her perfectionism, personalized attention and gentle demeanor.

1001 Fifth Avenue
New York, NY 10028
Tel: 212-452-2200   Fax: 212-452-2200

LE COQ AU VIN
Restaurants

Louis Perrotte's casual, French country restaurant is where other chefs dine on their nights off. Considered by many to be the best restaurant in Florida, Le Coq au Vin offers three dining rooms, accented in warm hues, offering an unpretentious feel. But it's the food and service that makes some fanatics hate to leave. Signature dishes include the restaurant's namesake, a braised chicken with red burgundy wine and a salmon with horseradish sauce on braised cabbage. Utilizing fresh, local ingredients, Perrotte changes the menu every two months to emphasize different regions in France.

4800 S. Orange Avenue
Orlando, FL 32806
Tel: 407-851-6980
Fax: 407-248-0658

CRÈME DE LA MER
Hair and Beauty

Crème de la Mer has been a legend since it was first created more than three decades ago. Inventor and NASA aerospace physicist Max Huber, set out to help himself after he suffered a horrific accident when a routine experiment exploded in his face covering him with disfiguring scars. Twelve years and over 6000 experiments later, he perfected a crème that would help give skin a dramatically smoother appearance.

Today, the legend has grown and La Mer has acquired a cult following with devotees that include Hollywood celebrities and New York socialites. Austrian Countess Lucienne von Doz swears that she has found the Fountain of Youth in the two-ounce jars. Leonard Lauder was also attracted to the cream because of its homemade roots, similar to the one with which his mother Estée launched her business.

Leonard Lauder was in fact so attracted to the formula that he acquired the company after Max Huber's death. The product continues to be made in the exact same way as day one, and still maintains its low-key marketing approach. Borrowing from the original vision, the followers of Max Huber have created the next generation of products that includes facial and body treatments. All are made in a manner as miraculous as the crème he originally pioneered. The legend continues. La Mer is available at Bergdorf Goodman and select Neiman Marcus and Saks Fifth Avenue locations.

767 Fifth Avenue
New York, NY 10153
Tel: 212-572-4322
Fax: 212-572-4040

THE COOPER-HEWITT NATIONAL DESIGN MUSEUM
Museums

Part of the Smithsonian Institution since 1967, the National Design Museum is housed in the historic Andrew Carnegie Mansion on Fifth Avenue, across from Central Park. Most popular are the Barbara Riley Levin Conservatory and magnificent Arthur Ross Terrace and Garden. International in scope, the collections are defined by four curatorial departments – industrial design and applied arts, textiles, wall coverings and drawings and prints. With over 500,000 volumes of design related reference material and 500 rare books, its new library is unparalleled.

2 East 91st Street
New York, NY 10128
Tel: 212-849-8420
Fax: 212-849-8401

THE CORCORAN GROUP
Property Consultants

The Corcoran group is the largest privately owned real estate firm in Manhattan, with over 10 offices, 500 brokers and $2 billion in annual sales volume. The firm's sales statistics and timely marketing data are recognized by local buyers, sellers and the media as the most accurate and reliable in the industry. Since the launch of their website in 1995, the Madison Avenue company has been setting records with over a deal a day and has become the premier global source for luxury properties. Founder Barbara Corcoran was recently named as one of New York's 100 Most Influential Women in Business.

660 Madison Avenue
New York, NY 10021
Tel: 212-355-3550   Fax: 212-223-6381

≈

CORCORAN GALLERY OF ART
Museums

Washington's first museum of art, founded in 1869, the Gallery is internationally known for its distinguished collection of historical and modern American art, as well as European painting, sculpture and decorative arts. Founded in 1890, the Corcoran College of Art and Design is the capital's only four-year, fully-accredited college of art and design, offering BFA degrees in three majors: Fine Arts, Graphic Design and Photography. The Open Program, which offers credit and non-credit classes for children and adults, draws more than 3000 participants each year. A major Andy Warhol retrospective is scheduled for the spring of 2001.

500 17th Street, NW
Washington, DC 20006
Tel: 202-639-1700

COSENTINO
Winemakers

Mitch Cosentino's first serious wine, a 1982 Reserve Cabernet Sauvignon, was a gold medal winner. The rest, as they say, is history. Cosentino vintages are made in small batches (typically 1000 case lots) which make them difficult to acquire but well worth the effort. "The goal," says Mr Cosentino, "is to make the best wine, not the best wine to fit a certain number of cases." The M Coz is particularly worth hunting out.

P.O. Box 2818
Yountville, CA 94599
Tel: 707-944-1220
Fax: 707-944-1254

≈

LA COSTA RESORT AND SPA
Spas and Clinics

At La Costa, there is no average day. The mammoth 75,000 square foot spa is one of North America's largest, including a championship golf course and a 21-court racquet club. Each of the 50 pampering treatments is tailored to the client's needs. From massage, pedicures and body wraps to more exotic services like milk baths and full body exfoliation, this Carlsbad gem is the perfect antidote to all of life's little, and big, troubles. Ask general manager John Peto to schedule you a La Costa Glow, a combination treatment of massage, exfoliation and wrap, or the loofah scrub, which opens your pores and prepares your skin for massage.

2100 Costa Del Mar Road
Carlsbad, CA 92009
Tel: 800-854-5000
Fax: 760-931-7585

COVE LANDING
Antiques

Soaring above the Connecticut River's southern shores, Cove Landing is a newly constructed antiques gallery voted "Best Retail Project" by *Interiors* Magazine in 1999. Architect and interior designer L.A. Morgan co-owns the business with respected author and antiques dealer Angus Wilkie, who honed his eye at Christie's. Cove Landing's spare presentation and unique surroundings echo the quality, scale and integrity of superb objects and furniture. An unusual selection chosen from diverse periods includes examples of Ming Dynasty, Irish Regency, Biedermeier and Twentieth century design.

Route 156, Lyme
Hadlyme, CT 06439
Tel: 860-526-3464   Fax: 860-434-3103

≈

COVINGTON & BURLING
Law Firms

Covington & Burling is one of the quintessential Washington, D.C. law firms, engaging business issues on a national level. Its cases are often tied into the national news; health law, regulatory legislation, environmental and high-profile civil cases are all covered by Covington's 400 attorneys. Other branches are found in New York, San Francisco, London and Brussels. Meticulous preparation and unwavering dedication allows the firm to engage in such prominent cases as Computer Associates' takeover of Lotus, the biggest software takeover ever.

1201 Pennsylvania Avenue, NW
Washington, DC 20044
Tel: 202-662-6000

CRAVATH, SWAINE & MOORE
Law Firms

Cravath, Swaine & Moore is one of the oldest, most prestigious legal establishments in New York. Cravath attorneys are trained to be generalists, rather than narrow-based specialists. Recruiting from the cream of the best law schools, CSW welcomes challenging cases that take advantage of its substantial intellectual resources. DuPont, Royal Dutch Shell and Time Warner have all benefited from Cravath representation in litigation and takeover matters. There are older firms, and there are bigger firms, but few can compete with Cravath's combination of well-rounded and intensely dedicated attorneys.

825 Eighth Avenue
New York, NY 10019
Tel: 212-474-1000
Fax: 212-474-3700

CROFTON ON WELLS
Restaurants

Suzy Crofton's 1200 square-foot dining room is a palette of light gray tones and varying textures. This graduate of the Minneapolis College of Art and Design accidentally began her career as a chef while working in a coffee shop. When the pastry chef broke her hip, Crofton stepped in. Today she is acclaimed across the country. Try her roast Guinea hen, served with morel mushrooms, fava beans, pancetta and white truffle oil, or the grilled venison, served with black mission figs.

535 North Wells Street
Chicago, IL 60610
Tel: 312-755-1790
Fax: 312-755-1890

THE CULINARY INSTITUTE OF AMERICA
Culinary Schools

Established in 1946, the Culinary Institute of America is devoted to an education in culinary skills. With a 150 acre campus in New York as well as the Greystone campus in St. Helena, the private, not for profit facility provides Associate and Bachelor degree programs. Students at the campus take advantage of the 55,000-volume Conrad N. Hilton Library and personal career counselors. Graduates include Walter Scheib, Executive Chef at the White House, Larry Forgione of An American Place Resturant and Paul Bocuse's son, Jerome.

433 Albany Post Road
Hyde Park, NY 12538
Tel: 914-452-9600
Fax: 914-452-9629

CULLMAN & KRAVIS
Architects and Interior Designers

When Elissa Cullman and Hedi Kravis submitted a screenplay to film producer Stanley Jaffe in the early 1980s, he told them in no uncertain terms that they had "absolutely no talent at script writing." However, he thought they had such a flair for decorating that he promptly hired them to decorate his Park Avenue apartment and their careers were launched. In 1984 Cullman & Kravis was born. Specializing in interior decoration for collectors of fine art and antiques, Cullman & Kravis effectively serve as curators to their clients, helping them analyze the aesthetic and financial prudence of their purchases within the parameters of the historical context and the marketplace. The designers attend to every detail, using layered lighting, antique carpets, one-of-a-kind textiles and decorative paint to create unique, comfortable interiors that are at once elegant and classic. At pains to avoid the traps of trendiness, over-designing and slavish recreations of period rooms, Cullman & Kravis will complete the design of an interior with customized furniture and

accessories, such as wastebaskets, lamps, tissue boxes and china. The firm once even custom designed a step for a client's miniature long-haired dachshund to enable him to climb onto her bed.

790 Madison Avenue
New York, NY 10021
Tel: 212-249-3874   Fax: 212-249-3881

CYPRESS POINT CLUB
Golf Clubs

If there is such a place as a golf heaven anywhere on this earth, it may well be found on California's Monterey Peninsula. One reason why is this very small, very private club, which, according to experts Robert Graves and Geoffrey Cornish, features "one of the world's greatest golf course layouts."

Designed in 1928 by Alister MacKenzie, the course includes two consecutive par fives (holes 5 and 6), as well as consecutive par threes (holes 15 and 16, the latter a 230-yard carry over the Pacific Ocean aced by singer Bing Crosby in 1947).

17 Mile Drive
Pebble Beach, CA 93953
Tel: 831-624-6444

DALLAS MUSEUM OF ART
Museums

From paintings by Monet, Degas, van Gogh and Renoir to the Southwest's most significant holdings in African art, DMA displays one of the most diverse collections of art in the world. The anchor of cultural offerings in the downtown Arts District, the museum houses a treasury of American artifacts and masterpieces by such artists as Edward Hopper, Georgia O'Keeffe and Andrew Wyeth. The Wendy and Emery Reves Collection is particularly impressive, recreating the idyllic lifestyle enjoyed by the couple in their home, Villa La Pausa, in the south of France. The museum is also a great spot for live jazz on Thursday nights and fascinating art history lectures.

1717 North Harwood
Dallas, TX 75201
Tel: 214-922-1200   Fax: 214-954-0174

D & M CHAMPAGNE
Wine Merchants

From an ultra-rare 1893 Chateau d'Yquem to a dignified line-up of port, D & M boast one of the most impressive selections of top quality wine in the country. Owners Mike and Joe Politz have a combined 79 years in the wine business. They also offer 300 types of Single Malt Scotch, Armagnac and top-quality Oaxacan Mezcal tequila. For traditional lovers of champagne, don't miss the vintage selections, like a Tattinger Vintage 1978 (with artwork by Victor Vasarely).

2200 Fillmore Street
San Francisco, CA 94115
Tel: 415-346-1325

Outside the Print-Seller's Shop, by Honoré Daumier

THE DAILY BLOSSOM
Florists

A veritable "Who's Who" among the world's financial, entertainment and media industries rely on the artisans at The Daily Blossom and their exquisite floral creations for gift giving and to grace their executive suites, corporate offices, private homes and numerous special events and charities. Owner Saundra Parks and her alluring flowers have been featured in everything from a television advertising campaign for American Express to articles in *The New York Times, Los Angeles Times* and other publications across the country. Located in the fashionable Chelsea district of Manhattan with a second location near the Rockefeller Center, Parks and her talented staff of dedicated perfectionists work closely with clients to create timelessly beautiful and provocative floral designs.

236 West 27th Street
New York, NY 10001
Tel: 212-633-9000   Fax: 212-633-0808

DALLAS POLO CLUB
Polo Clubs

This well-organized club maintains three full fields to accomodate its growing membership, comprising three levels: social, corporate and VIP. The illustrious arena player Bill Walton presides over a bracing year-round schedule of competitive polo at the Bear Creek Ranch and a staff of grooms care for more than 100 member and pro thoroughbreds. The most active polo club in North Texas also runs a prestigious polo school.

2906 Maple Avenue, Suite 204
Dallas, TX 75201
Tel: 214-979-0300   Fax: 214-979-0849

D'AMICO CUCINA
Restaurants

With a father who grew up on a farm and a pastry chef mother, it's no wonder that J.P. Samuelson is so passionate about food. When he's not mountain biking or playing basketball, he's serving up his signature wild acres roasted chicken, served with potato gnocchi, or his piadina, a delicious combination of Italian flatbread, gorgonzola cheese, prosciutto and rhododendron honey. D'Amico Cucina is influenced by Northern Italy, both on the menu and in the atmosphere. The main dining room is open and airy, accented in marble and romantic wooden beams. Table 51 affords a great view of the street and is the only real corner table. Many prefer the privacy of the wine room, where rare vintages are served for private parties.

100 North Sixth Street, Butler Square
Minneapolis, MN 55403
Tel: 612-338-2401   Fax: 612-374-1869

DALVA BROTHERS

Antiques

When Louis XIV was fitting out Versailles, the best craftsmen in Europe were drawn to Paris. The fruits of their labor are on show in Manhattan, where the Dalva brothers' collection of French furniture from the 17th and 18th centuries fills a five-story townhouse. The Dalvas have helped the Getty and the Metropolitan Museums build public collections of some of the most beautiful furniture ever made.

44 East 57th Street
New York, NY 10022
Tel: 212-758-2297

DANIEL

Restaurants

For a memorable night out on the town, some go to the theater and others go to Daniel, the namesake restaurant of French super-chef Daniel Boulud. Designed to evoke the Venetian Renaissance, the ambiance is clean and elegant with a gold-leafed bar, 18-foot stencilled ceiling and bronze-studded mahogany doors. Even the floor of the ladies room is laid with a third-century Syrian marble mosaic. But the decor will always be a backdrop to Boulud's powerhouse flavors. Try his signature dishes, like spiced rhubarb tuile with a light orange blossom cream, and roasted squab stuffed with foie gras, black truffle, winter vegetables and chestnuts. Call at least two weeks in advance.

60 East 65th Street
New York, NY 10021
Tel: 212-288-0033   Fax: 212-737-0612

DANIELS, DANIELS & DANIELS

Antiques

The Daniels brothers sell a diverse array of 19th century French and English antiques at their Hallandale and Aspen stores, from furniture that formerly graced the interiors of royal palaces, to that with a slightly less aristocratic past. Particularly interesting is a selection of French 17th and 18th century furniture. As a company brochure explains, "one is continually astonished by the extraordinary variety of materials used, the quality of the workmanship, and the individuality and beauty of virtually every piece." The firm exhibits at most of the country's more prestigious antique shows.

2520 South West 30th Avenue
Hallandale, FL 33309
Tel: 954-454-1395   Fax: 954-454-6452

DARRELL SCHMITT DESIGN ASSOCIATES

Architects and Interior Designers

Though his company is relatively young, Darrell Schmidt has been in the design business for more than 28 years, completing prestigious hospitality and residential installations throughout the world to the highest levels of quality and integrity. Working closely with James Northcutt, an acknowledged innovator in the field of hospitality design, for many years until his death, Schmitt worked on projects as varied as The Peninsula Beverly Hills Hotel, Four Seasons Resorts at Wailea, Hawaii and residential commissions from Indonesia to Saudi Arabia.

6399 Wilshire Boulevard, #1010
Los Angeles, CA 90048
Tel: 323-951-9283   Fax: 323-951-9231

DANIELLE

Specialty Shops

Danielle is a graceful mixture of different styles and origins, specializing in lovely 18th and 19th century European antiques and spirited 20th century American and European acquisitions. Expert Interior Design Services artfully meld lovely furnishings and accessories. With 25 years of expertise as an interior designer to some of the most affluent people in the world, owner Danielle Ellis exhibits tasteful, unique pieces, representative of her work in the field. From a French leaded crystal decanter set from the mid-19th century to an Indonesian colonial-era daybed covered in Clarence House fabric, clients can turn their homes into chic chateaus. Ellis goes the distance for her shop; at the time of writing, she is traveling to Europe in search of a rare 15-foot sideboard.

1111-12 Uptown Park Boulevard
Houston, TX 77056
Tel: 13-623-2800   Fax: 713-623-2830

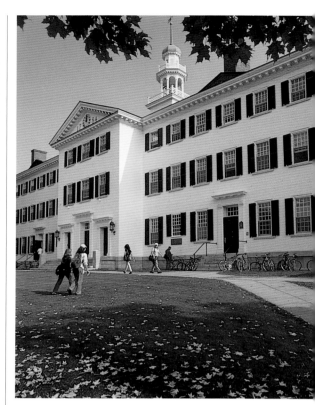

DARTMOUTH COLLEGE

Colleges

Established in 1769 in Hanover, New Hampshire, Dartmouth was the last college established under colonial rule. Intended to educate and instruct the "youth of the Indian Tribes in this Land...and also English youth and any others," the college has always traded in a more rugged experience than many of its Ivy brethren. Boisterous and famously loyal, the sons and daughters of Dartmouth cherish life at the historic outpost of civilization in the New England hills.

38 N. Main Street
Hanover, NH 03755
Tel: 603-646-3661

DAV EL

Chauffeur Services

Scott Solombrino saw a good deal when the opportunity to own this limousine service arose. Once the sole Boston franchisee for Dav El, Solombrino eventually snatched the company up from David Klein, who founded it in 1966. The Massachusetts based firm is now America's largest privately-held chauffeured transportation firm, with a network of affiliates in 350 cities around the world. Its vehicles are supplied with state-of-the-art equipment and luxurious features as standard.

200 Second Street
Chelsea, MA 02150
Tel: 617-887-0900
Fax: 617-884-2707

DAVID ANTHONY EASTON
Architects and Interior Designers

David Easton is renowned for recreating the sumptuous gentility of English country houses, although he is equally capable of working in other styles. For 25 years this dashing architect has designed homes for a very select clientele: Easton is the man who built John Kluge's massive house on a 12,000 acre Virginia estate from its humble beginnings as a sketch on the back of a napkin. His headquarters have recently moved from the Upper East Side to SoHo.

72 Spring Street
New York, NY 10012
Tel: 212-334-3820   Fax: 212-334-3821

DAVID JONES
Florists

A veteran florist, David Jones – who has lectured at the Smithsonian – lists the Bloomingdales, Mehtas and Annenbergs among his clients. His personal arrangements are invariably distinctive and delightful, and Mr. Jones is an old-fashioned character in the best sense of the term. One could not produce a list of America's best florists without including this fabulous man.

450 North Robertson
Los Angeles, CA 90048
Tel: 310-659-6347

DAVID LAVOY
Florists

David LaVoy turned his interest in flowers into a thriving business, focusing on weddings and other gala events throughout the South. His style is best described as classical and opulent, with a heavy emphasis on roses. Atlanta institutions like the Cherokee Country Club and the Piedmont Driving Club retain LaVoy for their weekly flower arrangements and Christmas decorations.

2126 Faulkner Road
Atlanta, GA 30324
Tel: 404-320-6677   Fax: 404-320-7788

DAVID STERN
Jewelry and Watches

David Stern creates cutting-edge pieces that withstand time; pieces, in short, that are hip but not whimsical. Specializing in platinum and gold, the designer works with his clients until the piece suits them perfectly. Particularly timeless are his white-gold custom necklace and white diamonds. The firm also has an impressive collection of fine time-pieces, including the most comprehensive collection of Piaget in Boca.

3013 Yamoto Road, Suite B20
Boca Raton, FL 33434
Tel: 561-994-3330

DAVID YURMAN
Jewelry and Watches

There is a sublime sense of artistry to everything David Yurman and his wife and partner, Sybil, do. Witness the couple's new Madison Avenue boutique. This stunning flagship store – or jewel box, as they aptly call it – envelops customers in a feeling of richness and harmony. Designed by Dakota Jackson in collaboration with the Yurmans, the boutique, with its dramatic black granite entrance, curved beechwood walls and hand-etched glass vitrines, illustrates the same attention to quality, craftsmanship and detail found in the company's jewelry.

David Yurman masterfully combines the aesthetics and craftsmanship of fine jewelry with an unerring eye for fashion. As a result, each piece from the Yurman collection is unmistakable; from the trademarked sterling silver and 18 karat gold Cable Collection; to the new Couture Collection, featuring one-of-a-kind pieces and limited editions; to the complete line of David Yurman Timepieces, including the recently launched Thoroughbred Watch Collection. Inspiration for these lines may come from simple, ordinary objects or the most precious piece of fine art. The couple, both of whom began their careers as fine artists (David apprenticed with sculptors Jacques Lipshitz and Theodore Rozark, while Sybil was an accomplished painter) find ideas everywhere. "My interest in design has always been touched by magical, ancient forms," says David. "I sense there is a common thread in recognizable symbols that seem to bind people together."

501 Madison Avenue
New York, NY 10022
Tel: 212-593-1122

DAVID TUNICK

Art Dealers

One of the leading art dealers in America today, David Tunick deals in fine prints and drawings by artists from the 15th to the mid-20th century. Works by masters like Durer, Rembrandt, Piranesi and Toulouse-Lautrec all feature strongly in a truly world-class inventory. Industry seniors Reed Masselink and David Tunick oversee day to day operations at the gallery, which is best viewed by appointment.

45 East 65th Street
New York, NY 10021
Tel: 212-570-0090   Fax: 212-744-8931

DAVID WEBB

Jewelry and Watches

At David Webb, the fantastical and the whimsical go hand in hand. Jewelry experts at the store combine materials like enamel, cabachon stone and crystals to create untraditional pieces that enhance a face or embellish a neck. The inimitable Stanley Silberstein, president of the firm, prides himself on maintaining close relationships with his clients. Silberstein has been known to make dinner reservations, purchase theater tickets, and have dinner with customers while on business trips.

445 Park Avenue
New York, NY 10022
Tel: 212-421-3030   Fax: 212-758-7827

DAVIS, POLK & WARDWELL

Law Firms

A large New York-based firm with over 20 areas of specialization, Davis, Polk & Wardwell has offices in Europe, Asia and Latin America. The firm serves old clients, such as J.P. Morgan, with its experience in mergers and acquisitions, as well as helping New Economy startups launch and finance themselves through public stock offerings. The management of such complex transactions has earned Davis, Polk & Wardwell a reputation among the first rank of American international law firms.

450 Lexington Avenue
New York, NY 10017
Tel: 212-450-4000

DE VERA

Specialty Shops   *Rising Star*

Founded in 1991, Federico de Vera's stores are just a few blocks from Union Square in the heart of San Francisco's shopping district. Each gallery displays a diverse collection of objects and artifacts from around the world, including de Vera's own unique designs in furniture and jewelry. Here you might find vintage Italian glass, Japanese lacquerware, Victorian jewelry, Tibetan deities and early 20th century decorative arts – each displayed by de Vera with museum-like quality and style.

580 Sutter Street
San Francisco, CA 94102
Tel: 415-989-0988   Fax: 415-989-0468

DEER VALLEY RESORT

Hotels

Truly a first class retreat, Deer Valley is consistently ranked among the top ski resorts in North America and it is not only because of the excellent skiing and lodgings: the chefs of Deer Valley's eight restaurants realized that the true path to skiers' hearts is to feed them well. And with eight restaurants to choose, there is no end of choice, from slopeside snacks to the superb and cozy Mariposa. And if you feel as most people do about their desserts, you can now buy Letty Flatt's long awaited *Chocolate Snowball* cookbook. The 2002 Olympic slalom events will be held here.

P.O. Box 1525
Park City, UT 84060
Tel: 435-649-1000   Fax: 435-645-6939

DEBORAH KOEPPER

Hair and Beauty

Deborah Koepper has earned a reputation as one of the nation's most skilled estheticians and make-up artists. Her résumé of career accomplishments speaks volumes. From serving as stylist to First Lady Nancy Reagan and the makeup artist of choice for visiting White House dignitaries and diplomats, working with the grooming needs of the Bush administration, to establishing the esthetics wing of one of Washington's most prestigious spas, Koepper's experience, education and training is unparalleled.

Over a decade ago Koepper moved south to Florida, establishing her own salon. Today, the salon on the fashionable island of Palm Beach has a loyal clientele that has grown to include Alex von Furstenburg, Queen Beatrix, Joan Rivers, Samantha Boardman and Brooke Shields, just to name a few. Koepper and her staff are in demand at the shows of such designers as Kors, Duke, Halston, Ferre and Mackie. From styling magazine covers and national advertisements, to articulating the on-air appearances of television news personalities, to being quoted as an expert source in national publications, Koepper is a sought-after leader in the industry.

The Deborah Koepper Salon is replete with all facets of esthetic skin, hair and nail care, medical skin treatments, personal styling and makeovers. Additionally, she has formulated an exclusive skin care treatment and cosmetics collection. Together with her team of professionals, Koepper has built an incredible business, while creating a unique environment that is all about beauty, care, tranquility and impeccably discreet service.

215 Sunset Avenue
Palm Beach, FL 33480
Tel: 561-833-6561   Fax: 561-659-9805

DE GUSTIBUS COOKING SCHOOL
Culinary Schools

Over the past 20 years, De Gustibus has featured over 500 of the world's greatest chefs in their demonstrational cooking program, commonly cited as the benchmark in the field. Held at Macy's Herald Square, the series includes exhibitions like *Great Luxury Products: Foie Gras, Truffles, Cheese and Caviar* and *An Afternoon with Italian Wine and Food*, where top chefs and cookbook authors reveal their culinary insights. Audience participants enjoy exploring farmer's markets, improvising with recipes and sharpening their sense of taste. Incidentally, Director Arlene Feltman Sailhac's husband, Alain, was the Executive Chef at Le Cirque for many years.

343 East 74th Street, Suite 14A
New York, NY 10021
Tel: 212-439-1714   Fax: 212-439-1716

DELANO HOTEL
Hotels

This deluxe, oceanfront hotel is in the heart of the Art Deco District and within walking distance of the bistros, shops and galleries of ultra-chic South Beach. Completely renovated by Philippe Starck and hotelier Ian Schrager in 1995, the hotel has retained a five star rating ever since. With an originally designed pool (with underwater music), a rooftop bath house spa and solarium, a state of the art David Barton Gym and the critically acclaimed Blue Door restaurant, it's difficult for guests to stay in their rooms; even those lucky enough to secure one of the eight poolside bungalows, with floor-to-ceiling marble bathrooms.

1685 Collins Avenue
Miami Beach, FL 33139
Tel: 305-672-2000   Fax: 305-532-0099

DELLA FEMINA
Restaurants

Caricatures of celebrity patrons like Billy Joel, Martha Stewart and Christie Brinkley line the walls of ad-man Jerry Della Femina's East Hampton mainstay, where seeing and being seen are an integral part of the package. Executive Chef Kevin Penner's contemporary American cuisine includes an excellent tartar of Hawaiian tuna and halibut served with a wild mushroom broth. Hotshots sit up front.

99 North Main Street
East Hampton, NY 11937
Tel: 631-329-6666
Fax: 631-329-3547

DELMONICO
Restaurants

Delmonico, an icon in the New Orleans restaurant industry, has been in business since 1895. Re-opening it as Emeril's Delmonico Restaurant and Bar in 1998, Chef Emeril Lagasse – who has also made quite a name for himself on television – has kept many of the classic items, while adding the inventive flavors for which he has garnered a number of awards. Located on the edge of the historic garden district (overlooking St. Charles Avenue) the building is over 100 years old. It has been described as both Victorian and Edwardian in design, with interiors reflecting a classic, understated elegance, with high ceilings, wood floors and large paneled windows.

1300 St. Charles Avenue
New Orleans, LA 70130
Tel: 504-525-4937
Fax: 504-525-0506

DEMPSEY & CARROLL
Specialty Shops

The ultimate keepsake from a wedding may be an engraved invitation printed by Dempsey & Carroll; but assuming that you might want to actually write something on their delightful engraved cotton paper, this is the place to come. Known worldwide for the quality of its luxury writing materials, this boutique occupies a niche at the top of an ever-scarcer field. Dempsey & Carroll paper and fine quill pens have been the choice of presidents, royalty and captains of industry for personal or official correspondence for over 100 years. The able staff will help you select your own royal writing instruments.

110 East 57 Street
New York, NY 10022
Tel: 212-486-7526
Fax: 212-486-7523

DEPASQUALE, THE SPA
Spas and Clinics

For a deeply relaxing massage, this spa's extensive menu includes Warm Stone Therapy or you may enjoy a soak in an authentic Japanese steeping tub, followed by an Italian "rainshower" and a candlelit massage. The very special DePasquale Experience can be enjoyed alone or with one other person and takes place in two adjoining suites. Everything from the architectural design and decor - incorporating original works of art and sculpture, along with a soothing waterfall - to the scents permeating the air

is designed to exhilarate the mind and body, making this spa a total sensory experience, which is just one of the reasons DePasquale, The Spa is so coveted as a venue for both private and corporate parties.

Route 10 East, Powder Mill Plaza
Morris Plains, NJ 07950
Tel: 973-538-3811
Fax: 973-359-8940

DAVID YURMAN

The Cable Collection™

FLAGSHIP STORE • NEIMAN MARCUS • SAKS FIFTH AVENUE
AND AUTHORIZED RETAILERS

DESIGN ASSOCIATES
Architects and Interior Designers

Design Associates has been providing comprehensive architectural services for construction, restoration and renovation work throughout New England since 1979. The company's projects are conceived and designed in a restorative manner, using siting, massing and period details to create buildings and structures that are sympathetic to a site, its context, and its architectural style.

432 Columbia Street
Cambridge, MA 02141
Tel: 508-228-4342

≈

DEVON YACHT CLUB
Private Clubs

Originally established in 1908 as the Gardner's Bay Boat Club, the Devon Yacht Club was incorporated in 1916 and had its first season in 1917, with 46 members. Today, its 350 members keep approximately 50 yachts in the marina and races are scheduled every Saturday. Besides yachting, the club offers tennis on eight clay courts, with instruction by pro Tim Snell. Lunch at the clubhouse is casual, but dinner requires a jacket and tie.

P.O. Box 2549
Amagansett, NY 11930
Tel: 631-267-6340

≈

DIAMOND CREEK WINERY
Winemakers

Al Brounstein, owner of Diamond Creek, is a very colorful guy – an aviator, skier and marvelous storyteller; apparently he once smuggled first growth cuttings from Bordeaux through Mexico and into California. Al and winemaker Bill Steinschrieber only produce wines from their own grapes. Their Cabernets are a story in themselves, possibly the best in Napa – which is saying magnums – and they get better with age. This year, four bottles went for $130,000.

1500 Diamond Mountain Road
Calistoga, CA 94515
Tel: 707-942-6926

DESIGN CUISINE CATERERS
Party Organizers and Caterers

"At its essence, the catering business is about food, equipment and staff," says Bill Homan, the President of Design Cuisine. "I like to think that when people come to us, they're looking for a lot more than that." Indeed they are. With 45 full time chefs and a client list that reads like *Who's Who*, this 20 year old firm is among the most prestigious caterers in the country. Clients include top brass politicians (look for their logo in the White House) and Washington Royalty like Sally Quinn and Katherine Graham, 'though in recent years it's the high tech corridor in northern Virginia which provides much of the firm's 'bread and butter' work.

2659 South Shirlington Road
Arlington, VA 22206
Tel: 703-979-9400   Fax: 703-979-8632

≈

DHS DESIGNS
Specialty Shops

Specializing in 16th to 19th century French carved, limestone mantelpieces and garden ornaments, DHS Designs also stocks 18th and 19th century continental furniture and decorative arts. Its two Maryland warehouses are open to the trade and the public seven days a week. The shop imports the mantels, many salvaged intact from manor houses in the Loire Valley, in numbered pieces that are reconstructed by stonemasons.

86 Maryland Avenue
Annapolis, MD 21401
Tel: 410-280-3466
Fax: 410-280-8729

≈

DIA CENTER FOR THE ARTS
Museums

With a mission to make the arts of our time accessible to an ever wider and increasingly well-informed audience, the Dia Center has played a vital role among arts institutions in New York. The permanent collection boasts Walter De Maria's *The Broken Kilometer*, works by Joseph Beuys, John Chamberlain, Blinky Palermo and Andy Warhol. In addition to the permanent collection, the museum offers Arts education workshops with teaching writers, artists and art historians. The *Readings in Contemporary Poetry* program, one of the country's foremost reading series, has featured Robert Creeley, Allen Ginsberg, Adrienne Rich, Mark Strand and Charles Simic.

548 West 22nd Street
New York, NY 10011
Tel: 212-989-5566
www.diacenter.org

DILLINGHAM & COMPANY
Antiques

Located in Jackson Square, San Francisco's historic antiques district, the Dillingham & Company gallery carries an exquisite array of English furniture from the 17th, 18th and early 19th centuries. While Dillingham is well-known for their English furnishings, European pieces are also well represented. This extraordinary Venetian bureau bookcase, c. 1740, employs a unique profusion of shells and waterfalls, serpentine sides as well as the original mirror plates. It would be hard to find a better example of 18th century Italian furniture in America today. All of the pieces in the collection are vetted for quality and execution of design – Dillingham & Company also carries period paintings and objects, including ivory dressing boxes, Chinese porcelain, colonial game boxes and Scandinavian bowls. Indeed, something for every taste.

700 Sansome Street
San Francisco, CA 94111
Tel: 415-989-8777
Fax: 415-989-5145

DIMSON HOMMA
Specialty Shops

Boasting a huge selection of art and antiques, Dimson Homma truly offers a bewildering array of delights. Founded in 1996 by Risë Dimson and Robert Homma, the shop appears to have no boundaries: with Ming Dynasty furniture, 1200 year old 22 karat gold jewelry, antique Turkish rugs, contemporary bronze sculpture and glassware by Elliot Rosenstein, the Manhattan treasure chest satiates even the most curious connoisseur. Incidentally, those live birds are Lady Gouldian finches — Queen Victoria thought them the most beautiful birds in the world.

20 East 67th Street
New York, NY 10021
Tel: 212-439-7950   Fax: 212-439-7960

DISTINCTIVE BOOKBINDING & STATIONERY
Specialty Shops

Bringing the glamour of the fashion world to stationery is a tall order, but one that is met with ease by Distinctive Bookbinding and Stationery. Their fine bookbinding services, handmade stationery and distinctive desk sets borrow the best of Milanese and Florentine design and tradition, offering a refreshingly sophisticated take on the business of writing.

1003 North Rush Street
Chicago, IL 60611
Tel: 312-867-7474
Fax: 312-867-7157

DIVA LIMOUSINES
Chauffeur Services

After 15 years of operation Diva has over 150 vehicles nationwide — roughly ten new cars each year. They are equipped with state of the art amenities such as on-board Teletrak satellite location tracking, two-way dispatch radios and cellular phones. Established by Bijan Zoughi with one car and a good driving record, the company now has exclusive accounts with Fox, Disney, Paramount and Condé Nast, where the caliber of your car is almost as important as the make of your shoes.

1670 North Sycamore Avenue
Los Angeles, CA 90028
Tel: 310-278-3482   Fax: 323-962-3803

DIXON AND DIXON OF ROYAL
Antiques

After traveling extensively throughout Europe and America, the Dixon family entered the world of antiques and fine art. Today the firm boasts three magnificent galleries in the heart of New Orleans' historic French Quarter, where, throughout some 20,000 square feet of gallery space, they display fine art, along with 17th, 18th and 19th century English, French, and Dutch furnishings, estate and antique jewelry, and antique carpets. The gallery uniquely guarantees an annual appreciation value of five percent on any purchase made there, indefinitely.

237 Royal Street
New Orleans, LA 70130
Tel: 504-524-0282
Fax: 504-524-7378

DOMINUS ESTATES
Winemakers

The wine produced by Christian Moueix (who owns Chateau Pétrus in Bordeaux) from grapes grown in the Napa Valley, reflects Californian climate and soil and the spirit of a great chateau. This combination results in distinctive reds, led by prominent Cabernet Sauvignon and Merlot varietals. The premier Medoc variety imparts intense aromas of cassis and cherries with notes of vanilla and licorice — it is powerful, intense, tannic and designed for the long haul. The key is to wait until the winemaker wants you to drink it, not before.

2570 Napanook Road
Yountville, CA 94599
Tel: 707-944-8954   Fax: 707-944-0547

DONALD HILL INTERIORS
Architects and Interior Designers

Donald Hill believes that a room has been well designed when it looks as though it has not been designed at all. The one time film location scout was so intrigued by a request to find an architectural site that he set out for Paris to study design and antiques. He has since helped some of the most influential people in the world mix design and function. Hill doesn't believe in just creating "pretty" space for the sake of aestheticism, although — according to one client — he does wonders with making fax machines and microwaves disappear!

167 Madison Avenue
New York, NY 10016
Tel: 212-686-5867

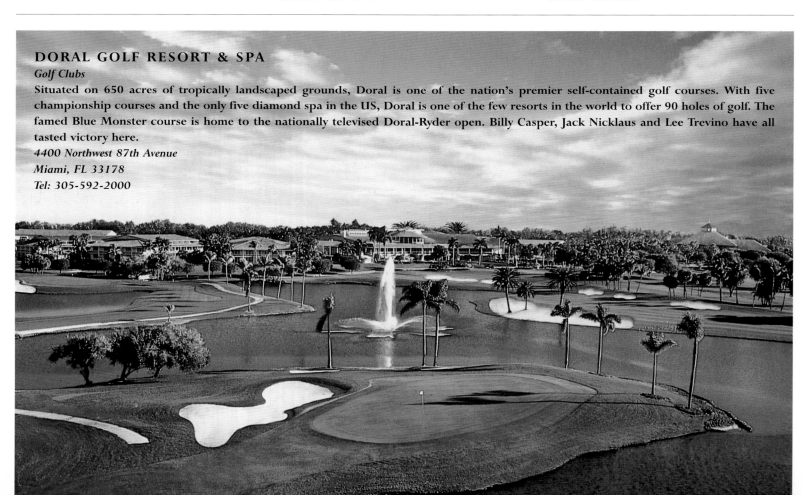

DORAL GOLF RESORT & SPA
Golf Clubs

Situated on 650 acres of tropically landscaped grounds, Doral is one of the nation's premier self-contained golf courses. With five championship courses and the only five diamond spa in the US, Doral is one of the few resorts in the world to offer 90 holes of golf. The famed Blue Monster course is home to the nationally televised Doral-Ryder open. Billy Casper, Jack Nicklaus and Lee Trevino have all tasted victory here.

4400 Northwest 87th Avenue
Miami, FL 33178
Tel: 305-592-2000

DOUBLES
Private Clubs

By their very nature, dining clubs are ephemeral. Like the glittering hordes who populate them, they come and go with alarming ease. Only a precious few survive the transition from upstart to institution. Doubles is one such club. Now 25 years old, it has weathered all sorts of abuse (not least from this quarter) and has emerged looking better than ever. This is largely due to the efforts of Andrew and Wendy Carduner, who run the operation with competence, charm and great aplomb. Discreet service, decent food and a truly convivial ambience keep junior (and not so junior) members of New York society clamouring for more.

783 Fifth Avenue
New York, NY 10021
Tel: 212-751-9595

JEFFREY DOVER, M.D.
Cosmetic Surgeons

After his graduation from Harvard, Jeffrey Dover spent a year in England, studying at the prestigious St. John's Hospital for Diseases of the Skin. Returning to Harvard, he began to publish his studies on laser research. Today, Dover is one of the most sought-after experts in his field — from birthmarks, varicose veins, liver spots to broken facial blood vessels, he and his colleagues, Dr. Michael Kaminer and Dr. Kent Arnt, offer every image-improving technique. With three operating rooms, 12 regular examining rooms and seven physicians on staff, you're guaranteed an appointment in two to three months. Dr. Dover explains his philosophies and techniques in one of his eight published textbooks: *Skin Deep*.

1244 Boyleston Street, Suite 302
Chestnut Hill, MA 02467
Tel: 617-731-1600   Fax: 617-731-1601

DOWNTOWN
Specialty Shops

A stylish haven for sybarites in search of mid-20th century furniture, Downtown is owned by a truly creative group. Paul Marra is an interior designer, Robert Wilson is an executive chef and David Serrano is an artist. Their vintage line is amazing but they also carry a line of original designs, inspired by classic modernists. The firm regularly works with leading designers, collectors and architects throughout the United States and Europe and their pieces are frequently up for auction at Christie's. Inspired by Dunbar, the trio tries to meet the needs of clients' imaginations — they once spent two weeks trawling the west coast for a bronze "fish lamp."

719 North La Cienaga Boulevard
Los Angeles, CA 90069
Tel: 310-652-7461   Fax: 310-652-4916

DONALD YOUNG GALLERY
Art Dealers

Donald Young worked for 10 years in Paris before opening this large, minimalist Chicago gallery in a less than glamorous part of town. It was an ambitious move, certainly, although Young clearly knew what he was doing. Today he represents artists like Richard Long and Rosemarie Trockel. Young has regularly shown large-scale video installations by Bruce Nauman, Gary Hill and Bill Viola. His other areas of expertise include American minimal, formal and conceptual artists from the 1960s and 70s, such as Dan Flavin, Sol LeWitt and Donald Judd.

933 West Washington Boulevard
Chicago, IL 60607
Tel: 312-455-0100   Fax: 312-455-0101

DORMEUIL PERSONAL TAILORING
Fashion

Founded in 1842, Ashley Dormeuil's family business has been providing exclusive custom tailoring for more than 150 years. Dormeuil clients have whirlwind lifestyles, so fittings are usually made at the customer's convenience. Dormeuil Personal has dressed Royalty, and the tailoring service is a favorite of Katie Couric. Custom shirts, suits and English bench-made shoes by Edward Green hark back to the golden days of Savile Row.

21 East 67th Street
New York, NY 10021
Tel: 212-396-4444
Fax: 212-396-0599

DUCKHORN VINEYARDS
Winemakers

Duckhorn Vineyards was founded in 1976 on a ten acre parcel at Lodi Lane and the Silverado Trail just north of St. Helena, California. The first harvest, in 1978, consisted of 28 tons, which became the first bottling of Three Palms Vineyard Merlot. The firm has grown to an annual crush capacity of 750 tons (approximately 45,000 cases). While the emphasis continues to be on Merlot (as we put it last year, "almost up in First Growth territory") the Cabernet Sauvignon is also superb, offering deep color, flattering roundness and exotic scents.

1000 Lodi Lane
St. Helena, CA 95475
Tel: 707-963-7108

DUNVILLE'S L'ANTIQUAIRE
Antiques

Edoardo Toros opened his antique shop in 1980, after moving to the United States from Italy. In 1995, he sold his business to Joseph Dunville, who convinced Toros to run the firm as general manager. Today, Toros presides over an outstanding collection of 18th and 19th century fine English and French furniture, English silver, Oriental porcelain, silver and works of art. At the time of writing, the collection included an exceptional set of 12 sterling dinner plates by Garrard, circa 1820 and a 1770 double-door, lacquered side cabinet with an original green marble top.

329 Worth Avenue
Palm Beach, FL 33480
Tel: 561-655-5774
Fax: 561-659-3038

DUOMO
Fitness

Former Mr. America Rich Barretta founded Duomo (Italian for sanctuary) to offer a total, personalized solution for today's health conscious individual. A 23,000 square-foot, bi-level gym, the space overlooks the lush greenery of Madison Square Park – more evocative of a sprawling Soho loft than a gym. The self-contained fitness area is divided into sections featuring upper body equipment, lower body equipment, free weights, a boxing section and a 1500 square-feet yoga and dance studio. Upstairs, members relax at the juice bar, play pool and enjoy light snacks. Nothing here says "franchise."

11 East 26th Street
New York, NY 10001
Tel: 212-689-9121
Fax: 212-689-9564

DUNEMERE ASSOCIATES REAL ESTATE
Property Consultants

Looking for a French country house within striking distance of Manhattan, an 18th century colonial or a turn of the century estate a stone's throw from the beach? Dunemere is recognized as the leading high-end broker in the Hamptons. Operating in one of the most competitive markets in the country today, it is the authority for rentals or sales from Southampton to East Hampton. With homes ranging from $750,000 to $25 million, average sales are in excess of $1.5 million. Representing the area as the exclusive affiliate for Christie's Great Estates, Dunemere is also listed in *Who's Who of Luxury Real Estate*. Founded in 1992, the agency

has offices in East Hampton, Southampton, Bridgehampton and Sag Harbor and and maintains a sales staff of 50 experienced, full-time brokers, dedicated to the luxury real estate business.

37 Newtown Lane
East Hampton, NY 11937
Tel: 631-324-6400   Fax: 631-324-6343

DUNTON HOT SPRINGS
Hotels

Dunton Hot Springs is the ultimate in a wilderness retreat – but don't get the wrong idea. Even the most pampered princess will find it hard to get bored in a place where the amenities include gourmet dining, riding, hiking, ice-climbing, snow shoeing, cross-country skiing and heli-skiing. Dunton is not open to the general public; instead, the resort specializes in customizing its services to select groups ranging from 8 to 24 guests. Highly recommended.

P.O. Box 818
Dolores, CO 81323
Tel: 970-882-4800
Fax: 970-882-7474

E & J FRANKEL

Antiques

E & J Frankel specialize in Chinese antiques, spanning from the Neolithic era to the 19th century, although the firm also deals in rare Japanese, Tibetan and Buddhist pieces. Joel and Edith Frankel opened their flagship on Madison Avenue in 1967. They concentrate on "home-market," that is, selections that are never exported out of China. This stipulation makes acquisition difficult but the showroom would have you think otherwise. Don't miss the Lei bronze wine vessels from the second millennium B.C. or the astounding collection of Chinese paintings. Incidentally, Edith Frankel founded the program on Chinese Art at the New School University, where she taught for 17 years.

1040 Madison Avenue
New York, NY 10021
Tel: 212-879-5733
Fax: 212-879-1998

EAST BANK CLUB

Fitness

Recognized as Chicago's most gracious and dynamic fitness, sports and dining facility. The largest and most complete club in the country, EBC encompasses more than 450,000 square feet (two city blocks) spread over five levels. There are outdoor and indoor pools, a full-service salon, nine indoor tennis courts, five racquetball courts, one squash court, indoor golf, two basketball courts and four studios with more than 170 exercise classes. The Wellness Center offers smoking cessation programs, fitness evaluations, blood pressure monitoring and weight management counseling. Oprah Winfrey is a member.

500 North Kingsbury
Chicago, IL 60610
Tel: 312-527-5800
Fax: 312-527-5666

EDENHURST GALLERY

Art Dealers

Edenhurst Gallery's realm of expertise in the arena of fine art and antiques began in 1965, with exclusive sales in fine art beginning in 1985. Its newest gallery location on Melrose Avenue, on the Avenues of Art and Design of West Hollywood, opened its doors in early 1998. With new and elite showrooms in a museum-like setting, the gallery's inventory of fine and historic early California paintings is showcased in a comfortable and friendly atmosphere, catering to a clientele of astute and discerning buyers. At last bringing elegance and quality to the most prestigious fine art quarter in all of Southern California, Edenhurst's comprehensive and well-chosen inventory of 19th and early 20th century Californian, American and European paintings finally fills a long-awaited niche in the art market of Los Angeles. The Gallery routinely displays the best that is currently available in fine paintings by recognized California Impressionist painters such as William Wendt, Guy Rose, Granville Redmond, Maurice Braun, and Edgar Payne. Edenhurst's expertise in this field is sought by collectors, scholars, and museum curators alike.

The year 2000 marked the inauguration of a landmark yearly show, the "Spring Salon" whose goal is to showcase work by contemporary American artists, especially those who paint in the continuing tradition of impressionism. The show's in-part sponsorship by *Art & Antiques* magazine is judged by a prestigious panel that awards a $10,000 purchase prize. A sizable donation from profits thereof also helps in the building fund of the future California Art Academy and Museum in Pasadena, recognized to be the most important fine art museum that will come to the Los Angeles area since the new Getty Museum, and due to open in 2002. Regularly hailed as one of the most beautiful galleries in the world, Edenhurst makes for a particularly enjoyable visit. Owners: Tom Gianetto, Dan Nicodemo, and Don Merrill. Director: Ms. Susan Schomburg

8920 Melrose Avenue
Los Angeles, CA 90069
Tel: 310-247-8151   Fax: 310-247-8167

EAST HAMPTON GYM

Fitness

Unfortunately, watching the waves is not really a sufficient workout during your summer weekends at the beach. Instead, sign up for a three month membership at the no-nonsense East Hampton Gym, where Cybex equipment, cardio machines with a cardio theater and an Olympic weight room will keep you in shape. Look out for Cindy Crawford and Martha Stewart taking advantage of what's known as the "cleanest gym on Long Island."

2 Fithian Lane
East Hampton, NY 11937
Tel: 631-324-4499

~

EATON FINE ART

Art Dealers

Eaton Fine Art hosts exhibitions and sales of important 19th and 20th century and contemporary American and European painting, sculpture, photography and decorative art. Just next door to the art gallery, a new sculpture garden offers a peaceful green repose in the middle of a bustling urban area. Designed by Mary Anna Eaton, the garden sits on an acre of land and features a diverse range of tropical and indigenous flora. Currently the garden features Patrick Ireland's conceptual piece, *Magic Square* – a square grid composed of nine sections, with each section containing a column of glass blocks which vary in number from one to nine. Also look out for three *Arcs* by Bernar Venet; these sculptures measure up to thirteen feet high and consist of bars of steel bent into predetermined arcs of specific degrees.

435 Gardenia Street
West Palm Beach, FL 33401
Tel: 561-833-4766   Fax: 561-833-3134

EAST & ORIENT COMPANY

Specialty Shops   Best Kept Secret

Originally specializing in antiques from Asia, this store now carries mostly French, English and Continental European antiques from the 17th, 18th and 19th centuries, all of which are displayed in elegant salons in this spacious store. The store boasts a lecture hall for specialty talks by distinguished speakers, such as Princess Michael of Kent, and is host to all of Sotheby's talks. This is one of the best kept secrets in the industry.

1123 Slocum Street
Dallas, TX 75207
Tel: 214-741-1191   Fax: 214-741-2192

~

EDIFICEREX.COM

Websites   Rising Star

The premier building-specific Internet portal, EdificeRex is dedicated to serving those living and working in the firm's managed properties. The site updates daily, offering up to the minute information on your building, neighborhood, weather, news and traffic. They let you know what's on sale, what restaurants are hot (they're even brave enough to dismiss the mighty *Zagats*), and fill you in on upcoming charity events, the stock market, the art market and your children's schools. Acting as a personal manager, EdificeRex lets you know when you've received a package, gives you the super's phone number when you lose it and can give you tips on decorating your apartment. The site's "on the road" link shows the best travel routes for car, limousine or jet.

200 Park Avenue
New York, NY 10166
Tel: 888-550-9837

EDWARD LEE CAVE

Property Consultants

Edward Lee Cave leads the market in the sale of fine residential properties on Manhattan's Upper East Side and Central Park West. A former vice president at Sotheby's, Cave also handles the sale of international properties, like Hever Castle, which he sold for the Astor family. In the last year his firm has regularly negotiated sales in excess of $12 million – indeed, a "Cave apartment" often comes with ballrooms, solariums and eight working fireplaces. He and his team are renowned for satisfying even the most unusual request – Cave has found a marble-laden gymnasium for a client and a Victorian conservatory for a client particularly fond of orchids.

790 Madison Avenue, Suite 405
New York, NY 10021
Tel: 212-772-8510

EDWARD CARTER GALLERY

Art Dealers

An amateur photographer himself, Edward Carter had developed a particular affinity for the work of Ansel Adams, especially his landscapes of the American West – perhaps the best-known images ever recorded. Over the years, Carter built his collection of Ansel Adams's work under the guidance of James and Mary Alinder, close friends of the artist. When the Alinders realized that Carter's collection was the largest available inventory of Ansel Adams's work, they encouraged him to share it with the world. The Gallery was established in 1991 for private collectors in Europe and the United States. In 1999, a dramatic, new public space opened on Broadway, across from the Guggenheim Museum. While the core of the gallery is the world's largest available inventory of Ansel Adams's work, other masters of the 19th and 20th centuries are also featured.

560 Broadway, 4th Floor
New York, NY 10012
Tel: 212-966-1933   Fax: 212-966-2145

~

ELDORADO HOTEL

Hotels

Santa Fe's first AAA, four-diamond, four-star hotel, Eldorado is a stately landmark, conveniently located in the heart of town, directly across the street from the Georgia O'Keeffe museum. Built in New Mexico's pueblo-revival style, deluxe rooms and suites include kiva fireplaces, terraces overlooking the Sangre de Cristo mountains and personal butler service. Guests enjoy heated rooftop swimming and saunas with a panoramic view of the city. The business center offers an 18,000 square-foot ballroom for conference groups up to 700. For private parties, snag the 7000 square-foot penthouse patio.

309 West San Francisco Street
Santa Fe, NM 87501
Tel: 505-988-4455   Fax: 505-995-4555

ELEVEN MADISON PARK
Restaurants

The affable Danny Meyer can do no wrong — or so it seems. Armed with the talents of Kerry Heffernan (of Bouley and Mondrian fame) Meyer's latest looks set to stay the course. The dining room's soaring ceilings, art deco interior and impeccable service add to the pleasure of Heffernan's seasonal cuisine, highlighted with a French accent. Try the roasted duck breast, served with roasted fennel, beet borscht and chive crème fraîche or the crisped veal, served with shiitake mushrooms, baby carrots and wild leeks.

11 Madison Avenue
New York, NY 10010
Tel: 212-889-0905

ERIC JAVITS
Fashion

Nicole Kidman, Madonna and Lauren Bacall agree: Eric Javits is the milliner of choice. Since 1985, he has helped royalty, prominent social ladies and celebrities complete their styles with his one of a kind originals. A graduate of the Rhode Island School of Design, Javits studied painting and sculpture and became fascinated with altering the shape of the face through different shaped hats. His designs are sold in specialty and fine department stores and have appeared on the covers of *Vogue, Glamour* and *Elle* magazines. Javits has had the three-time honor of being named 'Hat Designer of the Year' and his functional yet elegant designs are included in the archives of the Metropolitan Museum of Art's Costume Institute.

406 West 31st Street
New York, NY 10001
Tel: 212-967-8410   Fax: 212-967-8571

L'ERMITAGE
Hotels

L'Ermitage was once a sanitorium where one recovered after plastic surgery. After a $35 million face-lift of its own, bedrooms are now equipped with 40 inch televisions, 88-inch bath towels, private humidors and a choice between towel or waffled cotton bathrobes. Rooms are huge and are delicately understated in pale, sycamore wood. Guests receive a personal cellphone and their own valets. And staff take privacy to a brand new level (instead of knocking, maids check motion detectors to see whether or not guests are in).

9291 Burton Way
Beverly Hills, CA 90210
Tel: 310-278-3344
Fax: 310-278-8247

ELITE YACHT CHARTERS
Powerboats & Yachts

Based in Beverly Hills, Elite Yacht Charters is world-renowned and specializes in the highest possible service in luxury yacht charters. Every aspect of an Elite yacht charter is totally customized — from menus to itineraries. Kelley Smitten, the company's founder, has been a charter specialist for 13 years and supplies luxury yachts for clients across the globe. Smitten is unique in that she tailors every trip that she arranges and personally inspects and visits the worldwide yacht charter fleet. She has cruised throughout Europe and the Caribbean and can offer insights into all cruising areas. Smitten personally oversees even the smallest detail, insuring that everything the client requests is on board waiting — from vintage wines to beluga caviar. With a clientele composed almost entirely of Hollywood VIPs and *Fortune 500* CEOs, confidentiality and discretion is assured at all times. Service is first and foremost, which reinforces Elite's sterling reputation. Elite Yacht Charters has recently been recognized by *Departures* magazine and has repeatedly been recommended by our readers.

468 North Camden Drive, Suite 200
Beverly Hills, CA 90210
Tel: 310-552-7968   Fax: 310-553-2551

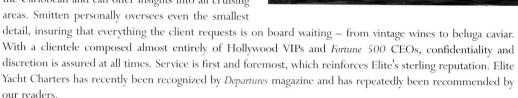

ELI WILNER & COMPANY
Specialty Shops

When the National Museum of American Art recently acquired three monumental paintings by Thomas Moran, the curators called Eli Wilner. Historic photographs revealed that the works had originally been adorned by elaborate period frames that had since been lost, and Wilner, with his unsurpassed expertise in locating, restoring and replicating 19th and early 20th century frames from America and Europe, was asked to replace them. After painstaking research that drew upon his shop's inventory of more than 3000 antique frames, Wilner and his staff of gifted craftspeople were able to reproduce exactly the right frame for each painting. The American Museum thus joined the ranks of such delighted Wilner clients as the Metropolitan Museum of Art, the Virginia Museum of Fine Arts, the Detroit Institute of the Arts and a roster of additional museums, galleries and private collectors around the world that even includes the White House. Wilner and Company have, over the years, found just the right antique or reproduction frame to complement the works of Picasso, Monet, Degas, Renoir, Homer, Singer Sargent, and many other major artists of the last two centuries.

1525 York Avenue
New York, NY 10028
Tel: 212-744-6521

EDENHURST GALLERY
Fine Art

ESSENTIAL SETTINGS
Specialty Shops

Houston's own Essential Settings offers a classic, elegant and sophisticated range of china, crystal, silver and gifts from leading manufacturers. Fabergé exclusives make the shop a must-see for discriminating collectors from around the state. From dog bowls by Chaleur, Atoll votives from Kosta Boda and Imperial Rosebud Eggs, the firm completes many gift searches and is one of the chicest bridal registries in the Lone Star state. Imported crystal from the Czech Republic is particularly popular just now with brides-to-be.

1716 Post Oak Boulevard
Houston, TX 77056
Tel: 713-629-6244   Fax: 713-629-5677

EUPHEMIA HAYE RESTAURANT
Restaurants

Euphemia Haye is a dining haven on a barrier island, off the coast of Sarasota. Stephen King, John Mellencamp, Robert DeNiro and the late Audrey Hepburn have all been guests at the beautifully named restaurant. Chefs and owners Raymond and D'Arcy Arpke have won countless accolades and awards for their eclectic cuisine. And the 12-page wine list has often been cited by critics as one of the best in the state. Of tables within the four dining rooms, tables 3, 15 and 16 are recommended for their views of the garden. After dinner, ask Maitre d' Colin Wilson to escort you to the upstairs "hay loft" lounge, where desserts and cocktails are served.

5540 Gulf of Mexico Drive
Longboat Key, FL 94228
Tel: 941-383-3633

L'ESPALIER
Restaurants

A favorite of Boston's old-money set since 1978, L'Espalier is among the brick townhouses that comprise the Back Bay. Owner and executive chef Frank McClelland offers a new menu every day, always stocked with exotic ingredients and local, fresh fish. The restaurant hosts guests in three intimate dining rooms with only 10 tables in each. Ask maitre d' Louis Risoli for a seat beside a bay window, overlooking trendy Gloucester Street. Private dining is available, but call a few weeks in advance.

30 Gloucester Street
Boston, MA 02115
Tel: 617-262-3023   Fax: 617-375-9297

EVELYN S. POOLE
Antiques

This is the premier source in South Florida for quality decorative antiques from Italy, Russia, Sweden, France and England dating from the 17th, 18th and 19th centuries. With a reputation for distinct and exquisite antiques, objets d'art, silver and porcelain, Poole counts acclaimed interior designers and collectors among her clients. She travels the world in search of individual pieces for her spectacular 5000 square-foot showroom in the historic Miami Design District. Poole recently added a collection of important signed French Art Deco furniture and accessories.

3925 North Miami Avenue
Miami, FL 33127
Tel: 305-573-7463   Fax: 305-573-7409

EVEREST
Restaurants

The spectacular view from the 40th floor of a Chicago skyscraper makes Everest the city's most elegant place to dine. Since 1986, chef superstar Jean Joho has been serving his personalized menu, which changes seasonally and has been recognized by *The Chicago Tribune* with four stars. Joho has been *Food and Wine*'s Chef of the Year and is a recipient of the prestigious James Beard Award. His filet of beef poached with foie gras is superb and the wine cellar holds a huge collection of Alsatian vintages.

440 South LaSalle Street
Chicago, IL 60605
Tel: 312-663-8920
Fax: 312-663-8802

ESTATE ANTIQUES
Antiques

George Williams, a former Sotheby's intern, joined forces with Jim and Harriet Pratt in 1979 to display southern antiques because, as he says: "there is nothing else in the world I would consider doing." Located in Charleston's

antiques district, the showroom features pre-1820 American furniture, with an emphasis on southern decorative arts. The firm meticulously scrutinizes each piece that goes up for sale, and customers are educated on the history of the piece. Estate keeps files on every antique, administering a museum-like approach. To date, the firm's library holds over 5000 records. The Metropolitan Museum of Art, MESDA and the Charleston Museum have bought furniture, paintings, maps, prints, porcelain and brass through Estate Antiques.

155 King Street
Charleston, SC 29401
Tel: 843-723-2362   Fax: 843-723-2363

EVERGLADES CLUB
Private Clubs

Architect Addison Mizner opened this club in 1919; the clubhouse that he designed still stands today. The Everglades offers top-notch golf, tennis and dining in a truly elegant environment. However, admittance is strictly reserved for the approximately 1100 members and their guests. The club hosts black-tie parties every Saturday night during February and March. The waiting list for membership is at least five years.

356 Worth Avenue
Palm Beach, FL 33480
Tel: 561-820-2620

FAIRMONT SCOTTSDALE PRINCESS

Hotels

Located in Scottsdale, yet away from tourism, the Fairmont Scottsdale Princess is a sophisticated, quality establishment specializing in luxury accommodation. Heaven for golfers, the Princess has two 18-hole championship golf courses (one was a site of the PGA Tours Phoenix Open). The hotel offers elaborate spa services in its 1500 square foot facility. La Hacienda is North America's only four-star/AAA four-diamond Mexican Restaurant. The hotel's other eatery, The Marquesa, has five diamonds for Catalan cuisine. The Scottsdale Princess has nightly "dive-in" movies. Guests can enjoy food and drink service in the pool between improving their golf handicap.

7575 East President Drive
Scottsdale, AZ 85255
Tel: 480-585-4848   Fax: 480-585-0086

FAO SCHWARZ

Specialty Shops

When people enter FAO they are in Never Never Land, Candyland and Fairyland all rolled into one. That's why it is so hard to pull them back out. Kids (and grown ups alike) love this "toy" store where there is simply never too-much. Alas, when FAO moved in the 1980s, the train room of yore couldn't be replicated, but there are laser game consoles and plenty of other bewildering diversions. One piece of advice: do your Christmas shopping early – even if your name is Santa Claus, it's hard to stay jolly during the holiday rush.

767 Fifth Avenue
New York, NY 10153
Tel: 212-644-9400

FAR NIENTE VINEYARDS

Winemakers

Nestled in the heart of California's beautiful Napa Valley, Far Niente Vineyards distinguishes itself from some of its more famous winemaking neighbors with an almost religious attention to detail. Not only do they hand-pick the grapes that go into their Chardonnay, Cabernet Semillon and Dolce, they are one of the few wineries that actually hand-sorts them. Look out for Gil Nickel's new winery, Nickel and Nickel, which he hopes to launch with son Jeremy by 2002. It will specialize in single vineyard wines, also under the supervision of Far Niente's current director of winemaking, Dirk Hampson.

P.O. Box 327
Oakville, CA 94562
Tel: 707-944-2861   Fax: 707-944-2312

FAIRFAX & SAMMONS

Architects and Interior Designers

Richard Sammons began his career in the office of David Anthony Easton in New York and Anne Fairfax ran private architectural practices in Honolulu. Nowadays Richard and Anne are partners in business as well as in marriage. Offering a full scope of architectural services, Fairfax & Sammons designs, constructs drawings and supplies on-site construction administration. Committed to innovation, the firm is responsible for the addition to a H.T. Lindeburg House and a Palladian inspired villa in Hong Kong. Fairfax & Sammons have developed a body of work which reflects theories of proportion and order through scholarship and meticulous attention to detail. They have offices in both New York and Palm Beach.

67 Gansevoort Street
New York, NY 10014
Tel: 212-255-0704
Fax: 212-229-9517

THE FEDERALIST

Restaurants

As charming as it is delicious, The Federalist makes a grand success out of combining the old with the new in a city where the two sit side by side. The dining room, soothing in cream and cocoa hues, is accented with busts of historical figures and gray architectural pillars (most are equipped with data ports, for those who can't make it through lunch without checking their e-mail). The gold domed state house is a coin toss from the financial district and Old North Church. Make sure that you try the Hudson Valley foie gras and the sautéed Californian abalone.

15 Beacon Street
Boston, MA 02108
Tel: 617-670-2515

FELIDIA

Restaurants

Opened in 1981 by Lidia Mattichio Bastianich in a converted old brownstone on Manhattan's Upper East side, Felidia is one of the leading italian restaurants in the city. Formerly of Villa Marchese in Sicily, chef Fortunato Nicotra prepares heavenly grilled baby octopus and a braised veal, served with barley risotto, saffron and parmesan. Centering the menu around seasonal produce, Lidia's other restaurants include Frico Bar and Becco, both in New York, and Lidia's in Kansas City. Incidentally, with 980 selections, Felidia has one of the most comprehensive wine lists in the United States.

243 East 58th Street
New York, NY 10022
Tel: 212-758-1479

FERRARI CARANO WINERIES

Winemakers

When husband and wife team Don and Rhonda Carano decided to seek sanctuary from the stresses of running a large casino in Reno, they moved to Alexander County, with an ambition only to sell grapes to local producers. Curiosity led the couple to sign up for a few enology courses and before long, they were smoothing namesake labels over bottles of Chardonnay, Fumé Blanc and Zinfandel. Led by winemaker George Bursick, Ferrari Carano is now one of the standout vineyards in Sonoma. The 1995 Trésor is particularly sublime, although each of the wines produced under the Ferrari Carano moniker has something to recommend it.

8761 Dry Creek Road
Healdsburg, CA 95448
Tel: 707-433-6700
Fax: 707-431-1742

FELISSIMO
Specialty Shops

When serious shoppers – women such as Oprah Winfrey, Susan Sarandon and supermodel Linda Evangelista – need a break from the bustle of Fifth Avenue, they drop into Felissimo, a five-story urban oasis, created according to the principles of feng shui. Acclaimed designer Clodagh's style artfully blends minimalism with luxurious earth-friendly materials for a relaxing shopping experience. Enter the store's luminous mirrored foyer, then flow up to the ch'i level and choose a talisman from the Feng Shui collection. Don't leave Felissimo without stopping at its renowned tea room for a cup of rejuvenating Haiku tea. You might just spot Monica Lewinsky at the next table.

10 West 56th Street
New York, NY 10019
Tel: 212-247-5656

FERRÉE FLORSHEIM CATERING
Party Organizers and Caterers

Newly renamed Food For Thought – Ferrée Florsheim Catering, this top Chicago party consulting and catering company is still dishing up some of the most innovative and elegant cuisine around. Partners Susan Florsheim and Anne Ferrée pride themselves in serving unique foods with élan. Mashed potatoes topped with caviar, for instance, are presented in martini glasses by an impeccably trained staff. Chicago's smart set can't get enough of the Double-F Brigade, whether it's an intimate dinner party, a high-profile celebrity wedding or a charity ball.

7001 Ridgeway
Lincolnwood, IL 60712
Tel: 847-982-2608
Fax: 847-982-0884

FIELD MUSEUM
OF NATURAL HISTORY
Museums

The exterior of The Field Museum is closely patterned after the Erechtheium, one of the Athenian Acropolis temples. Founded to house the biological and anthropological collections assembled for the world's Colombian exposition of 1893, today it houses more than 20 million artifacts and specimens drawn from the fields of anthropology, botany, geology and zoology. The Museum is home to "Sue", the largest and most complete Tyrannosaurus rex in the world. It also has an active staff of scientists who conduct research in evolutionary biology, anthropology and paleontology in conjunction with local universities.

1400 South Lakeshore Drive
Chicago, IL 60605
Tel: 312-922-9410

FIFTEEN BEACON
Hotels   *Rising Star*

Paul Roiff is the owner of Fifteen Beacon, a new 61-room luxury boutique hotel, located in the heart of historic Beacon Hill, within walking distance of Boston's financial district and the famed Newbury Street. After a $25 million renovation, it is now one of the hottest spots in the city. Interior designer Celeste Cooper juxtaposes cutting-edge technology with classical Jeffersonian styling to create an atmosphere of worldly charm. The hotel occupies a turn-of-the-century 10-story Beaux Arts building and many of its original features have been preserved. Rooms come adorned with working gas

fireplaces, mahogany paneling and flanking bookcases. Each room features an original design scheme with grand canopy beds, custom furniture and 300 thread count Italian linens. Fifteen Beacon offers guests personalized business cards on arrival, imprinted with their own phone and fax numbers at the hotel. The Federalist Restaurant is a culinary destination with an atmosphere allusive of the world's most prestigious clubs. The signature of "The Fed" is Boston's most extensive wine cellar.

15 Beacon Street
Boston, MA 02108
Tel: 617-670-1500   Fax: 617-670-2525

FIORIDELLA
Florists

Whether in the market for a spray of exotic Ecuadorian roses, or a delicate bouquet of springtime blossoms, chic San Franciscans have been turning to Fioridella for over twenty years. Known for stunning window displays that feature innovative yet elegant arrangements – like orchids artfully wrapped in burlap. They also carry an assortment of unique gifts from across the globe, from Moroccan room screens to tobacco boxes handmade in India.

1920 Polk Street
San Francisco, CA 94109
Tel: 415-775-4065
Fax: 415-775-6396

FIRESTONE AND PARSON
Antiques

In 1946, Edwin I. Firestone began his career in fine and antique jewelry. Today, he is joined by his son David in supplying major collectors and museums with rare stones and silver – Firestone claims that he has sold more silver by Paul Revere than all other antique dealers and auction houses in the United States combined. Renowned for great attention to detail and demand for high quality, his acclaimed firm shows annually at the International Art and Antique Dealers Show.

8 Newbury Street
Boston, MA 02116
Tel: 617-266-1858
Fax: 617-266-0117

~

FINE ARTS MUSEUM OF SAN FRANCISCO
Museums

The Fine Arts Museum was created in 1970, when the California Palace of the Legion of Honor merged with the De Young Museum. The elegant French neoclassical building was dedicated to the memory of the 36,000 Californian men who had lost their lives on the battlefields of France during World War I. Six additional gallery spaces were set around a sky lit court in 1995. Focusing on Greek, Etruscan, Roman, Egyptian, Medieval, Renaissance, and 17th through 20th century art, the palace showcases 80,000 works.

233 Post Street
San Francisco, CA 94108
Tel: 415-863-3330

FISHERS ISLAND COUNTRY CLUB
Golf Clubs

Breathtaking views are the hallmark of this ultra-exclusive, Seth Raynor designed course off the coast of Long Island. Measuring 6566 yards from the back tees, the course is a shotmaker's delight despite the everpresent windy conditions. The par four 4th is consistently among the top 100 holes in America. The scenery is enhanced by frequent perspective shifts caused by numerous elevation changes throughout the course. While its geographic location ensures a high degree of privacy, Fishers Island is also the only course rated among America's 100 Greatest which has asked to be excluded from the list. Not for the rabbit or the socially insecure.

Fishers Island, NY 06390
Tel: 631-788-7221

FIRST UNION NATIONAL BANK
Wealth Management

For excellent financial advice conveyed with warm southern hospitality, individuals with $1 million or more in investable assets often turn to First Union National Bank. The North Carolina-based institution operates a Private Client Group, designed to offer discreet personalized assistance with investment and financial planning needs. Clients are assigned their own relationship manager to assist in trust and estate planning, tax advantage strategies and business valuations.

First Union Corporation
301 South College Street
Charlotte, NC 28288
Tel: 704-374-6161   Fax: 704-383-0699

~

FISH & NEAVE
Law Firms

A leader in the burgeoning field of intellectual property law, Fish & Neave maintains offices both in New York and Palo Alto. With direct access to the centers of technological development, the firm has specialized in patent and trademark infringement, copyright enforcement, and complex intellectual portfolio management. No firm has a better pedigree in this field: the Wright Brothers, Thomas Edison, and Alexander Graham Bell were all clients, as are Ford, Time Warner, Polaroid and many others today.

1251 Avenue of the Americas
New York, NY 10020
Tel: 212-596-9000

FISHER TRAVEL
Travel Consultants

Creating the perception that a product or service is desperately exclusive is a key tenet of luxury marketing. Bill Fisher has utilised this knowledge to considerable acclaim. The Brooklyn-born travel consultant has carved a lucrative niche for himself as travel agent to the stars. Tom Cruise, Diane Sawyer and Calvin Klein are among the oh-so chic 500 who can claim that "Bill does my booking."

200 East 42nd Street, Suite 1411
New York, NY 10017
Tel: 212-867-4040

~

FISHER ISLAND SPA
Spas and Clinics

Fisher Island vacations include a private, chauffeured limousine service to and from Miami International Airport, accommodation in a Junior Suite, the use of a golf cart for on-island transportation, three meals a day and unlimited exercise classes. The 216 acre island offers soft, white beaches, five fine restaurants, a championship golf course and tennis courts. Reserve a seven night stay and you'll receive five aromatherapy massages, a seaweed body wrap, two target massages, a manicure, a pedicure and exceptional treatments from the topnotch beauty salon. One of the best spas on the east coast.

1 Fisher Island Drive
Fisher Island, FL 33109
Tel: 305-535-6000   Fax: 305-535-6036

FLEET BANK
Wealth Management
With a high staff-to-client ratio and a range of portfolio services designed to fulfill the needs of the most discriminating investors, the Fleet Private Clients group has won the praise of customers and industry experts alike. Each new client (with investable assets of $1 million or more) is assigned both a personal relationship manager and an investment officer to assure individualized service. Among the areas in which Fleet is particularly strong are diversification of assets, intra-generational planning and tax-effective philanthropy.

100 Federal Street
Boston, MA 02110
Tel: 617-346-4000

FLEXJET
Airplanes
FlexJet, a program of Bombardier Aerospace – the world's third largest producer of civil aircraft, after Boeing and Airbus – entered the fractional ownership market in 1995. Depending on the share level you enter at, you may have 100-400 flying hours per year, and no matter which program you select, you will always be guaranteed an aircraft with the comfort, convenience, safety and privacy that ownership affords. In as few as four hours you may have a Learjet, Challenger, or Global Express (the world's fastest, ultra-long range business jet) waiting for you at any of 5000 airports in the U.S.

14651 Dallas Parkway, Suite 600
Dallas, TX 75240
Tel: 972-720-2536   Fax: 972-720-2435

FLIGHT OPTIONS
Airplanes   *Rising Star*
If you are tired of having your plans dictated by the schedules of others then you might want to consider buying a share in an aircraft. Flight Options' complete service includes a customized ownership plan so you can buy a share that suits your budget as well as your transportation needs. Best of all, they guarantee to have the aircraft you need at any of more than 5000 airports in the US within four to six hours of your request. It is like having a jet at your command at every airport in the country. And if you decide to start taking the train or simply need cash in a hurry, they also guarantee liquidity. Among the aircraft in their fleet are the Citation II, Beechjet 400A and the Hawker 800.

26180 Curtiss Wright Parkway
Richmond Heights, OH 44143
Tel: 216-261-3500

FLEUR DE LYS
Restaurants
Some people come to Fleur de Lys just to check out its unusual dining room, which feels almost like a garden tent. Once you have sampled the romantic ambiance – and Hubert Keller's award-winning French food – you will know why they keep returning. Keller's fans include President Clinton, for whom he cooked as the first guest chef in the history of the White House.

777 Sutter Street
San Francisco, CA 94109
Tel: 415-673-7779

FLORAL EVENTS UNLIMITED
Florists
Planning a gala or wedding in Washington, D.C.? If you have a large budget then you might as well use the floral designer who dressed both of President Clinton's last inaugural balls. Often cited as one of the most successful florists in the region, Angelo Bonita's company receives frequent accolades from wedding and party planners. Senator and Mrs. Jay Rockefeller are regular customers.

2700 Garfield Avenue
Silver Spring, MD 20910
Tel: 301-585-2772

FLOWERS
Winemakers
Walt and Joan Flowers once ran Moon nursery (which dates back to 1767) farming over 1000 acres. The Pennsylvanians then set out for Camp Meeting Ridge, less than two miles from the Pacific, elevated at 1300 feet – optimum growing conditions for Pinot Noir and Chardonnay. The estate uses an all gravity flow, allowing a natural "fall and gather" collection before grapes are sorted and crushed. Their 1996 Camp Meeting Ridge Pinot Noir was served at the White House for the 50th Anniversary of NATO, reputedly causing a few explosions among the French contingent.

28500 Seaview Road
Cazadero, CA 95421
Tel: 707-847-3661

PETER B. FODOR, M.D.
Cosmetic Surgeons
Peter Fodor is recognized as a leader in the field of Aesthetic Plastic Surgery. Board certified in both general and plastic surgery, the doctor recently opened Century Cosmetics which specializes in anti-aging treatments and advanced skin care. Despite the many awards he has received, Fodor insists that his greatest satisfaction comes from seeing the effect his work has on his patients' lives.

2080 Century Park East, #710
Los Angeles, CA 90067
Tel: 310-203-9533
Fax: 310-203-9798

THE FORD DETROIT INTERNATIONAL JAZZ FESTIVAL
Events
Since 1980, Labor Day Weekend has brought thousands of jazz aficionados to the Ford Detroit International Jazz Festival. Held in the heart of downtown Detroit in an Art Deco-style Music Hall, the festival features emerging artists such as Brasil Brazil as well as living legends like Nancy Wilson and Dr. John. Conveniently located near Detroit's best hotels and restaurants, the Festival is traditionally the last of the big summer music get-togethers.

350 Madison Avenue
Detroit, MI 48226
Tel: 313-962-4307   Fax: 313-963-2462

FOUR SEASONS BOSTON
Hotels

The only hotel in New England to be awarded the AAA Five Diamond Award and the Mobile Five-Star Award, the Four Seasons Boston combines the unsurpassed service of a world-class luxury hotel with the comfort and charm of a traditional Beacon Hill home. Boasting 275 elegant rooms and suites, the hotel is located just minutes from the city's renovated Theater District.

200 Boylston Street
Boston, MA 02116
Tel: 617-338-4400   Fax: 617-423-0154

FOUR SEASONS LAS VEGAS
Hotels

This non-gaming hotel is an oasis of sorts, yet it is only minutes away from diverse entertainment, world-class shopping and the natural wonders of the scenic southern Nevada corridor. 424 deluxe guest rooms, including 86 suites, are located on five floors of the 43-story Mandalay Bay Resort & Casino tower. The highest rated hotel in Las Vegas offers dozens of little luxuries including walk-in closets, down duvets and deep soaking tubs. With an 8000 square foot freeform pool, a full-service spa and a full range of cardiovascular and weight training equipment, it's a serene escape from the sometimes maddening casino crowds.

3960 Las Vegas Boulevard South
Las Vegas, NV 89119
Tel: 702-632-5000
Fax: 702-632-5195

FOUR SEASONS NEW YORK
Hotels

"Classic elegance that transcends time and fashion." That's I.M. Pei describing the Four Seasons New York, which the famous architect designed. From the graceful, steeping spire of the exterior to the subtle yet sumptuous Art Deco interior, this bastion of *haute chic* is as cool and sleek as its inhabitants. The people-watching in the hotel's bar is, at times, a better show than anything on Broadway – and for an amusing second-act, the Fifty Seven Fifty Seven restaurant offers global cuisine on a par with the hotel's high style. As in all of the Four Seasons hotels, the service is truly immaculate. From being addressed by one's name to having newspaper preferences remembered by the hotel staff, every last whim is catered to.

57 East 57th Street
New York, NY 10022
Tel: 212-758-5700   Fax: 212-758-5711

FOUR SEASONS HUALALAI
Hotels

Set on 32 acres of tropical land, the Four Seasons Hualalai boasts a rich Polynesian ambiance, coupled with every modern convenience imaginable. The Bungalow-style suites are decorated in teak wood, and are littered with fresh, tropical flowers. Each suite comes with its own Jacuzzi tub and outdoor showers. Guests enjoy spa services, yoga, kickboxing lessons and leisurely dining in the waterfront Lava Lounge.

100 Kautulehu Road
Kona, HI 96740
Tel: 808-325-8000
Fax: 808-325-8100

FOUR SEASONS PALM BEACH
Hotels

This private, oceanfront resort is the highest rated hotel in the state of Florida. Renowned for impeccable personal service and attention (attendants "spritz" guests on the beach), the hotel grounds are lush, flanked by palm trees and tropical flowers; no detail is missed. The same philosophy continues inside the hotel, where suites are lavishly appointed and offer spectacular ocean views. Three dining rooms offer executive chef Hubert Des Marais's seasonal French cuisine: he was recently listed among America's Best New Chefs by *Food and Wine* magazine.

2800 South Ocean Boulevard
Palm Beach, FL 33480
Tel: 561-582-2800
Fax: 561-547-1374

FOUR SEASONS RESTAURANT
Restaurants

Birthplace of the power lunch, the Four Seasons continues to reach new heights 40 years after its creation. Featuring a timeless design by Philip Johnson (who has a corner table reserved for him daily) and a myriad of loyal and high profile regulars, the experience of dining at this New York landmark is not to be missed. Creations from executive chef Christian Albin are complimented by a wine list that includes arguably the country's largest selection of Brunello di Montelcino wines. If it's a memorable impression you want to make, this is the place.

99 East 52nd Street
New York, NY 10021
Tel: 212-754-9494
Fax: 212-754-1077

FOX RESIDENTIAL GROUP
Property Consultants

Ranked as one of the top real estate brokerage houses in New York by *Crain's*, Fox Residential Group have handles the sale and lease of upscale cooperative and condominium apartments and townhouses for many of the city's top movers and shakers, including Walter Cronkite and theatrical producer Harold Prince. The firm also offers complete corporate relocation services. Founder Barbara Fox is a recipient of the Henry Foster Memorial Award for outstanding achievement in residential real estate.

1015 Madison Avenue
New York, NY 10021
Tel: 212-772-2666   Fax: 212-535-5450

FRAENKEL GALLERY

Art Dealers

When he started his gallery more than 20 years ago, Jeffrey Fraenkel took on a challenge. Besides offering one of the country's premier collections of 19th and 20th century photography, he began showing the works of important modern masters whose photographs were, up until then, hard to come by on the West Coast. Among those whose pictures he championed – and still represents – are now established artists like Garry Winogrand, Lee Friedlander, Diane Arbus and Irving Penn. Along with co-owner, Frish Brandt, Fraenkel has lent a number of the gallery's photographs to major museums across the country, among them the Museum of Modern Art, the Metropolitan Museum of Art and the National Gallery.

49 Geary Street
San Francisco, CA 94108
Tel: 415-981-2661   Fax: 415-981-4014

FRANCISCAN ESTATES

Winemakers

At the core of the Oakville viticultural area, Franciscan Estates is defined by blue-ribbon terroir – the location and climate ensure heavenly grapes. A neighbor to Mondavi and Opus One, the 240 acre vineyard produces a flagship Bordeaux style blend "Magnificat" and classic Cabernet Sauvignon, Merlot and Zinfandel. The unfiltered barrel-fermented Cuvée Sauvage, a big, oaky, rich Chardonnay, is what first earned the estate its reputation. Ralph Hersom, Wine Director at Le Cirque 2000, says "they set out to make one wine which stands comparison with their French cousins. They have succeeded."

1178 Galleron Lane
St. Helena, CA 94574
Tel: 707-963-7112   Fax: 707-963-7867

FRANK & BARBARA POLLACK

Antiques

It was while furnishing her own home that Barbara Pollack first fell in love with and began acquiring American naive art from the 18th and 19th centuries. After holding what she calls "the world's largest garage sale" to make room for her new passion, Barbara put together a collection that now boasts first-rate works by American itinerant artists, including watercolors by Sheldon Peck and the renowned married painters, Samuel and Ruth Shute. Call for an appointment to view these works plus other exquisite examples of American textiles, pottery, folk art and 20th century decorative arts and jewelry. Frank Pollack also handles rare books, with an emphasis on murder mysteries.

1214 Green Bay Road
Highland Park, IL 60035
Tel: 847-433-2213

FRASER YACHTS

Powerboats & Yachts

When a particularly rushed client needed a brand new super yacht delivered in the brief week between Christmas and New Years, he called Stuart Larsen, one of the top brokers at Fraser Yachts. A whirlwind of urgent meetings and several transatlantic flights later, Larsen arrived in New York to do the impossible – hand over contracts and keys to the newly appointed luxury craft, now fully staffed and ready to sail. His client, delighted by the extraordinary care he received by this prestigious global brokerage service, no doubt rang in the millennium from the deck of his new yacht.

2230 South East 17th Street
Fort Lauderdale, FL 33316
Tel: 954-463-0600   Fax: 954-763-1053

FRAMED ON MADISON

Specialty Shops

Gene Elter opened his Madison Avenue shop in 1942; at the time, it was the only store in the city dedicated exclusively to classic European picture frames, some from the early 1800s. The connoisseur quickly established a niche on the Upper East Side. Right after his wife had a baby, Daniel Koren happened to be in the shop, purchasing frames. The college professor soon developed a friendship with Elter, eventually purchasing the firm in 1985. In the tradition of his predecessor, Elter acquires frames at auction and from private collectors around the world.

740 Madison Avenue
New York, NY 10021
Tel: 212-734-4680
Fax: 212-988-0128

FRED JOAILLIER

Jewelry and Watches

When Fred Samuel opened his first boutique in Paris in 1936, his mission was to present stunning one-of-a-kind jewels, using the finest and rarest stones available in the world. Continuing that mission today, sensuality, design and exuberance are the three core values in Fred designs. Magnificent pieces by artists like Braque, Buffet and Cocteau have ensured a reputation for exclusivity as well as quality. From Paris to Cannes and from Monte Carlo to Beverly Hills, Brigitte Bardot, Princess Stephanie of Monaco and the Sultan of Brunei are among the long list of satisfied and demanding clients. Many of the world's largest single stones were sold by the firm, such as the Soleil d'Or, a 105.54 carat yellow diamond, and the Blue Moon, a faceted sapphire of 275 carats.

401 North Rodeo Drive
Beverly Hills, CA 90210
Tel: 310-276-1277   Fax: 310-274-1057

FRED LEIGHTON

Jewelry and Watches

Fred Leighton opened a shop in Greenwich Village as a young man. As he puts it himself, it was "full of colorful paper flowers, happy painted sculptures and hand-embroidered garden-party and wedding dresses." But his passion for rare jewelry soon overcame other concerns, and he began searching the world for the treasures he is now synonymous with. Together with his wife, the delightful Glorya, Fred launched a jewelry business 25 years ago. Today it is regarded as one of the premier sources of rare jewelery, with one of the largest and most prestigious collections of Estate and Antique jewelry in the world. The Leighton's devotees includes everyone from Nicole Kidman to Peggy Lipton.

773 Madison Avenue
New York, NY 10021
Tel: 212-288-1872

FREDERICK SCHULTZ
ANCIENT ART

Antiques

As president of the National Association of Dealers in Ancient, Oriental & Primitive Art, and a founding member of the International Association of Dealers in Ancient Art, Fred Schultz is recognized as one of the leading figures in his field. His Manhattan gallery specializes in museum quality art from Ancient Greece, Rome, Egypt, the Near East and Europe. Its impressive variety even includes an exquisite collection of Prehistoric Eskimo ivories.

41 East 57th Street
New York, NY 10022
Tel: 212-758-6007   Fax: 212-832-0448

FREEDMAN JEWELERS

Jewelry and Watches

Working with fine jewelry has been a tradition in Maurice Freedman's family for over a century. The third-generation jeweler creates important original pieces from exotic diamonds and colored gemstones for individuals and corporate clients. His store in Huntington also carries a variety of exquisite pieces from prestigious houses like Mikimoto and Tiffany.

345 New York Avenue
Huntington, NY 11743
Tel: 516-423-2000   Fax: 631-673-4466

FRENCH CULINARY INSTITUTE

Culinary Schools

Located in the heart of New York City's SoHo district, The French Culinary Institute is the preeminent American training school for classic French cooking. The Institute models its program on that of France's official training school. Many of the instructors are local gastronomic legends, such as Alain Sailhac of Le Cirque, and former chef-owner of Lutèce, André Soltner. The Institute is also open to amateurs for a 22-week Saturday program, La Technique.

462 Broadway
New York, NY 10013
Tel: 212-219-8890   Fax: 212-431-3054

THE FRENCH LAUNDRY

Restaurants

Ask to be seated outside in the country garden, among the vintage roses, perennials, seasonal herbs and vegetables and take in the rustic beauty of this stone cottage, built in 1900 as a French steam laundry, while you enjoy award-winning American cuisine with a French influence. A veteran of some of the great kitchens of the world, Chef Thomas Keller is renowned from coast to coast for his innovation and dedication. Don't miss his classic *pot au feu*.

6640 Washington Street
Yountville, CA 94599
Tel: 707-944-2380   Fax: 707-944-1974

FRENCHWAY TRAVEL

Travel Consultants

In the giddy worlds of finance and fashion, experienced travelers appreciate the Frenchway touch. Kate Moss, and Patrick Demarchelier depend on them to arrange their vacations. Frenchway is dedicated to satisfying even the most difficult requests with Gallic charm and passion, from exotic excursions and honeymoons, to business trips and last-minute getaways.

11 West 25th Street
New York, NY 10010
Tel: 212-243-3500   Fax: 212-243-3535

THE FRENCH ROOM

Restaurants

If the lobby of The Hotel Adolphus, with its multimillion dollar art collection, is a feast for the eyes, the French Room is a feast for all the senses; inspired by the 18th century, this sumptuous dining room has 18 foot arched ceilings framed with gilt borders, hand blown Murano glass chandeliers, marble floors and vast floral and plant arrangements. Maitre d' Jim Donohue is a real gentleman, and Chef William Koval's light and modern interpretation of classical French cuisine is a winner. His signature dishes include a jumbo Lump Crab cake, served with a whole grain mustard demi and tomato confit.

1321 Commerce Street
Dallas, TX 75202
Tel: 214-742-8200   Fax: 214-651-3588

FREER GALLERY OF ART

Museums

This was the first museum of fine arts within the Smithsonian Institution when it opened in 1923. In conjunction with the Sackler Gallery, the Freer is home to a superb collection of Asian art, modern ceramics, works on paper and 19th and early 20th century American art. Recent highlights include the Vever Collection, a grouping of Islamic art, assembled in turn-of-the century Paris by Henri Vever, a celebrated jeweler and connoisseur.

12th Street & Jefferson Drive
Washington, DC 20560
Tel: 202-357-2700

FRENCH COUNTRY LIVING

Specialty Shops

On a self-created sabbatical, Sally and Bringier McConnell founded French Country Living from a garret apartment in Paris in 1985. Seduced by the French style they saw in their neighborhood, the couple began researching furniture and decorative arts in libraries and along the French countryside. Before long, their collection included hand-painted tile of Carrelages du Marais, Alsatian furniture and forged iron from the Rhone valley and Provençal fabrics. Since bringing their collection to Virginia, the couple still collect French pieces – only now, French craftsmen have agreed to make dining chairs a little wider, to support American bottoms.

10205 Colvin Run Road
Great Falls, VA 22066
Tel: 703-759-2245

THE FRICK COLLECTION

Museums

Europeans love the Frick, which feels like a palazzo or a chateau and yet remains quintessentially American. Henry Clay Frick's mansion on Fifth Avenue is an anthology of some of the most distinguished works of Western art from early Renaissance through the late 19th century – including masterpieces by Titian, Boucher, Corot, El Greco, Renoir and Velázquez, as well as Renaissance bronzes, French sculpture of the 18th century and Chinese porcelain.

1 East 70th Street
New York, NY 10021
Tel: 212-288-0700   Fax: 212-628-4417

GABELLINI ASSOCIATES
Architects and Interior Designers

"You could describe my approach as portraiture," Gabellini says. "It has to reflect these people the way a set imitates actors." One of the world's most sought-after designers, his award-winning team includes architects, project managers, furniture, lighting and sourcing specialists as well as designers. The Pennsylvania native got his break with the late Jay Smith before branching out on his own in 1991, quickly building a reputation as a master of minimalism – utilizing spare, clean furnishings, such as a single limestone shelf, to enhance a room.

665 Broadway
New York, NY 10012
Tel: 212-388-1700

GALAXY AEROSPACE
Airplanes

Galaxy Aerospace is revolutionizing the way business is conducted at the highest echelons. At the company's launch in 1997, President & CEO Brian E. Barents promised to produce, market and support a line of advanced-technology business aircraft. Eliminating the use of "heavy iron," Galaxy has made it easier to reach world markets – covering a nautical-mile-range that previously was the domain of more expensive business jets. Able to travel nonstop from New York to Paris, New York to Los Angeles, Moscow to Beijing and Rio de Janeiro to Cape Town, the Galaxy is configured with an interior layout for eight passengers on long-range missions with true standing headroom – six feet, three inches.

One Galaxy Way
Fort Worth, Texas 76177
Tel: 817-837-3715   Fax: 817-837-3862

GAGOSIAN GALLERY
Art Dealers

Since 1980, when he opened a gallery in Los Angeles, Larry Gagosian has built up an empire in California, New York and London, showing mostly contemporary works. This world-class networker has the resources to attract and keep the hottest artists, including the likes of Richard Serra and Francesco Clemente, as well as more controversial figures such as Damien Hirst. His Beverly Hills gallery was designed by Richard Meier; he has shown Warhol, Basquiat, Picasso and Cy Twombly among others since it opened in 1995.

980 Madison Avenue
New York, NY 10021
Tel: 212-744-2313

GALERIE MICHAEL
Art Dealers

When you first enter Galerie Michael, you might easily mistake it for your basic high-end Beverly Hills establishment. Those in the know, however, head straight for the back room, where affable owner Michael Schwartz keeps the largest collection of Rembrandt etchings in the United States. His client list, which includes some of the entertainment industry's most prominent players, depends on Schwartz to help them build and curate their private old master collections.

430 North Rodeo Drive
Beverly Hills, CA 90210
Tel: 310-273-3377   Fax: 310-273-3452

GALILEO
Restaurants

Roberto Donna, born in the Piedmont region of Italy, is a highly regarded ambassador of Italian cuisine. A James Beard Award-winning chef and restaurateur, he believes in creating pure, simple cuisine using only the freshest ingredients. Galileo is the best of his eight restaurants, where he keeps the capital's elite clamoring for authentic Italian fare. Off the main dining room are two private cellars that are perfect for intimate gatherings, as well as a large terrace for dining outside in the summer. Try to snag the chef's table: it seats eight and is nestled in the corner of the kitchen. Better yet, the new *Laboratorio del Galileo* is a dining room inside the main dining room where 30 lucky diners sample from a 12-course tasting menu. Reserve three weeks in advance.

1110 21st Street, NW
Washington, DC 20036
Tel: 202-293-7191   Fax: 202-331-9364

GALLERY PAULE ANGLIM
Art Dealers

Scratch a gallery owner and you'll find a frustrated artist. However, in the case of Paule Anglim, those canvas dreams have been channeled into creating one of San Francisco's pre-eminent contemporary galleries. Since 1972, the Quebec-born Anglim has dealt in photography, painting, sculpture and multimedia installations. Up-and-comers are represented as well as established artists such as William Tucker, Louise Fishman, Paul Kos and Deborah Butterfield.

14 Geary Street
San Francisco, CA 94108
Tel: 415-433-2710
Fax: 415-433-1501

GARDEN GATE
Florists

Junior Villanueva became interested in floral design in High School; as homecoming and prom chairman, he had to investigate how long different flowers last. After college, he and his wife, Maria, founded Garden Gate, using flowers from all over the world to create designs that are more works of art than mere ornaments. Villanueva explains that today's bouquet is composed of monochromatic color and kept in antique and crystal vases rather than simple, earthy containers. The Mansion on Turtle Creek and the Adolphus Hotel both use Garden Gate on a weekly basis. Junior and Maria's work at the annual Beaux-Arts Ball, benefiting the Dallas Museum of Art, is also a good illustration of their talents.

2615 Roth Street
Dallas, TX 75201
Tel: 214-220-1272   Fax: 214-220-1275

GARY DANKO
Restaurants   *Rising Star*

Open less than a year and already a Mobil five-star restaurant, Gary Danko has given the bay area something to talk about that doesn't end in dot-com. Known as a spot where guests can linger all night if they desire, the service is orchestrated perfectly — you're not sitting at the table waiting, but you're not left feeling rushed and annoyed either. The prize-winning menu includes innovative French dishes like horseradish-crusted salmon and roast squab with couscous. Select a vintage from the mighty 900-bottle wine list and don't leave without tasting the chocolate soufflé with Grand Marnier sauce. Ask general manager Nick Peyton for a corner table in the low-lit dining room for the most commanding view.

800 North Point Street
San Francisco, CA
Tel: 415-749-2060

GALPER/BALDON ASSOCIATES
Architects and Interior Designers

When Leonard Nimoy's garden needed a new pavilion and Sharon Stone decided that a koi pond was the right finishing touch for her yard, both stars turned to the innovative landscape architecture firm of Galper/Baldon Associates, whose design philosophy champions the use of natural landscaping that complements the architectural style of clients' homes. From their offices on the boardwalk in Venice, California, the firm has designed thousands of unique gardens and swimming pools, pioneering in the process of such trends as raised pools, infinity edges and contour spa seating.

723 Oceanfront Walk
Venice, CA 90291
Tel: 310-392-3992   Fax: 310-392-9858

THE GARDENER
Specialty Shops

When it opened in 1984, The Gardener revived interest in gardening among smart Californians. What Alta Tingle succeeded in doing (where many had tried and failed) was to make the business of getting down on one's hands and knees sexy. Her Berkeley store continues to sell an eclectic mixture of furniture, tools and every conceivable accoutrement for both budding and veteran green fingers. Nowadays, there is also another branch of the operation in Healdsburg.

1836 Fourth Street
Berkeley, CA 94710
Tel: 510-548-4545
Fax: 510-548-6357

GARY E. YOUNG
Antiques

When he took over the family business (on Maryland's beautiful eastern shore) more than a quarter century ago, Gary Young also inherited his father's passion for 18th century English and Irish furniture. A stickler for pieces with fine patinas, especially those with their original paints and finishes, Young's antiques are sought after by private collectors and museum curators alike. His collection of portrait miniatures on ivory is among the best to be found in the country.

128 South Commerce Street
Centreville, MD 21617
Tel: 410-758-2132
Fax: 410-758-8755

GAME CREEK CLUB
Private Clubs

Inspired by similar clubs in Europe, the Game Creek Club offers its members (many of whom work in the high-pressure canyons of Wall Street) an opportunity to let off a little steam. Besides skiing at their lush Vail Mountain lodge, members can also take advantage of a reciprocal arrangement with the Eagle Club in Gstaad, or, a little closer to home, the brand new Aspen Mountain Club. Lita Hitchcock, Game Creek's charming director, arranges twice-yearly excursions for adventure-minded members, who enjoy exploits like river rafting through the Grand Canyon and helicopter skiing in British Columbia.

278 Hanson Ranch Road
Vail, CO 81657
Tel: 970-479-4280
Fax: 970-479-8010

GEARYS OF BEVERLY HILLS
Specialty Shops

Gearys is a fantasyland for connoisseurs of porcelain, linens, silver and glassworks. A celebrity clientele flocks to Beverly Hills' oldest retailer to snap up luxury home furnishings; since 1999 they have also been able to buy fine jewelry and timepieces as well. Over 600 china patterns, 300 silver patterns and 200 crystal sets are available, including the largest selection of Baccarat crystal in Southern California (no mean feat). The store is a blushing bride's dream, with one of the largest bridal registries in Los Angeles. And if the on-site shopping experience is not enough, Gearys' catalog has been awarded "Best Overall" by the *Wall Street Journal*.

351 North Beverly Drive
Beverly Hills, CA 90210
Tel: 310-273-4741
Fax: 310-858-7555

GAVERT ATELIER
Hair and Beauty

When not jetting off to the East Coast to highlight the locks of devoted Manhattanites, or trekking across Japan in a quest for the latest Asian haircare secrets, master colorist Stewart Gavert can be found at home in Los Angeles, tending to a high-profile celebrity clientele that includes the likes of Christine Lahti, Christina Applegate and Kurt Russell. Along with partner Cody Kusakabe, who wields the scissors, Gavert supervises a staff of five stylists and colorists. They perform their haircare magic at a sleek and serene Beverly Hills salon designed by Mako Tsuda.

9666 Brighton Way
Beverly Hills, CA 90210
Tel: 310-858-7898
Fax: 310-858-7216

GENE DOUGLAS DECORATIVE ARTS & ANTIQUES

Antiques

For the past 20 years, Gene Douglas has been a curator of fine art. In the 1980s, Gene and his late partner owned the fabulous store 3434, selling the best of the 20th century to private clients, designers and dealers from around the world. Douglas and his new partner, Barbara Rosin, house an eclectic mix of wonderfully designed pieces, dating from the Aesthetic Movement to the 1960s.

4621 1/2 N. Lincoln Avenue
Chicago, IL 60625
Tel: 773-561-4414   Fax: 773-561-6648

GENE JUAREZ SALON & SPA

Spas and Clinics

When fashion insiders are visiting Seattle and have the urge to be pampered – we're talking about such icons of glamour as Gwyneth Paltrow, Bianca Jagger and Josie Bisset – their destination of choice for a cleansing eucalyptus steam or some rejuvenating hydrotherapy is the Gene Juarez Salon & Spa. Even Melinda Gates, Bill's wife, has been known to arrange for home visits from this premier northwest spa. Of course, that means she misses out on such amenities as the European hydro-tubs and Vichy showers, not to mention the facility's discreet club-like atmosphere, which features fireplaces, velvet drapes and an intimate piano lounge.

1661 East Olive Way
Seattle, WA 98102
Tel: 206-323-7773

GEOFFREY BRADFIELD

Architects and Interior Designers

"To this day, I am amazed by the contrast between the rural beginnings of my childhood and the opulent sophistication of my adult life," explains Geoffrey Bradfield, who grew up on a farm near the Indian Ocean in South Africa. Now one of the most prominent interior designers in America, the charming New Yorker attributes his success to a passion for art (Bradfield will often design an entire room around a single antique). Recent projects include a showroom in Istanbul, a home in London, a townhouse in the south of France and a 12th century castle outside Rome. A true gentleman, Bradfield refuses to divulge the identities of his clients beyond saying that many are "silent celebrities."

105 East 63rd Street, 1B
New York, NY 10021
Tel: 212-758-1773
Fax: 212-688-1571

GENOA

Restaurants

Belmont Street's beloved Genoa has acted as an Italy away from Italy for the past 30 years. Famous for their elaborate and authentic seven course meals, Genoa has been called "the best Italian Restaurant in America" by renowned Italian cook Marcella Hazan. Owners Catherine Whims and Kerry DeBuse offer only 10 tables in their cozy restaurant, so calling at least a week before is recommended. Genoa received four stars in Mobil's travel guide this year, as well as Gourmet's Top Tables Award – and the Zagat survey named Genoa one of the top eight restaurants in the country.

2832 SE Belmont Street
Portland, OR 97212
Tel: 503-238-1464

GIOVANNI'S

Restaurants

Critically acclaimed for being one of the most "European" of eateries in the United States, Giovanni's on the Hill is the epitome of Italian dining in St. Louis. Giovanni Gabriele's son and executive chef Frank Gabriele prepares a classic Italian menu, including superb entrées like veal saltimboca alla Giovanni, and swordfish alla Ghiotta. Many famous palates have savored Chef Gabriele's unique pasta dishes, such as Giovanni's signature dish Presidential farfalline al salmone, created for President Reagan's inauguration in 1981, and melenzana alla Conca D'oro, a pasta and eggplant dish created some years ago for Paul and Linda McCartney; both creations have become staples on the menu. Other notable diners over the years include Presidents George Bush and Bill Clinton and Vice President Al Gore. The latter dined at Giovanni's for a celebration after announcing his 2000 candidacy for president. Satisfied customers and critics refer to this Italian eatery as one of the best dining experiences around, and no expedition to St. Louis would be complete without dinner here.

5201 Shaw Avenue
St. Louis, MO 63110
Tel: 314-772-5958   Fax: 314-772-0343

GEORGE L. JEWELL CATERING

Party Organizers and Caterers

Trained at Buckingham Palace and 10 Downing Street, George Jewell started his world-class catering service in Chicago in 1967. Today, his staff of 400 can handle up to 5000 guests with ease, serving a range of gourmet menus and vintage wines guaranteed to please the most discerning palate. Prince Charles and the late Princess Diana have enjoyed his hospitality, as well as President Clinton and Chicago mayor Richard Daley. Jewell also has experience producing events in Chicago's most appealing cultural and historic sites, and can recommend an appropriately beautiful setting for whatever the event requires.

424 North Wood Street
Chicago, IL 60622
Tel: 312-829-3663   Fax: 312-829-9791

LYNN NAKAMURA EXCLUSIVELY FOR GUMP'S
BAROQUE SOUTH SEA PEARLS WITH BAMBOO AND HAND-BRAIDED SILK CORD

GIBSON, DUNN & CRUTCHER
Law Firms

Gibson, Dunn & Crutcher spans America as well as London and Paris in its expertise in business law. Commercial transactions, entertainment and media law, finance, intellectual property, class action suits — Gibson Dunn has over 100 years of experience and 700 attorneys at the ready. Clients include multinational corporations in all major industries, commercial and investment banks, start-up ventures, emerging growth businesses, partnerships, government entities and individuals.

333 South Grand Avenue
Los Angeles, CA 90071
Tel: 213-229-7000

GIBSON'S
Restaurants

Epitomizing Chicago's exuberance, Gibson's is the quintessential steakhouse — as well known for its elbow rubbing as for its Filet Mignon. Packed with show-biz luminaries, politicians and CEOs on any given night, the whole show is perfectly orchestrated by manager Kathy O'Malley. Try the New York sirloin, delivering a meaty, flavorful punch, the sliced sirloin with red wine sauce (more warm and buttery) or for those who have cut out red meat, the Broiled Atlantic Salmon. Follow up with the Macadamia turtle pie and then retire to the bar, where veteran bartender Don LaMorge serves up his signature Martini.

1028 North Rush Street
Chicago, IL 60611
Tel: 312-266-8999
Fax: 312-787-5649

GILMARTIN STUDIOS
Specialty Shops

The line between furniture and sculpture is blurred at this small but impressive design studio, where Michael Gilmartin produces superb contemporary American furniture. Gilmartin's innovative designs embody movement and high-concept design. You've never seen plywood do this — a unique douglas fir composite that exceeds marine standards for strength is hand-buffed and polished to a rosy glow, which mellows and deepens with age. And these pieces pass the test of time in more than one way: Gilmartin furniture is on display at both the Brooklyn Museum and the High Museum of Art. We particularly like the Gilmartin Chair, which looks uncannily like a Manolo Blahnik stiletto.

1385 English Street NW
Atlanta, GA 30318
Tel: 404-351-7886

THE GOLDEN BEAR
Jewelry and Watches

In 1975 Lee Kirch arrived in Vail with her distinctive and casually elegant Bear designs. It didn't take long for members of the affluent communities of Vail and Beaver Creek Village to look upon the unique silver, gold and diamond creations as the symbol of the resort towns they love. Today, Vail Valley visitors and locals alike crave the precious earrings, necklaces, bracelets, rings and watches of The Golden Bear line, with this year's brand new Millennium Bear pieces proving to be an especially collectable hit. These stunning baubles, made to celebrate the year 2000, include limited edition pendants in both 18 carat yellow and white gold, each pavéd with 45 brilliant diamonds. Through their two boutiques, mail-order catalogue and the newly redesigned web site (www.thegoldenbear.net) this firm also sells a beautiful array of clothing, accessories, jewelry and home fashions from other high-end designers.

286 Bridge Street
Vail, CO 81657
Tel: 970-476-4082

MARY GINGRASS, M.D.
Cosmetic Surgeons

Mary Gingrass possesses an invaluable combination as a plastic surgeon: her qualifications as a researcher and teacher are second to none, and her emphasis on informed consent helps shape realistic expectations for clients. Her private clinic treats local and out-of-town clients in a hospital setting. Specialties include body sculpting and ultrasonic liposuction, a cutting-edge European technique pioneered in this country by Gingrass herself.

2021 Church Street, Suite 806
Nashville, TN 37203
Tel: 615-340-4500

GITTINGS
Portrait Painters and Photographers

Gittings portrait photographers do not simply take pictures — they create heirlooms. Preferred firm of the Clinton, Bush and Reagan administrations, the youngest photographer working here has 30 years experience behind the lens. The late Paul Lynwood Gittings founded the firm in 1928; since then, five studios have spread throughout the Lone Star state. General manager Rick Bettinger will send a team anywhere in the world. Recent trips include capturing the president of Continental Airlines on top of a jet, venturing to France to take a head shot of a client and photographing tigers from a tree-top refuge.

1111-07 Uptown Park Boulevard
Houston, TX 77056
Tel: 713-965-9304

GIVENCHY HOTEL & SPA
Spas and Clinics

Givenchy Spa is an intimate 104 room luxury resort set on 14 exquisite acres, with gardens featuring more than 8000 roses. The desert gem was recently named one of the top 10 spa destinations in the United States by *Conde Nast Traveler, Travel & Leisure* and *The Robb Report*. With the famous Givenchy Spa, six tennis courts, two outdoor pools, golf programs, croquet lawn and the fusion of French and American cuisine, Givenchy relaxes and rejuvenates even the most demanding guest.

4200 East Palm Canyon Drive
Palm Springs, CA 92264
Tel: 800-276-5000
Fax: 310-858-7956

GLADSTONE ANTIQUES SHOW
Events

Held each September, this insider's treat draws 50 of the East Coast's best antique dealers for one event-filled weekend. The show is actually held in the stables (don't worry, they've been cleaned) of the United States Equestrian Team, where a variety of 17th, 18th and 19th century collectibles are shown. Reserve early, for social events abound — Champagne Hunt breakfast, daily carriage driving and dressage demonstrations. You may leave the Gladstone with a newfound passion for horses!

c/o U.S.E.T. Pottersville Road
Gladstone, NJ 07934
Tel: 908-580-0051

GLEN GATE
Architects and Interior Designers
Glen Gate takes the simple concept of a swimming pool and raises it to the level of art, constructing total landscape environments and providing a full service approach to high-level residential exteriors. Many of Fairfield County's finest estates feature such 'outdoor rooms' designed as complete conceptual spaces. Landscape architects, horticulturists, construction crews, even plant health-care and pest control professionals are provided on a long-term, maintenance basis.

644 Danbury Road
Wilton, CT 06897
Tel: 203-762-2000   Fax: 203-762-9070

GLORIOUS FOODS
Party Organizers and Caterers
New York's pre-eminent caterer, Glorious Foods has catered many of the city's most high-profile events over the last ten years. *Fortune 500* CEOs regularly engage the caterer's services for private and corporate events, and charity galas of all kinds, including regular bashes at the Metropolitan Museum of Art and Lincoln Center. Under the vigilant eye of Sean Driscoll, several hundred highly trained staff serve multitudes with great charm – be they celebrities or mere mortals.

504 East 74th Street
New York, NY 10021
Tel: 212-628-2320   Fax: 212-988-8136

GOLDEN DOOR
Spas and Clinics
This award-winning spa provides lavish service, personalized programs and sumptuous accommodation for 39 guests per week. With a staff to client ratio of four to one, guests are guaranteed expert and attentive service. Programs and facilities are crafted to blend physical and mental challenges with healing and restorative therapies. Set in the perfect Southern California climate, with 377 acres of gardens and hillside, this is a perfect destination for a restful and rejuvenating respite from the information culture.

777 Deer Springs Road
San Marcos, CA 92069
Tel: 760-744-5777   Fax: 760-471-2393

GOLDEN BRIDGE YOGA
Fitness
Much more than a new-age layer added to a fitness center, Golden Bridge integrates fitness into a complete mind-body yoga program. The yogic idea of union with the self reigns supreme here; in addition to meditating and practicing yoga with premier L.A. guru Gurmukh Kaur Khalsa, nutritional counseling, aromatherapy, Ayurvedic healing, acupuncture and a variety of other spiritual and body treatments are available. The appeal is universal: celebrities as diverse as Cindy Crawford, Al Pacino, and Madonna have all made Golden Bridge a step in their search for nirvana.

5901 West 3rd
Los Angeles, CA 90036
Tel: 323-936-4172

GOLDEN WEST INTERNATIONAL
Wine Merchants
San Francisco residents are not the only ones who have discovered this dedicated purveyor of top-rated vintage Port, Bordeaux, Cabernet and Champagne. Through their growing mail-order business, Golden West has been reaching wine connoisseurs worldwide with their impressive inventory, strict selection criterion and careful use of temperature controlled storage.

2443 Fillmore Street
San Francisco, CA 94115
Tel: 800-722-7020   Fax: 415-931-3939

LA GOULUE
Restaurants
For more than 25 years this New York version of a smart French bistro has offered a welcome respite among the great shops of the Upper East Side. Excellent French cuisine is served in two smart, oak-paneled dining rooms (the best people watching is in the front room). If you have trouble snagging a reservation, ask for Craig, the incomparable Scottish Maitre d'. With its refreshingly liberal ethos, La Goulue will particularly appeal to Milanese and Parisians who enjoy smoking after dinner.

746 Madison Avenue
New York, NY 10021
Tel: 212-988-8169   Fax: 212-396-2552

GOLDENER HIRSCH INN
Hotels
Set in the mountains outside Salt Lake City, Goldener Hirsch Inn is a replica of the famous Goldener Hirsch Hotel in Salzburg – complete with outdoor jacuzzi, indoor sauna, massage, fireside lounge and an acclaimed restaurant, where Miguel Hernandez prepares international fare with an Alpine accent. 20 opulent suites are each decorated with eclectic antiques, stone fireplaces and thick, down comforters. The property is managed with great style by husband and wife team Walter and Phyllis Nassi.

7570 Royal Street East
Deer Valley, UT 84060
Tel: 435-649-7770
Fax: 435-649-7901

GOLDMAN, SACHS & CO.
Wealth Management
Goldman Sachs is legendarily picky in its choice of employees as well as clients. Raiding the Ivy League and the cream of the business school crop year after year, Goldman's brainpower is the envy of Wall Street. And this pays off: specializing in stock offerings and underwriting as well as market analysis, the firm has an enviable track record of growth through both good and bad times. Private banking and investment services are available, with a minimum of $5 million in personal liquidity.

85 Broad Street
New York, NY 10004
Tel: 212-902-5400

THE GOVERNOR

Hotels

Celebrating Oregon's unique history and spirit, The Governor Hotel is a testimony to Native American history, as well as the expeditions of explorers Lewis & Clark. Built in 1909, the original structure still stands, although it has been updated with funky furniture and a hip, shabby chic ambiance. Designer Candra Scott uses oak leaf wallpaper, black and white portraits of Native Americans, leather homestead chairs and ceremonial drums to lend character along the way. Incidentally, Jake's, the in-house restaurant and bar, is one of the busiest places in town.

611 Southwest 10th
Portland, OR 97205
Tel: 503-224-3400   Fax: 503-241-2122

GRAND HAVANA ROOM

Specialty Shops

New Hollywood meets here to smoke in a decidedly Old-Guard setting. This is a private club, with private humidors; Arnold Schwarzenegger, George Clooney and Tom Cruise all have their own. Of course, the offerings are not limited to cigars: you will find fine spirits and conversation here too. If, when asked about your love life, you describe your latest cigar, you will like it here.

301 North Cannon Road
Los Angeles, CA 90210
Tel: 310-247-2900

GRAND HOTEL

Hotels

Open only from May through October, this mighty 343 room resort undergoes intensive renovation through the winter. Although it is over a hundred years old, there is nothing stuffy about the Grand. Interior designer Carleton Varney has (literally) brought the outside in; hallway ceilings are sky blue and the 660 foot porch is lined with geraniums – as are the suites and dining rooms. Overlooking the Straits of Mackinac, the hotel offers spa services, fitness classes, hiking tours of the Island (80% state park), and an 18 hole golf course. Breakfast and dinner are included in the room rate and a 3500 foot strip is available for private aircraft.

1 Grand Drive
Mackinac Island, MI 49757
Tel: 906-847-3331
Fax: 906-847-3259

GRANT SELWYN FINE ART

Art Dealers

Anthony Grant and Marc Selwyn became partners in November of 1998, after serving as longtime collaborators with Sotheby's and Pace Wildenstein. Their 3000 square-foot East Coast gallery was designed by acclaimed architect Michael Gabellini, internationally noted for the design of Giorgio Armani and Jil Sander boutiques, while Frederick Fisher and Partners was the firm responsible for the equally impressive LA gallery. Exhibiting artists include Dan Asher, Mel Bochner, Johnathan Callan, Peter Halley, George Stoll and Francisca Sutil.

341 North Canon Drive
Beverly Hills, CA 90210
Tel: 310-777-2400
Fax: 310-247-8993

GREATER HOUSTON LIVERY

Chauffeur Services

Greater Houston Livery was founded, quite literally, due to popular demand. Ali Fazeli's clients from a company he worked for urged the stickler for detail to venture out on his own. 24 years later, GHS has a rock-solid clientele, composed of *Fortune 500* bigwigs, celebrities and professional athletes. Through the firm's affiliation program, clients can be accommodated anywhere in the world. Privacy and anonymity are a priority here – extra security is available for VIPs and valuable cargo.

3772 Richmond Avenue
Houston, TX 77227
Tel: 713-237-1717   Fax: 713-225-5473

GREEN CLASSIC LIMOUSINES

Chauffeur Services

Rated one of the top three limo services in the United States by a leading industry publication, Green Classic Limousines is the choice of Michael Jordan and Elton John when they visit Atlanta. Owner Jeff Green takes pride in offering his clients courteous service, which explains why demanding local establishments, from the Ritz Carlton and Four Seasons hotels to the Coca Cola Company, also rely on his firm.

2330 Defoor Hills Road
Atlanta, GA 30318
Tel: 404-875-3866
Fax: 404-875-0076

GREENBAUM INTERIORS

Specialty Shops

How to describe Greenbaum Interiors? You could simply say that they do interiors – everything from producing the highest quality furniture on-site to offering design services. This is a furniture lover's mecca: if you don't find the right antique in their vast showroom, their expert staff of designers and artisans can interpret and construct whatever is required. The gargantuan showroom features 125 settings that mix antiques, *objets d'art* and custom and imported furnishings, from armoires to bookshelves.

101 Washington Street
Paterson, NJ 07505
Tel: 973-279-3000
Fax: 973-279-3006

GREENBERG VAN DOREN GALLERY
Art Dealers

The Central West End of St. Louis just happens to possess a world-class art gallery. American and European modern and contemporary art are the specialties here. The list of past and present acquisitions is a who's who of the twentieth century, including drawings, paintings and sculpture by Calder, Christo, de Kooning, DuBuffet, Hockney, Rauschenberg and Warhol – hard to beat that roster in any cosmopolitan city, let alone in the Midwest.

44 Maryland Plaza
St. Louis, MO 63108
Tel: 314-361-7600

THE GREENBRIER
Hotels

Nestled in the Allegheny Mountains of West Virginia, the Greenbrier has pampered, renewed and restored its patrons since the early 19th century. In the beginning, the social set were drawn to the healing properties of the local sulfur waters, and although research suggests that it has no wondrous powers, people still flock to this mountain oasis, enjoying the spa, tennis, rafting, billiards and hiking. But golf reigns supreme: Dwight Eisenhower, the Prince of Wales and Bob Hope have enjoyed the Greenbrier's courses. Incidentally, a huge nuclear bunker, built by the U.S. government during the Cold War, lies under the hotel, enhancing its appeal for travelers who need something to worry about.

300 West Main Street
White Sulfur Springs, WV 24986
Tel: 304-536-1110
Fax: 304-536-7818

THE GREENHOUSE
Spas and Clinics

This exclusive retreat attracts visitors from all over the world, eager to entrust their tired minds and bodies to skillfully trained hands. With locations in Beverly Hills, Dallas, Chicago, Greenwich and Manhasset, the Greenhouse offers both destination and day-spa services. The real treat is the Sunday-to-Sunday stay in Dallas, which includes chauffeured limousine service from the airport, leading to an intensive mind/body cleansing experience that leaves clients glowing and renewed. (Sorry, women only). In addition to the usual spa amenities, laser facials and peels are offered, along with yoga and Pilates classes; a personal aesthetician can concoct a take-home beauty regimen tailored to each customer.

P.O. Box 1144
Arlington, TX 76004
Tel: 215-643-2954

GREENLEAF & CROSBY
Jewelry and Watches

The oldest jeweler in Florida, Greenleaf and Crosby has been adorning its clients since 1868. The firm's custom work is known worldwide. If they wish, clients can design their own jewelry – no request is too unusual and no stone is impossible to find. Owner Paul Henry apprenticed as a goldsmith and soon became interested in retail. A charming, knowledgeable connoisseur, he will happily sell you anything from a 132 karat Colombian emerald to the firm's signature Riviera diamond necklace.

236 Worth Avenue
Palm Beach, FL 33480
Tel: 561-655-5850

LA GRENOUILLE
Restaurants

With an atmosphere reminiscent of "stepping out" to dinner rather than simply of a place to eat, this formal French restaurant is an impressive landmark. Luminaries such as Charlie Chaplin, Greta Garbo, Marlene Dietrich and Jean Gabin were among the many artists who were in attendance during the glory days of this watering hole. Now finely aged, La Grenouille remains a chic destination for haute cuisine lovers in midtown Manhattan.

3 East 52nd Street
New York, NY 10021
Tel: 212-752-0652
Fax: 212-593-4964

GRAYSTONE INN
Hotels

Originally known as "The Bridgers Mansion," this romantic inn was built in 1905 by Elizabeth Haywood Bridgers, widow of Preston L. Bridgers, local merchant and two time representative to the confederate congress. Arguably the most elegant structure in Wilmington, the Inn has been completely restored under innkeepers Paul and Yolanda Bolda. Seven elegantly appointed guest rooms feature – in no particular order – Egyptian cotton sheets, PC dataports and clawfoot tubs. Frequently serving as a motion picture set, this elegant respite is walking distance from Wilmington attractions, shops and restaurants. Try to snag the Bellvue Suite, where Goldie Hawn stayed; it is the most comfortable.

100 South 3rd Street
Wilmington, NC 28401
Tel: 910-763-2000
Fax: 828-862-5689

GRGICH HILLS CELLARS
Winemakers

The name may not sound particularly French or Italian, but the California vineyards under Croation Mike Grgrich's green thumb produce award-winning wines that transcend national origin. The ex-Robert Mondavi oenologist has produced his own vintages for over 25 years, and continues to marry the best of California grape culture with old-world production methods. At his four vineyards, supreme Chardonnays, Sauvignon Blancs and Cabernets are aged in Limousin oak casks, before being snapped up by connoisseurs the world over – look for Grgich Hills in the presidential cellars at the White House.

1829 St. Helena Highway
Rutherford, CA 94573
Tel: 707-963-2784
Fax: 707-963-8725

GRILL ON THE ALLEY
Restaurants

A bastion of straightforward, classic American cuisine, the Grill is one of Beverly Hills' "must-do" places for those who require civility, charm and a view to who's sitting where. With a martini list that battles the impressive wine list, this bar and grill is a regular stomping ground for stars like Barbra Streisand and Mikhail Baryshnikov. Although it gets crowded very quickly, it's worth trying to get a table – the Chilean seabass and steak tartare make even the celebrities seem bland in comparison.

9560 Dayton Way
Beverly Hills, CA 90210
Tel: 310-276-0615
Fax: 310-276-0284

GUMP'S
Specialty Shops

Searching for the perfect gift? As synonymous with San Francisco as the Golden Gate Bridge or cable cars, Gump's has been providing all kinds of specialty goods to the city by the bay since its founder Solomon Gump first opened its doors in 1861. Today it remains an iconic shopping experience for natives and newcomers alike. For the past century Gump's has taken advantage of its Pacific Rim location. Creating an East meets West emporium, Gump's retains a certain cachet by offering all things Asian, unusual and interesting. With an established reputation as one of the finest purveyors of exclusive and high quality merchandise, offerings include an outstanding jewelry gallery with designer Lynn Nakamura, whose signature jewelry collection includes impressive pearl and jade designs. Gump's also features an array of contemporary designers, as well as custom, classic and estate jewelry. For some of the best glass sculptures and Asian and American artifacts, as well as contemporary and traditional antiques, visit the master crafts gallery. The world's best crystal and china, a vast collection of silver and bed, bath and fragrance selections complete this singular store's offerings, making Gump's an absolute haven for the gift buyer.

135 Post Street
San Francisco, CA 94108
Tel: 415-982-1616   Fax: 415-984-9379

THE GUARISCO GALLERY
Art Dealers

Guarisco abides by a philosophy that puts top quality, condition and aesthetics at a level of equal importance. The Washington space is run by Laura Guarisco and Jane Studebaker, who have been collecting 19th and early 20th century European and American paintings, sculpture and watercolors for 19 years. The 4000 square-foot gallery holds 600 paintings from the Victorian, Belle Epoque, Impressionist and Postimpressionist eras. This year, the gallery exhibited Georges d'Espagnat and an equally well received show on beautiful women in 19th century genre pictures.

2828 Pennsylvania Avenue, NW
Washington, DC 20007
Tel: 202-333-8533   Fax: 202-625-0834

GUNTHMAN AMERICANA
Antiques   Best Kept Secret

William Gunthman's passion became his profession when he founded this American antiques firm in 1966. Specializing in colonial and federal period military and historical materials, such as weapons, powder horns, and documents, Gunthman has helped to complete the collections of many museums and private connoisseurs. Gunthman Americana offers one of the most comprehensive collections of American Indian pieces in the country, including a number of revolutionary war swords.

P.O. Box 392
Westport, CT 06881
Tel: 203-259-9763   Fax: 203-319-0882

GWATHMEY SIEGEL & ASSOCIATES
Architects and Interior Designers

Charles Gwathmey and Robert Siegel came together 31 years ago to form this prestigious architecture and interior design firm, which uses a modernist vocabulary to design private residences, art museums and corporate interiors, including the Zumikon residence in Switzerland and the 1992 addition to the Guggenheim in New York. Gwathmey and Siegel designed Quelle Barn, Steven Spielberg's compound in the Hamptons, as well as homes for Jerry Seinfeld and David Geffen in Manhattan.

475 Tenth Avenue
New York, NY 10018
Tel: 212-947-1240   Fax: 212-967-0890

GULFSTREAM AEROSPACE
Airplanes

The corporate chieftain's choice for over 40 years, Gulfstream jets continue to set standards in the industry. The long-awaited G5 will be available this summer, albeit with a long waiting list, but for good reason: the plane will fly nonstop from New York to Tokyo. Large interiors are another Gulfstream specialty, and the furnishing of these interiors is a cottage industry unto itself, with numerous contractors available to custom-build one's home away from home in the sky. Of course, Gulfstreams are owned by the biggest names in business, finance and entertainment, and one-upmanship is the name of the game in specifications and interiors. Warren Buffett, however, opts for self-effacement; his G4 is named "The Indefensible."

P.O. Box 2206
Savannah, GA 31402
Tel: 912-965-3000
Fax: 912-965-3775

H. M. LUTHER

Antiques

"We make a point of not being a specialist antique dealer," says Daniel Harrison. "Rather, we are expert dealers with a broad range of interests." Harrison and his partner, H.M. Luther, have over 75 years of experience between them. Clients have included luminaries like Paul Mellon and Nelson Rockefeller. In two outlets – an intimate boutique at the Carlyle Hotel and a large loft in the Village – Harrison and Luther stock a superb array of European and Asian furniture and *objets d'art* from the 17th to the 20th century.

61 East 11th Street
New York, NY 10003
Tel: 212-505-1485   Fax: 212-505-0401

H.P. KRAUS

Specialty Shops

H.P. Kraus have specialized in the sale of illuminated manuscripts and rare books for nearly 60 years. An essential source for the private book collector (and blue-chip firms like Sotheby's), the firm has a tremendous library ranging from the curiously unique to the miraculous find. Owner Mary Anne Mitchell has everything from Guttenberg Bible leaves to Homer manuscripts.

16 East 46th Street
New York, NY 10017
Tel: 212-687-4808   Fax: 212-983-4790

HALL AND HALL RANCH BROKERS

Property Consultants

One of the largest property consultants in the world, by acres managed, Hall and Hall assist in the purchase and sale of top quality farms, ranches and scenic retreats in the Rocky Mountains. After the sale, H&H also supplies consulting, appraisals, long-term financing – and will even search for ranch managers.

2290 Grant Hall
Billings, MT 59102
Tel: 406-252-2155   Fax: 406-656-7550

HAMILTON JEWELERS

Jewelry and Watches

For three generations, Hamilton Jewelers' mantra has been to "exceed clients' expectations." Specializing in custom and designer jewelry, watches and accessories by such names as Cartier, Bulgari, Mikimoto, Chanel, Omega and Ebel, the oufit has four locations: a Princeton flagship (located in a building which once served as a dormitory for Princeton University), a Lawrenceville store and two smart boutiques in Palm Beach. Don't miss their distinctive collections of glass, pottery, china, crystal and antique silver.

92 Nassau Street
Princeton, NJ 08542
Tel: 609-683-4200   Fax: 609-771-8250

HAMMER GALLERIES

Art Dealers

Founded in 1928 by Dr. Armand Hammer, the Hammer gallery originally specialized in Russian icons and brocades. It later introduced the work of Karl Fabergé, the celebrated court jeweler, showcasing his exquisite collection of Imperial Easter Eggs. Today, impressionist, post-impressionist and early modern paintings are among Hammer's specialities, while the contemporary art collection includes work by Andrew Wyeth, Eric Sloane and over 40 Picasso ceramics.

33 West 57th Street
New York, NY 10019
Tel: 212-644-4400   Fax: 212-644-4407

HAMPTON COUNTRY REAL ESTATE

Property Consultants

In the decade since they established Hampton Country Real Estate, owners Robert Camerino and Joseph Gaites have seen Eastern Long Island explode from a tony second home location for well-heeled Manhattanites to *the* summer playground for bigshots from all over the country. Their firm specializes in the sale of prime waterfront building sites and historic farmland to an international clientele, ranging from European and Asian investors to the titans of Wall Street and Hollywood.

19 Corwith Avenue
Bridgehampton, NY 11932
Tel: 631-537-2000
Fax: 631-537-2004

HARBOUR COURT

Hotels

Harbour Court Hotel offers 203 beautifully appointed bedrooms and a private ambiance not available in larger hotels. Location is key at this resort; shopping complexes are located across the street and Camden Yards is just a brief walk away. Guests enjoy massage, swimming, indoor and outdoor Jacuzzi and a fully equipped fitness center. Hampton Restaurant is a four star establishment, offering the finest in new American cuisine.

550 Light Street
Baltimore, MD 21202
Tel: 410-234-0550   Fax: 410-659-5925

HARBOUR TOWN GOLF LINKS

Golf Clubs

Harbour Town is part of the South Carolina Golf Club, the oldest golf club in North America. While it is a public course, the best chance of getting a tee time is during the offseason between November and February. The signature par 4, 478-yard 18th hole, which runs along the Calibogue Sound and plays out to the lighthouse at the harbor, is one of the most photographed holes in golf. The course is currently undergoing a complete restoration to its original design, an effort headed by Pete Dye. Reopening is slated for January 2001.

11 Lighthouse Lane
Hilton Head Island, SC 29928
Tel: 843-842-8484

HARGRAVE YACHTS
Powerboats & Yachts

With over 7000 boat designs of all types to his credit, including his classic line of yachts for Hatteras, the late naval architect Jack Hargrave is credited with inventing the American yachtsman look. So when Hargrave passed away in 1996, entrepreneur Michael Joyce, himself a respected veteran of the boat business, vowed to continue the tradition Hargrave had started – to design the very best in personal luxury craft, custom tailored to meet the specific needs of even the most exacting client. Joyce, however, went one step further. In 1997, his company began building their own designs and the result is maritime magic.

901 South East 17th Street
Fort Lauderdale, FL 33316
Tel: 954-463-0555
Fax: 954-463-8621

HARLAN ESTATE
Winemakers

When his passion for wine became an obsession, William Harlan opened his 230-acre winery on a forested piece of property, west of Martha's Vineyard, with steep hillsides offering multiple elevations and exposures. The grapes are hand-picked, hand-sorted and fermented in small lots, then aged in French oak barrels for two years. The result is an amazingly potent, powerful Cabernet Sauvignon made by the great Bordeaux winemaker Michel Rolland and veteran Robert Levy. Production is up to 1300 cases – perfect for aging, it is hoarded by those lucky enough to get a single bottle.

PO Box 352
Oakville, CA 94526
Tel: 707-944-1441
Fax: 707-944-1444

HARTMANN LUGGAGE & LEATHER GOODS
Specialty Shops

From its earliest days as a manufacturer of luxury steamer trunks, Hartmann has specialized in rich hand-craftsmanship, using the finest materials. Their square leather briefcase, a favorite among CEOs, is an indication of the kind of practical luxury that has prevailed here for over 120 years. New materials are always being explored, and the latest generation of exquisitely crafted computer cases are all the rage with new economy laptop-dependent executives.

1301 Hartmann Drive
Lebanon, TN 37087
Tel: 800-621-5293

HARVARD
Colleges

If the pre-eminent brand name in American higher education still conjures images of Cabots, Lodges and Lowells (not to say Kennedys and Roosevelts), dinners at the Porcellian Club and eights on the Charles, please do not be deceived: at millennium's turn, Harvard's $13 billion endowment and international reach have enabled the university to assemble, among many other things, the foremost Afro-American studies department (chairman Henry Louis Gates's dream team of Cornell West, William Julius Wilson et al) in the United States. These formidable intellects are just one facet of a diverse, contemporary university that retains its formidable character while acting as a national think-tank.

8 Garden Street
Cambridge, MA 02138
Tel: 617-495-1000   Fax: 617-495-8821

HATTERAS YACHTS
Powerboats & Yachts

Hatteras Yachts pioneered the practice of constructing large fiberglass motor yachts (now the industry standard) with the completion of the Knit Wits, a 41' sport fishing convertible in 1959. Today, Hatteras manufactures sport fishing convertibles and cruising motor yachts from 50-100 feet, including the Hatteras Custom Yacht Series beginning at 82 feet. The 65' Convertible was launched in August 2000, the firm's first 100' Motor yacht in their elite series. In February of 2001, the 63' Raised Pilothouse motor yacht will hit the water.

110 North Glenburnie Road
New Bern, NC 28560
Tel: 252-633-3101   Fax: 252-634-4819

HARRY WINSTON
Jewelry and Watches

As America's premier jeweler, three generations of the Winston family have furnished celebrities, industrialists and princesses (royal and not so royal) with beautiful jewels. However, the most impressive names attached to the firm are Jonker, Mabel Boll, Taylor-Burton and Hope – glittering members of Winston's legendary "Court of Jewels." Unique among high fashion jewelers for the extensive wholesale and manufacturing operations it runs in addition to its retail salons in New York, Beverly Hills, Geneva, Paris and Tokyo, Harry Winston also carries a treasure trove of precious colored stones and pearls.

718 Fifth Avenue
New York, NY 10019
Tel: 212-245-2000
Fax: 212-765-8809

HAVERFORD COLLEGE
Colleges

A community of only 1100 undergraduates nestled on Philadelphia's tony Main Line, Haverford represents the pinnacle of the liberal arts college ideal and the antithesis of mass-market education. Quaker traditions place emphasis on group discussion, while all senior faculty reside on campus so as to remain available for discourse, both social and intellectual. In short, an academic boutique – with rigor to spare.

370 Lancaster Avenue
Haverford, PA 19041
Tel: 610-896-1037
Fax: 610-896-4231

THE HAY-ADAMS HOTEL
Hotels

A special atmosphere of timeless grandeur prevails at the Hay-Adams Hotel, situated across Lafayette Square from the White House. The historic landmark was built in the Italian Renaissance style, in the mid 1920s. Amelia Earhart, Sinclair Lewis and Ethel Barrymore have stayed here; this stately residence continues that venerable tradition by housing celebrities, dignitaries and discerning visitors from around the globe. Each of the 32 luxuriously appointed guest suites offer elegant furniture, richly woven fabrics, period ceilings and grand views of the White House or St. John's Church.

One Lafayette Square
800 16th Street, NW
Washington, DC 20006
Tel: 202-638-6600
Fax: 202-638-2716

HIGH MUSEUM OF ART
Museums
Founded in 1905 as the Atlanta Art Association, this is one of the South's premier fine art museums. The permanent collection is noted for its 19th and 20th century American art, as well as an acclaimed collection of decorative art, including the comprehensive Virginia Carroll Crawford Collection of American Decorative Arts. Other collections include Italian paintings and sculptures from the 14th to 18th centuries, French Impressionism, Post-Impressionism and German Expressionism. The museum has had a number of ambitious exhibitions in the last two years, including *John Twachtman: An American Impressionist*, which featured several recently discovered paintings.
1280 Peachtree Street, NE
Atlanta, GA 30309
Tel: 404-733-4400

KIM HEIRSTON
Art Consultants   *Rising Star*
Kim Heirston is an advisor specializing in contemporary art from the 1960s to the present, with an emphasis on cutting-edge and emerging talent. Former director of Pace, Robert Miller and Stux, the Yale graduate currently advises international clients, traveling to arts fairs in Paris, Cologne and Basel. These travels include major art expositions such as Documenta, Munster and the Venice Biennale. Kim Heirston has lived and worked in two of the primary arteries of the art world, London and New York City.
44 East 65th Street
New York, NY 10021
Tel: 212-734-0464   Fax: 212-734-0607

HEITZ WINE CELLARS
Winemakers   *Best Kept Secret*
The joke goes that if you stand still long enough in the Napa Valley someone will start a vineyard on you, although it was not that way when former teacher Joe Heitz and his wife Alice arrived in 1961 — there were fewer than a dozen. The couple's children, David and Kathleen, now oversee the business. Both are committed to furthering the tradition of producing sublime Cabernet Sauvignons. Try to snag a bottle of the 1995 Bella Oaks Cabernet or the 1968 Cabernet Sauvignon, one of the finest ever produced in California.
500 Taplin Road
St. Helena, CA 94574
Tel: 707-963-3542   Fax: 707-963-7454

HELMUT LANG
Fashion
Back in 1977, Austrian designer Helmut Lang began sewing clothes to order for Vienna's cognoscenti. Over the course of the next two decades, the low-key designer has risen to the pinnacle of his profession, so much so that his new partnership with Prada and surprise move to New York was enough to throw the fashion world into turmoil, making him one of the most talked about and influential designers in the process. Lang's signature style — hip yet casual basics that avoid trendiness — is perfect for those who enjoy luxury but usually shun designer labels. The quintessential Helmut Lang wearer wants, as one fashion insider put it, "to seem like they'd just kind of hit on their own personal look." Check out the designer's sleek, monochromatic SoHo flagship.
80 Greene Street
New York, NY 10012
Tel: 212-334-1014   Fax: 212-334-8018

THE HESS COLLECTION WINERY
Winemakers
Hess Vineyards is located on the steep slopes of Mt. Veeder, the southernmost mountain in the Mayacamas range of the Napa Valley. Founder Donald Hess, a Swiss entrepreneur, renovated the turn-of-the-century winery in 1989, returning a charming Napa landmark to active use. Inside, you'll find a three-story art gallery, including pieces by Robert Rauschenberg, Francis Bacon and Robert Motherwell.
4411 Redwood Road
Napa, CA 94558
Tel: 707-255-1144   Fax: 707-253-1682

HIROMI PAPER INTERNATIONAL
Specialty Shops

Although paper making dates back to AD 105, paper conservation is a relatively new field. With the influx of computer technology, it is hard to imagine that paper would have a growing market. But it does. Hiromi Katayama is the primary supplier of imported Japanese conservation papers to the Los Angeles County Museum of Art and the Getty Center. The former avant-garde artist's shop walls are lined with hundreds of textured and colored paper samples, from an 80-cent sheet of masa to a $480 roll of crown paper, used for printmaking.

2525 Michigan Avenue
Santa Monica, CA 90404
Tel: 310-998-0098
Fax: 310-998-0028

HIRSCHL & ADLER GALLERIES
Art Dealers

Hirschl & Adler specializes in American and European paintings, watercolors, drawings and sculpture from the 18th through the early 20th centuries; American prints of all periods; and American decorative arts from 1810 to 1910. Their modern section shows American and European art from the postwar period. Each year, the gallery assembles about a dozen special exhibitions exploring historical and contemporary themes, or examining the work of individual artists.

21 East 70th Street
New York, NY 10021
Tel: 212-535-8810
Fax: 212-772-7237

HOLLIS REH & SHARIFF
Jewelry and Watches

The elaborate exterior of this prestigious estate jeweler hides a suitably romantic history. A Romeo and Juliet of the jewelry world, Hollis Reh and Sal Shariff (whose families are both long established in the trade) met while bidding for the same brooch in Paris. Shariff lost the bid but won Reh's hand in marriage: unlike their fictional counterparts, this enterprising couple have enjoyed a decidedly upbeat fate. Today they run what *Town and Country* dubbed "Southampton's premier jewelry source for those in the know." With a remarkable selection of gems from prestigious houses such as Boucheron, Harry Winston and Cartier, the store has also won an impressive client base: Sally Jesse Raphael and Whoopi Goldberg are both devotees.

2 Job's Lane
Southampton, NY 11968
Tel: 631-283-6653

HOUSTON POLO CLUB
Polo Clubs

Houston's Polo Club has the largest membership in Texas, and is host to the Deloitte & Touche Texas Open and the Stanford Group USPA Silver Cup. The Isla Carrol team, past winners of the U.S. Open and the Gold Cup, are based at the club, which is located inside the loop near the old money haven of River Oaks. Texan Tommy Lee Jones plays here regularly. The club's Paella Festival and Robert Mondavi Cup tournaments are among the big social events on Houston's calendar.

8552 Memorial Drive
Houston, TX 77024
Tel: 713-622-7300

HOUSTON COUNTRY CLUB
Private Clubs

Houstonians are rightly proud of the oldest and most prestigious club in the lone star state, a place where social aura and family trees mingle. The two-story, white columned clubhouse overlooks an 18-hole golf course, a pool and tennis courts, all built on 165 acres. With only 1200 members, membership of the H.C.C. is one of the most sought after status symbols in the city. A private playground for prestigious clans like the Cullinans, Bakers and Newhouses, prospective members must be "old guard" and far more than rich to apply.

1 Totomac Drive
Houston, TX 77057
Tel: 713-524-9419
Fax: 713-465-7455

HOWARD KAPLAN ANTIQUES
Antiques

From formal to country, Howard Kaplan specializes in 19th century French and English furniture, with an accent on unique bathroom sinks and accessories. Dealing only with interior designers and a select private clientele, the collection includes custom dining tables, lighting, armoires, basins, chandeliers and chests. This year, the outfit is offering its first catalog, representing a comprehensive showcase of reproductions.

827 Broadway
New York, NY 10003
Tel: 212-674-1000
Fax: 212-228-7204

HR BEAUTY GALLERY
Spas and Clinics

SoHo has been invaded by new spas recently, but few combine years of experience in the cosmetics industry with the latest in skincare technology. Entering Helena Rubinstein's flagship on Spring Street is like stepping into a particularly serene version of the future. A wide range of spa treatments, created in collaboration with leading dermatologists, are available, including the "HR Express" for women on the go, which offers a manicure, pedicure and facial in 60 minutes. Try to leave time, however, to explore the spa's shopping gallery, where innovative interactive displays make getting beauty advice fun.

135 Spring Street
New York, NY 10012
Tel: 212-343-9966

HUGH NEWELL JACOBSEN
Architects and Interior Designers

Internationally acclaimed for his sparse and linear design, Hugh Jacobsen is among America's premier architects, especially when it comes to cutting-edge residential design. His award-winning Forbes residence and garden in Michigan, as well as the elegant McKinney residence in North Carolina, are evidence of this charming Yale-trained veteran's delightful observation that, "Good architecture never shouts: it is like a well-mannered lady who is polite to her neighbors."

2529 P Street NW
Washington, DC 20007
Tel: 202-337-5200
Fax: 202-337-3609

HUNTINGTON'S PRIVATE FINANCIAL GROUP
Wealth Management

"If you would know the value of money," wrote Benjamin Franklin, "go and try to borrow some." On the other hand, if you have lots of money to invest in a broad array of financial instruments – and if you particularly enjoy being pampered – then we recommend the good people at Huntington. Their Private Financial Group offers high net worth clients an impressive array of services, including personal trust, asset management, investment advice, insurance, deposits and loans.

41 South High Street
Columbus, OH 43235
Tel: 941-594-5900   Fax: 941-594-8330

HYDE PARK ANTIQUES
Antiques

Founded in 1965, Hyde Park Antiques is a leading source for fine late 17th, 18th and early 19th century English furniture. Pieces have often been acquired for institutions like the Victoria and Albert Museum in London, The National Museums of France, and the De Young in San Francisco. The erudite, multi-lingual staff deal with an international client base, offering everything from Queene Anne, Georgian and Regency pieces, to important Worcester and Chinese export porcelains. In the tradition of the gallery's founder, Bernard Karr, the current régime continues to occupy a pivotal place in the American art market.

836 Broadway
New York, NY 10003
Tel: 212-477-0033
Fax: 212-477-1781

THE HUNTINGTON
Hotels

Set high on Nob Hill, with postcard views of Huntington Park and the city's magnificent skyline, The Huntington remains a favorite among visiting dignitaries, celebrities, discriminating travelers and native San Franciscans alike. Built in 1924 as a residential hotel, it was the first brick and steel high-rise west of the Mississippi and the majority of the rooms, which are individually decorated, offer a taste of that old-world style and grace. Incidentally, the Big Four Restaurant – named after the four 19th century founders of Nob Hill – is specifically where Tony Bennett is said to have left his heart.

1075 California Street
San Francisco, CA 94108
Tel: 415-474-5400
Fax: 415-474-6227

GERALD IMBER, M.D.
Cosmetic Surgeons

Acclaimed for his pioneering work in anti-aging and youth-maintenance procedures, Dr. Imber is among the best known cosmetic surgeons on the east coast. He has performed more than 5000 facial surgeries and counts among his patients many luminaries in the worlds of politics and entertainment. His achievements have been acknowledged in *Vogue*, *Town and Country*, and *New York* magazine. Dr. Imber is also the author of *The Youth Corridor*.

1009 Fifth Avenue
New York, NY 10028
Tel: 212-472-1800
Fax: 212-249-2370

THE INN AT LITTLE WASHINGTON
Hotels

Set in a romantic village in the foothills of the Blue Ridge Mountains, the Inn at Little Washington is owned by Patrick O'Connell and Reinhardt Lynch. For 22 years, it has provided a benchmark for excellence in American cooking. George Bush used to helicopter over for dinner from the White House. Selections from the award winning menu include duck with polenta, and medallions of veal sautéed with local morels, Sauternes and Virginia country ham. The Inn is under constant refinement. Following a recent $3 million renovation, a new, state-of-the-art kitchen allows guests to eat in the heart of the action. Meanwhile, bedrooms are compared to 'jewel cases', clad in the finest antique furniture and country linens. The Inn at Little Washington was the first establishment to win two five-star Mobil awards, one for the restaurant and one for the accommodation.

PO Box 300
Washington, VA 22747
Tel: 540-675-3800
Fax: 540-675-3100

INN AT THE MARKET
Hotels

This 70-room boutique hotel enjoys a prime location at Seattle's famous Pike Place Market. Floor to ceiling windows in guests rooms offer panoramic views over beautiful Elliot Bay and of Mount Rainier and the Olympic Range. An ivy-draped courtyard and the lobby, conservative in design, blend the beauty of traditional Northwest art enhanced by classic European design. A Guy Anderson masterpiece serves as the focal point, creating a sense of calmness as you transition from the movement in the market to the tranquillity of one of Seattle's most popular destinations. Furnishings are influenced by the Biedermeier style, applying simply elegant lines with an emphasis on color and texture. Chenille, silk and cotton fabrics in soothing blues, beige and taupe tones give an overall effect of warmth and sophistication, to highlight the decor of the individual rooms. Guests choose from rooms with views of the city, the market, the courtyard or the bay. Those seeking something particularly special may be interested in one of the seven townhouse or parlor suites.

86 Pine Street
Seattle, WA 98101
Tel: 206-443-3600

INN AT SAW MILL FARM
Hotels

Fashioned from a 1797 barn, The Inn at Saw Mill Farm has neither telephone nor television in any of the 20 rooms (there are no locks on the doors either). Although determinedly old-fashioned, the Inn is a Relais & Chateaux property and it is considered to serve the finest foods and wines in Vermont. The comprehensive wine selection includes a 36,000 bottle cellar. Guests enjoy monstrously big brick stone fireplaces, an elaborate library and English countryside decor. Gentlemen are required to wear jackets to all events after 6pm.

Rt 100 Grosstown Road
West Dover, VT 05356
Tel: 802-464-8131   Fax: 802-464-1130

THE INN AT SPANISH BAY
Hotels

The Inn at Spanish Bay is a world-class hotel with the closest domestic equivalent to a Scottish links on its doorstep. Situated on California's dramatic central coast on the famous 17-mile drive, each suite offers a residential setting, some with dining rooms, grand pianos and balconies offering ocean or forest views. The Spanish Bay Club offers state-of-the-art fitness equipment, eight tennis courts, outdoor swimming, jacuzzi and a massage studio. Golfers will appreciate the friendly golf staff and the preferred tee times at the Pebble Beach, Spyglass Hill and Del Monte Golf Clubs.

2700 17-Mile Drive
Pebble Beach, CA 93953
Tel: 831-647-7500   Fax: 831-644-7955

INN AT NATIONAL HALL
Hotels
Nicknamed "Beverly Hills East," Westport is a mecca for the world of theater and the arts. This elegant, stately mansion in the center of town is the preferred address of celebrities and dignitaries from around the world. The property boasts 15 suites, all thematically different. Our favorites are the India suite, a regal corner room with river views and floor-to-ceiling, hand-painted murals, and the Turkistan Suite, which boasts a two-story bookcase, 12-foot high windows and Napoleon striped swag drapes. At the Mirimar restaurant Chef Rick Gencarelli prepares innovative Mediterranean cuisine for stars like Robert Redford, Paul Newman and Martha Stewart.

2, Post Road West
Westport, CT 06880
Tel: 203-221-1351   Fax: 203-221-0276

THE INTERNATIONAL FINE ART AND ANTIQUE DEALERS SHOW
Events
As Brian and Anna Haughton's "International Show" enters its second decade at the Seventh Regiment Armory, its reputation as the preeminent showcase for art and antique dealers looks secure. Strict vetting ensures that only top dealers are represented at the October Fair. New exhibitors last year included. The Gala preview is usually one of the more glittering events of the year.

2565 Broadway
New York, NY 10025
Tel: 212-642-8572

IRON HORSE VINEYARDS
Winemakers
Founding partners Audrey and Barry Sterling and Forrest Tancer shared the conviction that Iron Horse could, and therefore would, produce great wines. Today, 240 acres are dedicated to the production of Chardonnay and Pinot Noir with 60 acres reserved for Cabernet Sauvignon, Cabernet Franc, Sangiovese, Merlot, Viognier and Sauvignon Blanc. Iron Horse sparkling and still wines have traditionally been served at White House state dinners going back three administrations – George Bush selected the Vintage Brut for the signing of the START treaty in Moscow.

9786 Ross Station Road
Sebastopol, CA 95472
Tel: 707-887-1507   Fax: 707-887-1337

ISABELLE GREENE & ASSOCIATES
Architects and Interior Designers
One of America's most influential landscape architects, Isabelle Greene has done installations across the U.S., always relating to each particular terrain, client and climate. Her expertise in plants and knowledge of their aesthetic character has led to the design and execution of the country's most photographed landscapes. With a degree in Botany and post-graduate work in studio art, she is particularly influenced by Japanese garden design.

2613 De La Vina Street
Santa Barbara, CA 93105
Tel: 805-569-4045   Fax: 805-569-2270

ISLAND WEISS GALLERY
Art Dealers
With appointment only galleries in both New York and Los Angeles and an international celebrity clientele, Island Weiss has been dedicated to supporting and promoting the arts for more than 25 years. In the oeuvre of important 19th and 20th century American paintings, as well as contemporary American and European art, Weiss remains actively involved in artist representation, art brokerage and organizing fine art exhibitions and lectures worldwide.

201 East 69th Street, Penthouse M
New York, NY 10021
Tel: 212-861-4608   Fax: 212-861-0093

ISRAEL SACK
Antiques
When Israel Sack began his career in 1903, there were only a handful of Americana collectors and virtually no museum displays. He remained at the forefront of the burgeoning interest in American antiquities – museum collections at Kansas City, St. Louis, Chicago and the Henry Ford Museum are testaments to Sack's achievements during that era. The firm is now run by sons Robert, Albert and Harold, whose three Manhattan showrooms encompass more than 11,000 square feet and offer clocks, desks, highboys, sideboards, sofas and chests. Don't miss the collection of curious 17th century fire tools.

730 Fifth Avenue
New York, NY 10019
Tel: 212-399-6562   Fax: 212-399-9252

THE IVY
Restaurants
Set your phone on redial and go on with your day. Reservations are difficult to secure at The Ivy but with good reason. Besides housing handfuls of celebrities on any given night, chef Richard Irving prepares international fare that keeps the heated patio and more intimate dining room packed. The Maine lobster, spinach ravioli and stone crabs are all recommended – for smaller appetites, the grilled vegetable salad and crab cakes are particularly good.

113 North Robertson Boulevard
Los Angeles, CA 90048
Tel: 310-274-8303   Fax: 310-274-8170

Festival of Spring, by E. Blashfield

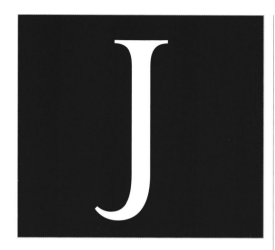

THE J. PAUL GETTY MUSEUM
Museums

The much anticipated Getty Center, which took 16 years of planning and building before opening at the end of 1997, unites the J. Paul Getty Museum and the Getty's institutes and grant program on one site. Home to a wide range of art works, including antiques, ceramics, sculpture, illustrated manuscripts, paintings by European Masters and photography, the museum collection is particularly strong on dead, white artists. Situated in the foothills of the Santa Monica Mountains in the historic Sepulveda Pass, this magnificent art complex is a haven for dedicated art lovers.

1200 Getty Center Drive
Los Angeles, CA 90049
Tel: 310-440-7330
Fax: 310-440-7722

JACOB MAARSE
Florists

With designs known for their "bold beauty," Jacob Maarse's imaginative creations have adorned exotic dinner parties, weddings and events – including the LA Opera, the Hollywood Bowl and Las Madrinas Ball. Maarse has also created bouquets for the Rose Queen and her court, as well as for innumerable weddings. A native of Holland, Maarse was raised with a passion for flowers, inspired by his father who cultivated hydrangeas to great acclaim. He settled in California in 1966, opening his floral design center, where among his vast offerings is an assortment of home grown roses. Continuing the family tradition, his son Hank now works side by side with his father and a staff of more than 50, including more than 15 designers.

655 East Green Street
Pasadena, CA 91101
Tel: 626-449-0246
Fax: 626-449-6169

JACK FHILLIPS DESIGN
Architects and Interior Designers

In the refined enclave of Palm Beach resides Jack Fhillips, who has gained a reputation as one of the chicest interior designers in the country. Serving as an interpreter for his clients' taste, Fhillips creates a vast array of styles, ranging from the clean, contemporary to museum-like interiors. With an artist's eye he deftly blends varying elements of time, taste and culture into one very distinctive style. Although most of the designer's work is executed in Florida, recent projects include homes in New York, Virginia, England and the West Indies. Fhillips' client roster includes the owners of football teams and automobile tycoons, as well as those who simply have good taste.

7 Via Parigi
Palm Beach, FL 33480
Tel: 561-659-4452   Fax: 561-659-0949

THE JACK S. BLANTON MUSEUM OF ART
Museums

Since its foundation in 1963, the Jack S. Blanton Museum of Art at the University of Texas at Austin has emerged as one of the foremost university art museums in the country. Encompassing 12,000 works, the Blanton's permanent collection spans the history of Western civilization, from antiquity to the present, with strong holdings in European art from the 16th through 18th centuries, 20th century American art, contemporary Latin American art and one of the finest collections of prints and drawings in the south west. The Suida-Manning collection stands as one of the finest Renaissance and Baroque exhibits in the country. The collection includes 250 paintings, 400 drawings and 50 sculptures by artists Boucher, Lorrain, Poussin and Rubens, among others.

23rd and San Jacinto
Austin, TX 78414
Tel: 512-471-2005   Fax: 512-471-7023

Study of the Head of a Youth, by Peter Paul Rubens

J. C. DENIRO
Property Consultants

Jack DeNiro specializes in opulent oceanfront and waterfront estates and other luxury properties in southern Florida. He attracts an international clientele through a worldwide marketing campaign and handles a wide variety of residential properties, with prices ranging from $100,000 to $39 million. With two offices and 30 agents, the company sold $60 million worth of property in just one month last year. Incidentally, Jack's nephew is actor Robert DeNiro.

822 E. Atlantic Ave.
Delray Beach, FL 33483
Tel: 561-278-7370

JACKSON-MITCHELL
Antiques

It was a former employee of DuPont and a former Psychotherapist who started this formidable gallery as a hobby in 1968 Pennsylvania, moving to Delaware in the mid-seventies. Jackson-Mitchell is an exclusive and elegant gallery specializing in the finest 17th, 18th and 19th century English furniture and accessories. From base metalware (brass, iron and copper) and longcase clocks, to a superb menagerie of Victorian Staffordshire animal figures, the company offers an extensive collection with a variety of styles and forms, wonderful colors and figures in wood and richly patinated surfaces and finishes. Located a mile from the acclaimed Winterthur Museum, Jackson-Mitchell has gained a client base that spans the country and regularly exhibits at the nation's top antique shows. Members of the Antiques Council and the Antique Dealers Association of America, Jackson-Mitchell recently celebrated their 20th year at the Winter Antiques Show in New York City.

5718 Kennett Pike
Centerville, DE 19807
Tel: 302-656-0110   Fax: 302-656-5664

JAMES KIERAN PINE
Architects and Interior Designers

James Kieran Pine has worked in both residential and commercial design for clients around the world. The designer began his career in the office of Carleton Varney at age sixteen, where he came to appreciate the benefits of marrying design sense with business savvy. Today, Pine owns the acclaimed Pennsbury Inn in Pennsylvania. This 18th-century farmhouse provides an ever-changing showcase for his design business, as well as for his retail store, Trade Secrets, dedicated to high-end residential furnishings.

880 Baltimore Pike
Chadds Ford, PA 19317
Tel: 610-388-8491   Fax: 610-637-3836

JANIS ALRIDGE
Antiques

If your heart is set on mechanical, architectural and natural-history engravings from the 17th through 20th centuries, you have found the right place — with three different venues. Stop into the store year-round in Washington, D.C.; view by appointment in New York; or browse seasonally on Nantucket Island. Expert presentation, framing and matting have earned Aldridge an impeccable reputation. The collection includes English School paintings, 18th and 19th century European antiques and a fabulous selection of hand-blown, hand-etched crystal lamps and English shades.

2900 M Street, NW
Washington, DC 20007
Tel: 202-338-7710

THE JEFFERSON
Hotels

The Jefferson has been a quintessential part of Richmond since 1895. Frequent host to the Barrymore, Vanderbilt and Richmond families, not to mention F. Scott Fitzgerald and Charlie Chaplin, the national historic landmark has undergone a $4 million makeover, completed in March 2000. 275 refurbished rooms and suites feature 57 different styles — all have unusually high ceilings, tall windows and custom designed, richly upholstered furnishings. From mahogany armoires to custom-woven carpets, the look is sumptuous but restrained. Don't leave without taking tea in the lobby, beside a life-sized statue of Thomas Jefferson and beneath the magnificent 35-foot Tiffany stained-glass skylight.

12 Kiawah Beach Drive
Town of Kiawah Island, SC 29455
Tel: 843-768-2912
Fax: 843-768-6828

JACQUELINE JASPER PORTRAITS
Portrait Painters and Photographers

Jacqueline Jasper's background in the fashion world brings a classic sense of style to her work as a portrait artist. Jasper specializes in painting children — she has an uncanny knack for capturing the personality and likeness of her subjects. Although she only commissions 10 portraits a year, these instant heirlooms are well worth the wait. Incidentally, Jasper is a founding member of the American Society of Portrait Artists.

360 Penn Estates
East Stroudsburg, PA 18301
Tel: 570-223-2390

JANOS
Restaurants

Janos Wilder's southwestern American cooking with a French touch relies on seafood from the Sea of Cortez and local vegetables and herbs. The result is cuisine cited for excellence by the James Beard Foundation. Wilder has added another restaurant in the same building called J BAR, offering a more casual atmosphere with a Latin American menu. Both command sweeping views of the Tucson valley.

3770 East Sunrise Drive
Tucson, AZ 85718
Tel: 520-615-6100   Fax: 520-615-3334

JAPONESQUE
Specialty Shops   Best Kept Secret

Koichi Hara's vibrant, minimalist gallery and art consultancy has grown in popularity largely through word of mouth and a recent catalog for Noguchi friend and collaborator, Izumi Masatoshi, which won an AIGA design award. Hara's collection includes Japanese antiques, distinctive for their contemporary, crisp feel. Clients include Thierry Despont, Geoffrey Beene and Donna Karan.

824 Montgomery Street
San Francisco, CA 94133
Tel: 415-391-8860   Fax: 415-391-3530

JAMES ROBINSON
Antiques

Bound for New York, James Robinson set sail from England in 1912. That same year, he established his antique store, which today is a fourth generation family run business, with Robinson's great-niece, Joan Boening, at the helm. Specializing in outstanding antique jewelry, silver, glass and porcelain from the 1700s to the 1930s, the firm carefully selects antiques based on authenticity, beauty, craftsmanship and condition. James Robinson also makes by hand 18 patterns of sterling silver flatware in the firm's 500 year old workshops and can also produce custom order designs. Presenting pieces as they would be displayed in the home, the showroom has a formal, yet relaxed atmosphere. Sensitive and knowledgeable collectors of the very best in

antique decorative arts are in good company with clients like fashion designers, art dealers, museum curators, several U.S. presidents and internationally known executives on the roster. Should a $5 million diamond and emerald necklace be what you are after, chances are James Robinson will find it.

480 Park Avenue
New York, NY 10022
Tel: 212-752-6166   Fax: 212-754-0961

JEAN GEORGES
Restaurants

The ongoing renaissance of Manhattan's Columbus Circle is clearly reflected in Jean Georges, an excellent addition to the restaurant empire of Jean-Georges Vongerichten with partners Phil Suarez and Bob Giraldi. Located in the Trump International Hotel, just a short stroll from the varied cultural offerings of Lincoln Center, the service is excellent, the decor is dazzling and Vongerichten's food lives up to all lofty expectations. The place to be is the terrace on a pleasant evening.

One Central Park West
New York, NY 10023
Tel: 212-299-3900

JEFFREY BILHUBER
Architects and Interior Designers

Jeffrey Bilhuber's American Classicism is a favorite of luminaries like Anna Wintour, Bob Pittman and Peter Jennings. Renowned for creating vital yet elegant spaces, the designer often tackles ten or more projects at a time, in addition to teaching at the Parsons School of Design and – most recently – mounting a major photography exhibition at the Metropolitan Museum of Art. Beware: don't suggest installing a banquette in your dining room. Bilhuber loathes them.

330 East 59th Street
New York, NY 10022
Tel: 212-308-4888

JENSEN-SMITH
Property Consultants

Historic Southport, Connecticut is home to Jensen-Smith's real estate empire, which spreads over Fairfield County, the state's most desired living area. From beachfront estates to backcountry mansions, Betty Jensen, Melanie Smith and their 23 associates cover the historic towns of Westport, Weston and Easton, providing New England charm within 50 miles of New York.

411 Pequot Avenue
Southport, CT 06490
Tel: 203-255-1001
Fax: 203-255-2330

HOTEL JEROME
Hotels

A member of the *Leading Hotels of the World*, Hotel Jerome was established in downtown Aspen over 110 years ago. It has been renovated several times since then, but without sacrificing its original grandeur and old-fashioned ambiance. Located in the heart of town, the historical landmark offers 93 rooms, 16 of which are suites, equipped with king-sized beds, CD players and Jacuzzi tubs. Almost sinfully comfortable, the Jerome is renowned for its unobtrusive pampering and quiet elegance. A quick stroll from boutiques, restaurants, museums and skiing yet far enough to escape the crowds, the Hotel Jerome is a stunning tribute to the elegance and charm of a bygone era.

330 East Main Street
Aspen, CO 81611
Tel: 970-920-1000
Fax: 970-925-2784

JERRY DILTS AND ASSOCIATES
Party Organizers and Caterers

Jerry Dilts once served an elegant formal dinner party for 1000 people in a remote, moon-lit meadow deep in the Smokey Mountains. No request is too difficult for the former restaurateur who prides himself on an ever-expanding list of innovative recipes that take advantage of the best local produce. For the past 30 years, Dilts has worked his magic in many of the more elegant homes in Atlanta, including the Governor's mansion. Some of his impeccably trained staff have been on board for over 15 years, consistently providing the sort of professional service one expects from the very best caterers.

500 Bishop Street, NW
Atlanta, GA 30391
Tel: 404-352-0611

milano fax. 02.760 13051

kiton

JETSOURCE
Airplanes
Founded only four years ago to provide high-quality private charter services, JetSource has since expanded rapidly. Its original fleet of aircraft has quadrupled and, while still offering national and international charters via their private hangar at Carlsbad Airport, JetSource services now include sales, maintenance, avionics and management – virtually a "full-service luxury hotel for airplanes." Clients include movie industry bigwigs and Southern California executives, who prefer the more civilized environment at Carlsbad to the congestion of nearby San Diego Airport.

2036 Palomar Airport Road
Carlsbad, CA 92008
Tel: 760-804-1500
Fax: 760-804-1515

~

JOAN B. MIRVISS
Art Dealers
Joan B. Mirviss is one of America's leading dealers of Japanese Art. Specializing in Japanese prints, scrolls and screens of the 17th and 19th centuries, she also has an exemplary collection of modern and contemporary ceramics. Her museum clientele includes the Metropolitan Museum of Art, Phoenix Art Museum and the Los Angeles County Museum of Art. The author of three books on Japanese prints, Mirviss resides between Tokyo and New York, where new and important acquisitions are made available to American collectors.

PO Box 231095
New York, NY 10023
Tel: 212-799-4021
Fax: 212- 721-5148

from Eight Parlor Views, by Suzuki Harunobu

JEAN-PIERRE HEIM & ASSOCIATES
Architects and Interior Designers
With degrees from the University of Illinois and the école des Beaux-Arts, Jean-Pierre Heim straddles the Atlantic in more ways than one. While his Paris office handles most of his major international architecture projects, the New York branch covers high-end interior design for many of the city's (and the country's) most luxurious hotels, boutiques and private residences. In Paris, the Lanvin and Christian Lacroix boutiques, as well as Omar Sharif's apartment, have received Heim's attentions; in New York suites at the Essex and Carlyle hotels bear the Heim hallmarks – luminous luxury and mixed Mediterranean motifs.

160 Central Park South
New York, NY 10024
Tel: 212-315-4346   Fax: 212-582-1386

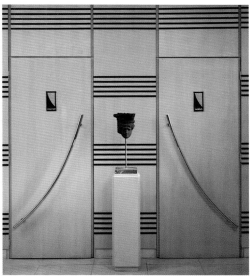

JOEL SOROKA GALLERY
Art Dealers
When you tire of Aspen's snow, check out Joel Soroka's intimate fine art photo gallery. The native New Yorker went public with his collection in 1993, after spending years as a private dealer. Soroka's inventory includes works by early 20th century artists such as Edward Quigley, Ilse Bing and Man Ray. Contemporary photographers represented include Beatrice Helg, Rod Cook and Vernon Miller among other exciting new talent. Don't miss the gallery's frequent vintage photography exhibitions.

400 East Hyman Avenue
Aspen, CO 81611
Tel: 970-920-3152
Fax: 970-920-3152

JOHN BARTLETT
Fashion

The usual trend is to start out in women's wear and then enter the men's domain. But Ohio native John Bartlett has always done things his own way. For the past three years the affable and handsome designer (whose menswear division has long been admired) has been stealing the focus of the New York women's collections – not simply with his unabashedly sexy designs but at times with the help of a stallion or hawk (yes, you read correctly). Antics aside, the Bartlett wardrobe – feminine, glamorous and flirtatious – can be seen on everyone from the ladies at the country-club to the ladies of the silver-screen – Halle Berry, Nicole Kidman and Julianne Moore, to name but a few. The future certainly looks bright for this Harvard grad – he was recently named as Creative Director for Italian fashion-house, Byblos.

650 Fifth Avenue
New York, NY 10019
Tel: 212-647-9409

JOHN ALLAN'S
Specialty Shops

Located across the street from the American Stock Exchange, John Allan's patrons, mostly Wall Street whiz kids, receive haircuts, manicures and shoeshines from a staff of 15 alluring, black-clad young women. The shop is decorated in traditional, green leather; it boasts a pool table and the token men's club mascot – a lion's head growling from the wall. Allan's doesn't open until 11 am, but Francisco, the club's unofficial father figure, will shine the shoes of guests who stop by earlier. Clients include Kevin Hynes, son of the Brooklyn DA, Charles, and Chris and Dan D'Amato, sons of senator Al. This spring, owner John Allan Meing will open a midtown branch.

95 Trinity Place
New York, NY 10006
Tel: 212-406-3000
Fax: 212-406-5896

JOHN BERGGRUEN GALLERY
Art Dealers

The art market's shifting trends have been represented at this San Franciso gallery since 1970. Following the contemporary art excesses of the late 1980s and the subsequent art-world consolidation of the early 1990s, Berggruen mixes and matches modern and contemporary works. Picasso and Matisse nestle up to contemporary luminaries like David Bates and Judith Shea, mirroring today's eclectic collecting patterns.

228 Grant Avenue
San Francisco, CA 94108
Tel: 415-781-4629

JOHN BARRETT SALON
Hair and Beauty

Located in New York's Bergdorf Goodman, in the penthouse apartment where three generations of the Goodmans once lived, John Barrett offers superior haircuts and styling, along with a spectacular view of Central Park. In 1996, Irish architect David Collins transformed the 6500 square-foot, 17-room residential penthouse into a state-of-the-art salon, with a private pedicure room, a relaxing shampoo room with lowered lighting and a coloring booth that boasts natural light from the north, south and east. Inspired by beauty, Barrett approaches clients in a very personal way, learning all that he can about them – a winning philosophy, making it unthinkable for them to trust the hands of anyone else.

754 Fifth Avenue
New York, NY 10019
Tel: 212-872-2700
Fax: 212-872-2709

JOHN'S ISLAND CLUB
Golf Clubs

Located on a barrier island between the Atlantic Ocean and the Indian River, this "very private" club maintains three golf courses, identified by points on the compass north, south and west. Tom Fazio made something of a stylistic departure in designing the unusually hilly west course; its 18th is one of the truly great holes in golf. The north and south courses were designed by Pete Dye in the late 1960s and early 70s, although they are currently being redesigned by Craig Schreiner and should be completed soon. The club is not currently taking new members.

3 John's Island Drive
Vero Beach, FL 32963
Tel: 561-231-1700

JOHN & PAUL HERRING
Art Consultants   *Best Kept Secret*

The Herring twins, Paul and John, have garnered a considerable reputation as dealers of the highest order, especially when discretion is not merely desirable. Flitting among New York, Paris and London, the brothers represent a select group of art collectors at key auctions around the world. Though many of their clients prefer to remain anonymous, they famously acquired a $50 million Cézanne still life for cosmetics heir Ronald Lauder. But the majority of their business is conducted behind firmly closed doors.

10 East 68th Street
New York, NY 10021
Tel: 212-628-5763

JOSEPH PHELPS
Winemakers

The chateau compound on this St. Helena vineyard is the first indicator of the 'old meets new' philosophy that underlies the best California winemaking. A century old wisteria-covered trellis abuts a modern redwood complex, where Cabernet Sauvignon, Sauvignon Blanc, Chardonnay and Merlot are vinted, as well as the occasional Muscat and Semillon. Members of the Phelps Preferred Club are first to taste limited releases, and have access to an exclusive on-site guest center. Phelps has spearheaded several wine movements in America, including Bordeaux-style blends and the revival of Syrah.

200 Taplin Road
St. Helena, CA 94575
Tel: 800-707-5789

JOHN DAUGHERTY
Property Consultants

John A. Daugherty is number one in listings and sales in Houston's most sought after neighborhoods. For four decades, his company has dealt with a range of properties in River Oaks, Rice and West University, Tanglewood and the prestigious Memorial district — comprising Sherwood Forest, Hunter's Creek, Hedwig, Piney Point and Bunker Hill. Houston's exclusive affiliate of Sotheby's International Realty, John Daugherty, Realtors has consistently held the record for the sale of the most expensive estate in the city.

520 Post Oak Boulevard
Houston, TX 77027
Tel: 713-626-3930   Fax: 713-963-9588

≈

JOHN VARVATOS
Fashion   *Rising Star*

"I believe today's man wants to look and feel at ease in any situation day or night," says John Varvatos, who has been the talk of the fashion world since the debut of his premier collection this past year. After long stints with both Ralph Lauren and Calvin Klein, the Michigan native clearly knows how to endure the fickle whims of fashion. Combining classic and new visions with luxurious fabrics and materials created by himself, Varvatos' philosophy is simple: "I dress men in a modern way while still paying attention to details and 'old world' quality." Look for the collection at Neiman Marcus.

26 West 17th Street
New York, NY 10011
Tel: 212-812-8000

JONES, DAY, REAVIS & POGUE
Law Firms

Founded in 1893 in Cleveland and still based there today, Jones Day is one of the top American law firms. Its geographical diversity includes not only the usual legal capitals (New York, Boston, Chicago, Los Angeles), but also Midwestern and Southern America as well as Europe, the Middle East and Asia. The firm's 1200 attorneys have represented over half of the *Fortune 500* companies; Jones Day also serves smaller companies, foundations, educational institutions and individuals.

901 Lakeside Avenue
Cleveland, OH 44114
Tel: 216-586-3939

≈

JORDAN VINEYARD & WINERY
Winemakers

Tom Jordan founded this breathtakingly beautiful vineyard in 1972, laying out a 275-acre property in the lush Alexander Valley. Tended by the same vintners who planted the vines nearly thirty years ago, and aided by a crack team of winemakers, Jordan produces award-winning Cabernet Sauvignons, Merlots, Chardonnays and Cabernet Francs. Any visit to the vineyard should include a meal at the restaurant, where the cart leads the horse in the best way possible: the menu is selected according to the vintages available.

1474 Alexander Valley Road
Healdsburg, CA 95448
Tel: 707-431-5250   Fax: 707-431-5259

JOSEPH A. BANK CLOTHIERS
Fashion

An esteemed manufacturer of business and casual attire, Joseph A. Bank has recently upped its luxury credentials by entering into business with Loro Piana, one of Italy's premier manufacturers of cashmere and other luxury woolens. The resulting combination of American styling and old-world sourcing could be called 'world-class traditional.' Icing on the cake? These timelessly styled clothes are backed by an unconditional guarantee.

500 Hanover Pike
Hampstead, MD 21074
Tel: 410-239-2700
Fax: 410-239-5700

≈

JOSHUA & COMPANY
Property Consultants

Top-drawer treatment is the order of the day at this boutique real-estate firm. This is not surprising in Aspen, one of the nation's top winter gathering-spots for the East and West Coast elite, but the level of discretion is something else: houses are not publicly advertised, but are quietly for sale. The company's property management services offer everything from providing landscape gardeners to chauffeuring clients who arrive at the local airport.

300 South Hunter Street
Aspen, CO 81611
Tel: 970-925-8810
Fax 970-925-4349

JP KING
Auction Houses

From its Alabama headquarters, JP King conducts military-scale auctions for luxury properties and ranches across the nation. J. Craig King, president and representative of the family's fourth generation in the business, has been called a 'megabroker' for his marshaling and updating of auction techniques to meet modern needs. Each property is assigned its own team of auctioneers, realtors and project managers, who in turn conduct national marketing campaigns to ensure the largest bidding base. Calumet Farms, one of the nation's leading stud farms, recently sold at JP King Auction Company for more than $20 million.

108 Fountain Avenue
Gadsden, AL 35901
Tel: 256-546-5217

JOSIE NATORI
Fashion

Philippine-raised Josie Natori has been breaking down boundaries in the fashion world for over twenty years. From her position as Vice President at Merrill Lynch, she made the unusual move of starting a lingerie line, which has blossomed into evening wear. Her lavish bustiers blur the line between innerwear and outerwear. Pacific and Asian influences are apparent in the kimono-inspired jackets, tunics and fluid trousers, executed in luxury European fabrics and such exotics as pineapple leaf-fiber. Combining feminity and a touch of pampered luxury with businesslike rigor, the Natori line is available at Bergdorf Goodman, Saks and Neiman Marcus.

40 East 34th Street
New York, NY 10016
Tel: 212-532-7796
Fax: 212-679-9796

JP MORGAN
Wealth Management

JP Morgan's business came of age in the boom in financial services that occurred just after the turn of the 20th century. 100 years on the powerhouse firm is still making record profits. But success and tradition have not dulled its competitive edge: innovative money-management services deal with such modern problems as unlocking restricted stock value for the paper-wealthy. Private financial management is available for select clients.

60 Wall Street
New York, NY 10260
Tel: 212-483-2323
Fax: 212-634-8810

JUDITH RIPKA
Jewelry and Watches

Judith Ripka has amassed a global clientele, many of whom set the standards in the world of high fashion. The designer's classic creations continue to delight this most discerning group, with their superior quality and craftsmanship. Virtually every detail of every original design is carefully scrutinized by Ripka herself. The Dew Drop necklace is a perfect example of the unique, signature look. Simple and stunning, a circle of 61 bezel-set diamonds is set in 18k white gold, with a tiny dew drop suspended from each diamond. First Lady Hillary Clinton commissioned Ripka to design a historic pin for the Presidential Inauguration in 1997.

21 West 46th Street
New York, NY 10036
Tel: 212-391-2340
Fax: 212-644-5936

JULIE SKARRATT
Portrait Painters and Photographers

Australian-born Julie Skarratt became a Ford model in 1984 and soon began commuting between fashion shoots in Europe and New York. Working with many of the world's leading photographers, she became inspired to try her hand on the other side of the lens. Last year, clients included Jerry and Jessica Seinfeld and Maria Bartiromo and Jonathan Steinberg. Her book of wedding photos, *The Spirit of Celebration*, was published in 1997. At the time, *Town & Country* Editor Pamela Fiori declared "If I had to do it over, I know who I would choose to take my wedding pictures."

106 West 73rd Street, #11c
New York, NY 10023
Tel: 212-877-2604   Fax: 212-362-6631

JUPITER HILLS
Golf Clubs

Tom Fazio and his uncle, George Fazio, collaborated in designing the two courses at this popular club, founded by Bob Hope and William Clay Ford. The Hills course, the longer of the two with more water hazards, has been ranked among the top 100 courses in the country since it was finished in 1970. The signature ninth hole is a 194-yard par 3 that is all carry over sand to an island green. The Village course was completed in 1979. Of special note are the par threes and the unforgiving, fluffy sand.

11800 South East Hill Club Terrace
Tequesta, FL 33469
Tel: 561-746-5151

JULIUS LOWY FRAME & RESTORING COMPANY
Antiques

In 1907, Julius Lowy founded his small frame shop. Today, Lowy Frame and Restoration meets the needs of corporations, collectors, museums and leading galleries. Besides having its own curator service, Lowy regularly recreates period frames where originals do not exist. Craftsmen work in studios directly above the gallery, producing frames to complement outstanding works of art. Private clients include David Rockefeller, Ralph Lauren, and the Randolph Hearsts.

223 East 80th Street
New York, NY 10021
Tel: 212-861-8585   Fax: 212-988-0443

JOSEPHINE SASSO
Fashion   *Rising Star*

Josephine Sasso's clothes are oriented towards the woman who is comfortable with tradition and rich fabrics. Her catalog and showroom allow customers to choose basic silhouettes in everything from tank tops to tulle skirts; fabrics are then selected to create the garment. Her country and city clothes are ideal for mixing and matching since any shape can be chosen. Bergdorf Goodman and Saks also carry off-the-rack Sasso clothing.

93 East Lancaster Avenue
Paoli, PA 19301
Tel: 610-408-8599   Fax: 610-408-8717

JUST ASK PETER
Party Organizers and Caterers

For ten years, Peter Helburn has provided the ultimate weddings, galas and parties for the most demanding clientele in the United States. William H. Macy, Felicity Huffman and Hollywood moguls beckon Helburn to produce their soirées. Recent events include festivities for *Fortune 500* companies and Jazz Aspen's opening gala. Between parties, Peter Helburn donates his time to the local community, serving on the boards of the Aspen Valley Medical Foundation, Aspen Ballet Company and School, Roaring Fork Hospice and Les Dames d'Aspen.

608 West Hopkins Avenue, #2
Aspen, CO 81611
Tel: 970-925-3351   Fax: 970-544-0086

KACHEMAK BAY WILDERNESS LODGE

Hotels

Untamed Alaska at its best, Kachemak Bay can only be reached by boat, ensuring a relaxing, private retreat for guests, who are accompanied by experienced staff accompany guests on clam digging, hiking, canoeing and fishing expeditions. For relaxation, the lodge offers hot tubs, a sauna and solarium and natural wonders: smoke rising from distant volcanos, sea otters sleeping on the shore and panoramic views. Accommodating only 12 visitors per five day stay, service is truly immaculate.

China Poot Bay
Homer, AK 99603
Tel: 907-235-8910   Fax: 907-235-8911

FRANK KAMER, M.D.

Cosmetic Surgeons

Beverly Hills is the most cosmetically modified city on earth – celebrity makeovers are positively *de rigeur*. Frank Kamer has been responsible for quite a few of them, but you'll have to catch the names through the gossip mill, as the good doctor is tight-lipped about his client list. For mere mortals the long waiting list for appointments is rewarded by expert facial aesthetic and reconstructive work, as well as on-site recovery facilities.

201 South Lasky Drive
Beverly Hills, CA 90212
Tel: 310-556-8155

KAPSIKI

Specialty Shops

A whiff of exotic air in buttoned-down Palm Beach, Kapsiki sells sexy ethnic wear from around the globe. This bijou store (bright, sun-filled) is awash with luxury fabrics, vibrant colors, unusual textures. This is modern, chic world fashion, perfect for adding spice to a wardrobe or an up-to-the-moment new direction.

235 B Worth Avenue
Palm Beach, FL 33480
Tel: 561-832-7432

KAUFMAN, MEEKS & PARTNERS

Architects and Interior Designers

One of the leading design forces in the industry, Kaufman, Meeks & Partners specialize in all aspects of housing, including single and multi-family communities, mixed-use projects, mid rise and high rise commercial buildings, hotels and resorts. This vast array of experience has allowed the firm to design over 300,000 dwelling units worldwide with a construction value over $20 billion. They have worked in over 38 states and 7 countries and are staffed with over 100 professional architects, designers and planners. President and Chairman Mark Kaufman and Don Meeks set residential design trends while delivering maximum product for the dollar.

16000 Memorial Drive, Suite 100
Houston, TX 77079
Tel: 281-558-8787   Fax: 281-558-3337

KARL KEMP & ASSOCIATES

Antiques

New York's leading dealer of neoclassical furniture has been in business since 1987, selling the finest quality European furniture and decorative objects. Admire an elegant array of early neoclassical antiques at his showroom in downtown Manhattan, where you will also find a stylish collection of fine French art deco from the 1920s – clean and streamlined, with an emphasis on beautiful wood.

36 East 10th Street
New York, NY 10003
Tel: 212-254-1877
Fax: 212-228-1236

KEMBLE INTERIORS

Specialty Shops

Renowned for the creative work of its ten designers, Kemble Interiors sits a few blocks off Worth Avenue in a town devoted to the "pleasurable pursuit of luxury." Mimi McMakin and Brooke Huttig create homes that complement the spirit of the location and the owner's aesthetic. Creative whimsy, eclectic irreverence and a true understanding of the synchronicity between comfort and beauty explain why many clients have house after house 'done' by this family-focused business.

294 Hibiscus Avenue
Palm Beach, FL 33480
Tel: 561-659-5556   Fax: 561-833-3476

KENNEDY & VIOLICH

Architects and Interior Designers

Though small by corporate standards, Kennedy & Violich has made a major impact on the Boston cityscape. Founded more than twenty years ago by Frano Violich and Sheila Kennedy, a professor at the Harvard Graduate School of Design, recent projects include the Boston Theater District Master Plan, which won an American Institute of Architects award. The majority of the firm's work is in the public sphere, but the occasional private project is taken on as well.

160 North Washington Street
Boston, MA 02114
Tel: 617-367-3784
Fax: 617-367-3727

KERRY JOYCE

Architects and Interior Designers

"I love good design as well as comfort and I take it as a challenge to create an interior that will satisfy both," states Kerry Joyce, who deftly creates interiors that reflect a broad range of styles and personalities. The inimitable Los Angeles-based designer has won an Emmy award for set decoration, was named one of the best interior designers in America by *House Beautiful* and was chosen to help restore the Getty House, residence of the Mayor of Los Angeles. Recent projects include a Ricardo Legorreta house in Bel Air, a traditional home in the style of a Mississippi mansion, remodeling a 1930s Southampton beach house for Ian Schrager and the Manhattan home of MTV CEO, Tom Freston. Joyce's award-winning line of furniture is manufactured by master craftsman James Jennings and is available at showrooms nationwide.

115 North La Brea Avenue
Los Angeles, CA 90036
Tel: 323-938-4442   Fax: 323-938-0484

KENNETH W. RENDELL GALLERY

Antiques

Located on Madison Avenue (beside the Carlyle Hotel) and on Elliott Street in Wellesley, Massachusetts, The Kenneth W. Rendell gallery specializes in historical letters. Its collection of illuminated manuscripts and rare books has shown at the International 20th Century Arts Fair in New York and the International Fine Arts and Antique Dealers Show. The gallery includes fine rarities by Colette, Albert Einstein, James Joyce, Benjamin Franklin and Sylvia Plath.

46 Elliott Street
Wellesley, MA 01760
Tel: 781-431-1776   Fax: 781-237-1492

Samuel Phillips Savage, by John Singleton Copley

KENNEDY GALLERIES

Art Dealers

Established in 1874, Kennedy Galleries is one of the oldest and most respected dealers in American art, offering vast holdings of paintings, sculpture and drawings of the 18th, 19th and 20th centuries. At the request of Pope John Paul VI, the firm helped to develop the American art collection within the Vatican Museums. In addition, Kennedy helped to complete the private collections of John D. Rockefeller III and Winton Blount. Artists currently represented include Winslow Homer, Thomas Cole, Albert Bierstadt and John F. Peto.

730 Fifth Avenue
New York, NY 10019
Tel: 212-541-9600
Fax: 212-977-3833

KENSINGTON COUNTRY CLUB

Private Clubs

Florida's Gulf Coast, with its warm waters and plentiful beaches, is catching up to its Atlantic rival for prestige and luxury. A prime example is the Kensington, an enormous playground for golf, fitness and relaxation, located within the private, gated Kensington community. On-site villas and estates are available for those who want to take year-round advantage of the 18-hole, par-71 Robert Trent Jones golf course, as well as the tennis center (which has hosted the Nuveen Championship) and a 30,000 square-foot clubhouse. Interim memberships are available for non-residents.

2700 Pine Ridge Road
Naples, FL 34109
Tel: 941-649-4440   Fax: 941-649-0427

KIAWAH ISLAND GOLF & TENNIS RESORT
Hotels

This award-winning resort offers five championship golf courses, fashioned by greats like Jack Nicklaus and Clyde Johnston. Exceptional dining and tennis, and ten miles of pristine beach (don't miss the evening oyster roasts) lend it further appeal among sybarites and athletes alike. Guests stay at the newly renovated Kiawah Island Inn, or in one of many villas. For the truly inexhaustible, activities also include marsh creek canoeing, ocean kayaking and wildlife hikes.

12 Kiawah Beach Drive
Kiawah Island, SC 29455
Tel: 843-768-2121   Fax: 843-768-6828

KENTSHIRE GALLERIES
Antiques

Celebrating their 60th anniversary this year, Kentshire Galleries specialize in 18th and 19th century furniture, antique jewelry, paintings and decorative arts. The eight-story showroom is situated in charming period settings, reminiscent of a museum display, with antique wallpaper, wood molding and curious *objets d'art*. Known especially for its Georgian and Regency period furniture, Kentshire clients include interior designers, museum curators, architects and private collectors. At the time of writing, the inventory included a Regency bronze mounted library table and a set of George III Sheraton dining chairs, circa 1790.

37 East 12th Street
New York, NY 10003
Tel: 212-673-6644

∼

KENTUCKY DERBY
Events

The crown jewel of the Triple Crown of American horse racing (along with the Preakness and the Belmont Stakes), the Kentucky Derby has been held the first Saturday of May for over 100 years. On Derby Day, three-year old thoroughbreds race into history while Louisville society and its visitors enjoy mint juleps in the stands. Of course, the names are not what they used to be: in 2000, the race was won by Fus Aichi Pegasus (!), a far cry from the days of Old Rosebud and Black Gold.

700 Central Avenue
Louisville, KY 40208
Tel: 502-584-6383

KESWICK HALL
Hotels

Keswick Hall was built in 1912. Later owned by Sir Bernard Ashley, the country mansion (which is set in magnificent grounds) is clad in fine antiques and Laura Ashley fabric. Executive chef Rick Small offers Classical European cuisine in the Ashley Room. Afternoon tea is also offered daily. Keswick Hall features an 18 hole golf course, five tennis courts, indoor and outdoor swimming pools, Jacuzzis, fitness and steam rooms. Massage service is available around the clock.

701 Club Drive
Keswick, VA 22947
Tel: 804-979-3440   Fax: 804-977-4171

∼

THE KEYES COMPANY
Property Consultants

The Keyes Company opened its doors in 1926 and since then, has become one of the leading property consultants in Florida. The firm offers home sales, title insurance, financing, property management, commercial investment property and extensive relocation services. The family-owned mega-brokerage, led by Michael Pappas, handles multimillion dollar homes on private islands, luxury condos on Miami Beach and restored older houses.

1023 Lincoln Road
Miami Beach, FL 33139
Tel: 305-531-5803
Fax: 305-531-5883

KIMBELL ART MUSEUM
Museums

With a collection of selected works of art ranging from antiquity to the 20th century and spanning four continents, the Kimbell Art museum is a Fort Worth gem. Founded by Kay Kimbell in 1972, the museum has won acclaim for its classic, modern building, designed by the great American Architect Louis I. Kahn. The new installation throughout the south galleries features masterpieces by Fra Angelico, El Greco, Velasquez, La Tour, David, Monet, Cezanne and Matisse, an outstanding collection of Asian art and select groups of African and Mesoamerican antiquities.

3333 Camp Bowie Boulevard
Fort Worth, TX 76107
Tel: 817-654-1034

∼

KINDEL FURNITURE
Specialty Shops

Kindel does not so much reproduce furniture as bring back to life the entire production process of days gone by. Copying the detail work found in the best 18th century American furniture at the level of accuracy demanded means that it must be hand carved. All the original primary materials, including mahogany, walnut and cherry, are used in the "line for line" reproductions, which vary in their dimensions from the originals by less than one thirty-second of an inch.

100 Garden Street
Grand Rapids, MI 49501
Tel: 616-243-3676   Fax: 616-243-6248

KING & SPALDING

Law Firms

King & Spalding has produced some of America's top corporate attorneys, while maintaining a high level of community service. Former Attorney General Griffin Bell and Senator Sam Nunn both made their names at the firm. The present client list includes half of the *Fortune 100* companies, but the New Economy is well represented as well, with specializations in biotechnology and internet law. Attorneys keep in tip-top legal shape in the on-premises mock courtroom, allowing exacting preparation for litigation and familiarization with the latest trial technologies.

191 Peachtree Street, NE
Atlanta, GA 30303
Tel: 404-572-4600
Fax: 404-572-5100

~

KINGSMILL RESORT

Spas and Clinics

Cradled by the oaks and dogwoods that border the James River, the scenic and stately Kingsmill Resort is sculpted into the rolling hills of Virginia. Over 50 body treatments, massages and facials are offered. The Seaweed Peppermint Twist , an aromatic body-shaping treatment, uses fresh marine seaweed and peppermint oil to stimulate circulation and nourish the skin. The Botanical Mud treatment helps detoxify the skin with lavender, chamomile and rose petals. For the fitness-minded, take the Golfer's Package, which includes a lesson with a staff professional, an aromatherapy massage and a hydrating manicure.

1010 Kingsmill Road
Williamsburg, VA 23185
Tel: 800-832-5665
Fax: 757-253-8237

~

KINSEY MARABLE BOOKSELLERS

Specialty Shops

A throwback to the days before faceless superstores, this luxurious old-world retreat is a far cry from the typical miles-of-aisles anonymity that pervades bookselling today. The store stocks out-of-print books and first editions, with an inviting browsing policy encouraged by comfortable chairs and reading lamps. In this case, you can take the experience with you: Kinsey Marable specializes in building home libraries, not only stocking them (selecting the volumes himself for time-is-money clients) but providing design expertise as well.

18 East 67th Street
New York, NY 10021
Tel: 212-717-0342
Fax: 212-717-0374

KIESELSTEIN-CORD

Fashion

As a premier luxury designer and artist, Barry Kieselstein-Cord has applied his unique perspective to create extraordinary jewelry and accessories, becoming one of the world's most successful and revered designers. His pieces are sought by serious art collectors and are found among the collections of the world's finest museums. Throughout his lifetime, Kieselstein-Cord has resided in New York City, Long Island, Florida, Texas and New Mexico, which has provided him with a diverse environmental background, helping him to appreciate everything from the wildness of the Everglades to the concrete canyons of Manhattan. Kieselstein-Cord's work is actively collected by celebrities from Steven Spielberg to Oprah Winfrey, Giorgio Armani to Tom Hanks. His works are signed, dated and copyrighted. The Kieselstein-Cord designs include jewelry, handbags, eyewear, luggage, belts, gloves, small leather goods and home furnishings. These collections are available throughout the U.S. and Europe in the Kieselstein-Cord boutiques as well as through such fine retailers as Bergdorf Goodman, Neiman Marcus and Saks Fifth Avenue.

132A East 65th Street
New York, NY 10021
Tel: 212-288-0200   Fax: 212-288-3438

KITTANSETT CLUB

Golf Clubs

Kittansett offers the very best of New England golf. Designed by Frederick Hood in 1922, the course is famous for its treacherous 215-yard, par three 11th hole, classic old school design and the signature third hole, a 165-yard par 3 with a green surrounded by sand. Located on a small point at the southern end of Cape Cod Canal, the course is surrounded by water on three sides.

11 Point Road
Marion, MA 02738
Tel: 508-748-0148   Fax: 508-748-0518

~

THE KNICKERBOCKER CLUB

Private Clubs

This exclusive club is a favorite of transplanted French and old New York families. The gentleman's-only bar seems to have been removed cleanly from the last century, complete with formidable French barmen. The mixed drawing room is a pleasant respite from busy Madison Avenue, particularly during the winter when a fireplace is lit. Bedrooms are popular with overseas members from grand clubs in Europe, who rave over the sensation of staying "in a private home rather than a hotel."

2 East 62nd Street
New York, NY 10021
Tel: 212-838-6700

KNIGHT SECURITY SYSTEMS

Security Consultants

Knight does not sell packages; all work is customized to clients' specific requirements. This feature alone has made the firm the preferred consultants of high end homeowners and corporate clients, including the Dallas office of Fidelity Investments. President Malcolm Reed keeps a close watch over Texas and the firm will monitor systems anywhere throughout the South West.

11056 Shady Trail
Dallas, TX 75229
Tel: 214-350-1632   Fax: 214-350-8666

~

KROLL ASSOCIATES

Security Consultants

Staffed largely by ex-FBI and other government intelligence agents, Kroll is retained by top corporations and national governments for fraud and security work, as well as asset searches and analysis. Counter-terrorism, on both corporate and governmental levels, is another prime area of business. Many high-profile cases of recent years, including the investigation of the downing of TWA flight 800, have involved Kroll's services. The firm is also available on a private basis.

900 Third Avenue
New York, NY 10022
Tel: 212-593-1000   Fax: 212-593-3509

L.A. VIE L'ORANGE

Spas and Clinics

Sugar Hare's entrepreneurial career spans 30 years — she has won awards and international acclaim for her interior designs and has gained prominence in Texas as the owner of her own catering and special events company. Together with her daughter, Kelly Brown, she has created one of the most popular havens in Hollywood. The 'made fresh daily' menu is whipped in blenders right before your eyes. Services include custom hand and foot scrubs, masks, infusions, reflexology, herbal soaks and cranial massage. Every visit comes with fresh, home baked cookies.

638 1/2 North Robertson
West Hollywood, CA 90069
Tel: 310-289-2501   Fax: 310-289-2510

LAGOS

Jewelry and Watches

For 22 years Steve Lagos has created award-winning collections within a classic signature style — designed for luxury, comfort and, above all, timeless fashion. Of heirloom quality, each collection is versatile, enhanceable and interchangeable, giving a woman the opportunity to create magnificent jewelry wardrobes dictated by her own personal style. The Caviar Collection is fashioned from sterling silver, 18 karat gold, pearls and gemstones, featuring earrings, rings, necklaces, bracelets and pins. Pieces are dramatic and versatile and can be worn day into evening. Swiss made timepieces are hand-crafted and fully sculpted from sterling silver and 18 karat gold.

1735 Walnut Street
Philadelphia, PA 19103
Tel: 215-567-0770

LAKESIDE GOLF CLUB

Golf Clubs

Traditional in design with small greens, Lakeside has a colorful history as one of the original golfing playgrounds for Hollywood's rich and famous, notably members such as Bing Crosby, Dean Martin and Bob Hope. Designed by Max Behr in 1924, the course runs along the Los Angeles River and Toluca Lake, yet is devoid of any water hazards. Offering the ultimate challenge is the mammoth par 3, 240-yard 9th hole. Lakeside's discreetness regarding its contemporary celebrity members is an anomaly in the very public city it calls home.

4500 Lakeside Drive
Burbank, CA 91505
Tel: 818-984-0601

LAKE PLACID LODGE

Hotels

Lake Placid's lakefront cabins are filled with rustic twig and bark furniture, richly textured fabrics, Adirondack antiques, oriental carpets and local artwork. At once simple and luxurious, all guest rooms have large stone wood-burning fireplaces, deep soaking tubs and double headed showers. A classic example of the Adirondack style, Christine and David Garrett's seductive resort offers guests a frontier experience amidst the beauty of the Great Lakes wilderness, but with all the amenities of a full-service resort. Adjacent to the property is an 18-hole golf course and four tennis courts.

Whiteface Inn Road, P.O. Box 550
Lake Placid, NY 12946
Tel: 518-523-2700
Fax: 518-523-1124

L.A. LOUVER GALLERY

Art Dealers

Ever since opening L.A. Louver Gallery a quarter century ago, owner Peter Goulds has remained committed to mounting museum-quality exhibitions of the best in contemporary art. On the schedule for this year are shows featuring the works of Richard Deacon, Ed Moses, David Hockney and Ed and Nancy Kienhold. The gallery's striking building, designed by architect Frederick Fisher, is located just a block from lively Venice Beach.

45 North Venice Boulevard
Venice, CA 90291
Tel: 310-822-4955   Fax: 310-821-7529

LAMBERTSON TRUEX

Fashion

The rise of two-year-old accessory firm Lambertson Truex must certainly rank as one of the swiftest in the history of the apparel industry. Designers Richard Lambertson and John Truex produced a spectacular success with the structured handbag/tote they named the Box Car bag, which was suddenly spotted swinging from the arms of Manhattan socialites and Hollywood royalty alike. One major buyer's guide has designated the printed leather beauty their style pick of the year, calling it a "singular success to have and to hold for years to come." Look for the company's luscious bags and briefcases at Bergdorf Goodman and Neiman Marcus.

19 West 21st Street
New York, NY 10010
Tel: 212-243-7671
Fax: 212-243-5341

THE LARK

Restaurants

"Everyone in their life wants to accomplish three things: build a house, write a book and own a restaurant," remarks Jim Lark, who has accomplished all three. Located in the third wealthiest suburb in the US, The Lark has been consistently rated the most romantic dining experience in Michigan. Chef Marcus Haight, formerly of Le Bec Fin in Philadelphia, creates a superb Rack of Lamb Genghis Khan, (he has sent out over 50,000 servings.) In the spring and summer, the three tables beside the floor-to-ceiling windows are almost impossible to secure and year round, Saturday evenings need to be booked six to eight weeks in advance.

6430 Farmington Road
West Bloomfield, MI 43882
Tel: 248-661-4466

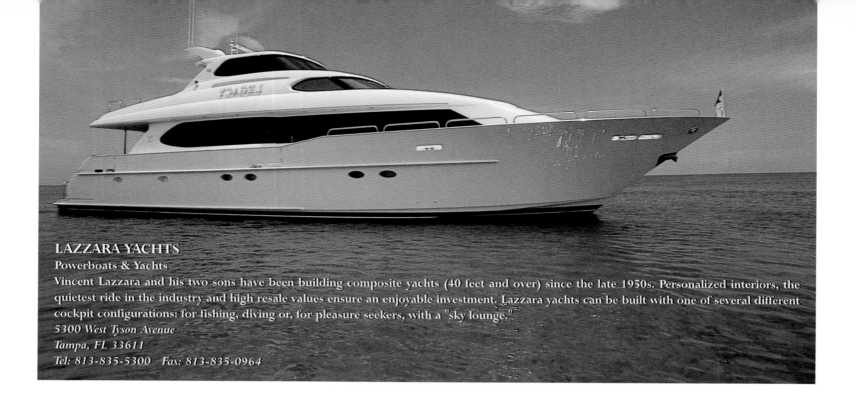

LAZZARA YACHTS
Powerboats & Yachts
Vincent Lazzara and his two sons have been building composite yachts (40 feet and over) since the late 1950s. Personalized interiors, the quietest ride in the industry and high resale values ensure an enjoyable investment. Lazzara yachts can be built with one of several different cockpit configurations: for fishing, diving or, for pleasure seekers, with a "sky lounge."
5300 West Tyson Avenue
Tampa, FL 33611
Tel: 813-835-5300   Fax: 813-835-0964

LADY PRIMROSE'S
Specialty Shops
Quintessential Texans and co-owners of Lady Primrose's, Caroline Rose Hunt and Vivian Young have created a shopping experience as interesting as their unique, English-themed merchandise. This two-story, 14,000 square foot emporium is chockablock with treats like English antiques, fine teas and chic bathing and skin luxuries. Customers are engulfed in a fantasy setting which includes façades of thatched cottages, an oversized, walk-in tea pantry, and a baronial hall that offers shoppers "a sense of discovery," eliminating dubious benefits of technology such as hard, fluorescent lighting.
500 Crescent Court, Suite 154
Dallas, TX 75201
Tel: 800-525-5066

LATHAM & WATKINS
Law Firms
This West Coast-based firm employs 950 attorneys, covering a wide range of corporate and individual areas of law. Founded in 1934, the firm has recently taken on a significant venture capital and technology practice, representing electronic merchants and biotechnology companies, as well as entertainment and more traditional corporate clients. Named the "best managed firm in the legal profession" by *The American Lawyer*, Latham & Watkins prizes its teamwork with clients. Its electronic and communications infrastructure, meanwhile, is second to none, ensuring that the firm is up to technological par both inside and out.
633 West Fifth Street, Suite 4000
Los Angeles, CA 90071
Tel: 213-485-1234

LAURELS
Florists
Robert Smith is the premier floral designer in Los Angeles — just ask Bette Midler, Tom Hanks or Julianne Moore. Specializing in custom floral design, decor and event planning since 1984, his firm has been showered with countless awards for unique designs and imagination. Smith was floral designer and set design consultant on a number of big new films, including *Town & Country* and *The Wedding Planner*, starring Jennifer Lopez. He recently organised the flowers for a 75-person wedding in Venice's Piazza San Marco. When he got back to the office he found another request to do a wedding, this time in Bermuda. Although there were 500 guests invited, the budgets were exactly the same.
7964 Melrose Avenue
Los Angeles, CA 90048
Tel: 323-655-3466

LEADING ESTATES OF THE WORLD
Property Consultants
A forum dedicated to estate life at its best, Leading Estates of the World is an international marketing organization — nearly 3.3 million copies of the eponymous magazine are distributed throughout the United States, Canada and 60 other countries. Robert H. Kelsey pioneered the publication, going on to showcase a stellar collection of famous personalities' estates, including Stanley Marcus, Barbra Streisand, Lucille Ball, Oliver Stone and Jacqueline Kennedy Onassis. If you are in the market for a really distinctive property, the magazine is a good first step.
1801 Avenue of the Stars
Los Angeles, CA 90067
Tel: 800-525-1122   Fax: 805-686-2086

LEE EPTING
Party Organizers and Caterers
Lee Epting has a passion for history. It's not unusual for this member of the Georgia Trust for Historic Preservation to combine his fascination with the past with his vocation as a party organizer and caterer, creating some truly memorable events in the process. The Athens Classics Center, Ted Turner and Rolex have all counted on him to put together everything from large-scale charity fund-raisers to intimate historical theme parties and candlelit plantation soirées. Epting has even been known to rent out his own lovingly restored home for the weddings of highly select clients.
2425 Jefferson Road
Athens, GA 30607
Tel: 706-353-1913
Fax: 706-353-7500

LEHMAN BROTHERS PRIVATE CLIENT SERVICES

Wealth Management

The complexity of managing modern super-wealth is addressed by a few select firms, of which Lehman Brothers is one of the most established, with worldwide reach to better serve clients' increasingly global needs. The Private Client Services Group (PCS) gives individual investors access to institutional-scale opportunities, the attention of senior money managers, institutionally priced stock derivatives and exclusive investment opportunities. Strong client relationships are the highest priority for the large (290-member) PCS staff.

Three World Financial Center
New York, NY 10285
Tel: 212-526-7000   Fax: 212-526-8896

LEONARD HUTTON GALLERIES

Art Dealers

For nearly 40 years, this Manhattan benchmark has maintained an active program of exhibitions, focusing on modernist movements from the first half of the 20th Century, particularly German Expressionism, Cubism, Futurism and Russian avant-garde. Artists most closely identified with the gallery include Kandinsky, Klee and Chasnik. Recent single-artist exhibitions have showcased Sonia Delaunay, Kazmir Malevich and Lazar Khdekel.

41 East 57th Street
New York, NY 10022
Tel: 212-751-7373
Fax: 212-832-2261

LEONARD N. STERN SCHOOL OF BUSINESS

Colleges

The Stern School of Business is found by heading to Manhattan's Washington Square and making a quick turn to the east. What may not be so readily apparent is that Stern sits at the vanguard of a decade-long transformation that has vaulted New York University into the uppermost echelons of higher education in the United States. Stern's spirit is that of aggressive pedogogical innovation and engagement with the dynamic business environment of New York City – look for it to seed the next wave of new media fortunes.

New York University
44 West 4th Street
New York, NY 10012
Tel: 212-998-0600
Fax: 212-995-4231

CAP B. LESESNE, M.D.

Cosmetic Surgeons

After witnessing the tragic results of a car accident while at Duke University's medical school, Cap Lesesne dropped everything else in his life to pursue a career in plastic surgery. Today, Dr. Lesesne is simultaneously Associate Clinical Professor of Plastic Surgery at New York University and Chief Resident at Cornell University Hospital, as well as maintaining private offices in New York and Paris. Listed as a top U.S. surgeon by *New York* and *Town and Country* magazines, his specialty is `rapid-recovery' facial surgery and body sculpting.

620 Park Avenue
New York, NY 10021
Tel: 212-570-6318

LES CONCIERGES

Specialty Shops

There is no specific category for Les Concierges within our directory, because this San Francisco based company is a self-styled panacea for all ills and an enabler and enhancer of all pleasures. Founder Jane Winter spent many years documenting the needs and whims of the rich before setting up a business which removes their burdens. As she puts it, "If the request is legal, ethical and not unkind, we'll arrange it. We are the ultimate middlemen." Typical requests include obtaining impossible tickets for the hot new show in town, or planning a client's wedding, while more exotic tasks may find Winter  and company in pursuit of the missing half of a rare set of cufflinks. And if your overbearing mother-in-law shows up on your doorstep, you can count on the firm to secure her a suite at even the most overbooked hotel. Les Concierges has a presence in 29 cities across the country, representatives in London and Paris, and the ability to satisfy clients' needs all over the world. Warmly recommended.

100 Bush Street, Suite 300
San Francisco, CA 94104
Tel: 415-291-1165   Fax: 415-291-0190

LIGHTHOUSE POINT YACHT & RACQUET CLUB

Fitness

Bathed in the beam of the historic Hillsboro Light on Florida's beautiful inter coastal waterway, Lighthouse Point revels in its leisurely, small town atmosphere. Though located in Broward County, this quiet residential hamlet seems a world away from the bustle of its big city neighbors. And nowhere is that peaceful lifestyle more evident than at the exclusive Lighthouse Point Yacht & Racquet Club, with its handsome clubhouse, sheltered boat docks, well-tended tennis courts and junior Olympic-size pool. A full-service spa and a singularly attentive staff add to the club's luxurious appeal.

2701 Northeast 42nd Street
Lighthouse Point, FL 33064
Tel: 954-942-3524   Fax: 954-942-3565

THE ULTIMATE GUIDE
TO LUXURY LIVING IN EUROPE

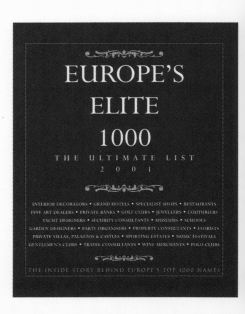

EUROPE'S
ELITE
1000
THE ULTIMATE LIST
2001

INTERIOR DECORATORS • GRAND HOTELS • SPECIALIST SHOPS • RESTAURANTS
FINE ART DEALERS • PRIVATE BANKS • GOLF CLUBS • JEWELLERS • COIFFUREURS
YACHT DESIGNERS • SECURITY CONSULTANTS • MUSEUMS • SCHOOLS
GARDEN DESIGNERS • PARTY ORGANISERS • PROPERTY CONSULTANTS • FLORISTS
PRIVATE VILLAS, PALAZZOS & CASTLES • SPORTING ESTATES • MUSIC FESTIVALS
GENTLEMEN'S CLUBS • TRAVEL CONSULTANTS • WINE MERCHANTS • POLO CLUBS

THE INSIDE STORY BEHIND EUROPE'S TOP 1000 NAMES

Visit Cadogan Publications - The Elite 1000 online @ www.elite1000.com
To order your edition in the USA Tel: 1-212-414 8776 Fax: 1-212-414 8779
To order your edition in the UK Tel: 44-20-77 95 01 82 Fax: 44-20-77 95 09 25

LILLIAN HEIDENBERG FINE ART

Art Dealers

Active in the international art world for over 25 years, Lillian Heidenberg began her career as the owner of a public gallery space (specializing in 19th and 20th century art) and then went private, buying and selling for clients at auction or through private hands. Specializing in early 20th century & impressionist art, Heidenberg maintains an extensive inventory that can be viewed by appointment only. It includes the works of Henry Moore, Picasso, Jean Miro, Henri Matisse and the culpture of Rodin. Also a resident of Boca Raton, Heidenberg has a strong client base in Palm Beach and Miami.

45 East 66th Street
New York, NY 10021
Tel: 212-628-6110   Fax: 212-628-4958

LILLIAN NASSAU

Antiques

Lillian Nassau opened her first antique shop in New York in the 1940s. For the first few years, Nassau's collection was mostly composed of 18th and 19th century porcelain glass and objets d'art. In the 1950s she bought her first Tiffany lamp, a Wisteria, for $200. She gradually added other objects of the Art Nouveau period, which spanned 1890 to 1915. In the next few years, Lillian Nassau's passion for Louis Comfort Tiffany sparked an interest among decorative art collectors like Walter Chrysler, Joe Heil, Ed Wormley and Edgar Kaufmann Jr. In 1967, Nassau moved to East 57th Street, where the firm remains to this day. Although the distinguished collector passed away in 1995, her store is run and preserved by her son, Paul.

220 East 57th Street
New York, NY 10022
Tel: 212-759-6062   Fax: 212-832-9493

THE LINKS CLUB

Private Clubs

If the Brook is the top gentleman's social club in New York, the Links is its business counterpart. With its formidible membership of Social Register and St. Grottlesex-trained bankers, the essence of the Links is comfort of that most genteel English sort. The club is perfectly maintained and yet the most recent renovations seem to have occurred around the time of V-J Day. With Eisenhower in his club tie smiling benevolently down from above the fireplace, smoked salmon on English muffins and black bean soup have never tasted better.

36 East 62nd Street
New York, NY 10021
Tel: 212-838-8181

THE LEVISON & CULLEN GALLERY

Antiques

The mother-daughter team of Deanne Levison and Suzanna Cullen are in the process of improving on perfection. Their extraordinary Atlanta gallery, which already offers some of the best examples of 18th and 19th century American furniture, decorative arts, and fine art, is about to start carrying a larger inventory. "We see that residences are becoming more eclectic with a wide diversity in periods, styles, and provenance," explain the ladies, who are, as always, making it a priority to meet the needs of their devoted clientele. As a result, they will now be carrying antiques from America, England and Europe of the 18th, 19th and 20th centuries, though only those items which meet their strict standards of quality. A new design service, in addition to their continued representation of clients at auction, will also be priorities. And, as ever, clients will be able to count on Levison & Cullen to be the authority on pieces from their native South.

2300 Peachtree Road
Atlanta, GA 30309
Tel: 404-351-3435   Fax: 404-351-5443

LISA LINDBLAD TRAVEL DESIGN

Travel Consultants

There is always something extraordinary about a vacation designed by Lisa Lindblad, whose personal contacts around the globe are eager to share their unique insights with her clients. Travelers to Indonesia are apt to make the rounds with the award-winning filmmaker of the TV series *Ring of Fire*, while art lovers who visit Florence go behind the scenes to the studios and ateliers of the city's finest artisans with one of their most knowledgeable peers. In London, Lisa's luxurious touch means visitors will be sailing the Thames at twilight in a historic mahogany and teak boat. No matter what your interest, this well-connected travel maven will be sure to customize a first-class vacation you will never forget.

27 East 95th Street
New York, NY 10128
Tel: 212-876-2554   Fax: 212-722-2797

THE LITTLE NELL
Hotels

Nestled in the heart of the Colorado Rockies, The Little Nell blends naturally into the landscape, giving the appearance of being carved into the mountain. A haven of comfort, style and elegance, this is the resort of choice for the likes of Arnold Schwarzenegger, Christie Brinkley, Jane Fonda and Ted Turner; guests feel as if they are spending a weekend in their own country home. No two rooms are alike although all have outstanding views of either the town of Aspen or Aspen Mountain. The most luxurious and coveted accommodation is the 2500 square foot Elizabeth Paepcke suite on the top floor of the hotel, with its private keyed entrance. In case you are not getting enough exercise, try working out in the fully equipped exercise center, then pamper yourself in the indoor spa with its steam room and three massage rooms.

675 East Durant Avenue
Aspen, CO 81611
Tel: 970-920-4600   Fax: 970-920-6345

LITTLE PALM ISLAND
Hotels

Located only an hour from Miami, Little Palm Island feels like Tahiti or Bali. Just off the lower Florida Keys, this private retreat (which is accessible only by boat) has served as a secluded haven for Presidents Roosevelt, Truman, Kennedy and Nixon. 30 deluxe suites in thatched-roof villas are furnished with exquisite British colonial pieces. A variety of water sports and recreational amenities are offered, including windsurfing, day sailing and pontooning. Arrangements can be made for SCUBA diving, snorkeling, back country and deep sea fishing, sunset sailing cruising and guided nature tours. Little Palm has a full-service, 10 slip marina, which can accommodate vessels up to 100 feet overnight, or simply for lunch or dinner. The resort's decadent spa, Bali Hai, offers massage, manicures, pedicures, facials and waxing. Chef Adam Votaw prepares 'Floribbean' dining with Asian and French influences.

28500 Overseas Highway
Little Torch Key, FL 33042
Tel: 305-872-2524   Fax: 305-872-4843

LIZ O'BRIEN
Specialty Shops   *Rising Star*

When furniture dealer Liz O'Brien moved uptown from SoHo last year, the critics could not contain their glee: "Let's talk location," cried *The New York Times*. "The Pierre Hotel is across the street, and Barneys is right around the corner." O'Brien has been wowing all-comers with her vintage-modern gems for many years, and her new space is a brilliant showcase for a sublime array of decorative arts, 20th century furniture and accessories. Many are one-of-a-kind European pieces, although leading American designers are also represented. If you want a sound investment, look out for anything by André Arbus or Billy Haines.

800A Fifth Avenue
New York, NY 10021
Tel: 212-755-3800   Fax: 212-755-3810

LODGE AT SKYLONDA
Hotels

The Lodge at Skylonda is located in the thick of the Redwoods in the Santa Cruz mountains. Whether you're looking to slip into one of their oversized soaking tubs, join in some morning yoga, or hike and explore, the common denominator is elegant simplicity. The 16-room lodge is composed completely of bleached wood, exuding a feeling as clean as the surrounding air. After a hike, guests of the lodge can visit the 10 room spa. Luxury services include hot stone treatment, facials, pedicures, manicures, steam room, dry sauna and countless methods of massage.

16350 Skyline Boulevard
Woodside, CA 94062
Tel: 650-851-6625   Fax: 650-851-5504

THE LODGE ON LITTLE ST. SIMONS ISLAND
Hotels   *Best Kept Secret*

Accessible only by boat and accommodating only 30 overnight guests, Little St. Simons is situated on one of the last privately-owned barrier islands along the Georgia coast. Guests have the entire 10,000-acre island to themselves, including an incredible seven-mile strand of shell-strewn beach and they are treated to a spirit of hospitality that dates back to the early 1900s. Days are as full or as absent of activities as a guest desires. After breakfast, guests can relax on the porch or pool side, canoe or boat through meandering tidal creeks or join in a birding exhibition. Saltwater fly fishing, surfcasting, bicycling and hiking are all popular, along with simple strolls within the solitude of the exclusive terrain.

P.O. Box 21078
St. Simons Island, GA 31522
Tel: 888-733-5774   Fax: 912-634-1811

LONGORIA COLLECTION
Specialty Shops

Interior designer Sylvia Longoria Dorsey opened her stylish emporium in 1993 to provide elegant home furnishings in combination with her interior design services to create lifestyles for people of discerning taste. Her collections exude classicism with a relaxed edge and include bed and bath fine linens, custom handmade beds, tables, lamps, chandeliers and a host of unique gift items such as Han, Tang and Ming Dynasty artifacts. The philosophy at Longoria Collection is to find beauty in the everyday and if the everyday needs a bit of a tweak, the perfect perfumed candle or fragrant soap will help create or enhance a mood conducive to relaxation

and reflection. Longoria Collection also carries custom furniture, lighting and tabletop accouterments by Bernardaud, Raynaud, Ralph Lauren, Simon Pearce, Saint Louis and Versace, among others. Their bridal and baby registries are especially popular, with such irresistable offerings as Peacock Alley's "babybed" linens.

1101-02 Uptown Park Boulevard
Houston, TX 77056
Tel: 713-621-4241   Fax: 713-621-4242

LONDON JEWELERS
Jewelry and Watches

In business for over seventy years, London Jewelers has long been one of the most prestigious names in jewelry on the east coast. With three stores within six miles of each other and a store in East Hampton, it is one of the few remaining family-run jewelry stores in the area. In addition to the new platinum-and-diamond line (designed by Candy Udell, wife of London CEO Mark), Bulgari, Cartier and Mikimoto all have in-store boutiques. London aficionados include clients as diverse as Secretary of State Madeline Albright, Patti Hansen and Cindy Crawford.

2046 Northern Boulevard
Manhasset, NY 11030
Tel: 516-627-7475
Fax: 516-627-1168

LOU MAROTTA
Antiques   Best Kept Secret

It's impossible to mistake Lou Marotta's shop for any other in the world. His unique inventory includes a wide range of both traditional antiques and truly unusual pieces, all personally selected by Marotta because they appeal to his passion for natural forms and original painted surfaces. This singular collection boasts French, Italian, Swedish and Spanish furniture dating back to the 17th century, plus more recent pieces inspired by plant and animal life, including tables masquerading as trees and whimsical armoires that appear to have come straight from an enchanted forest.

243 East 60th Street
New York, NY 10022
Tel: 212-223-0306   Fax: 212-223-4744

LOUIS BOSTON
Fashion

Louis Pearlstein was a pawnbroker who accepted the suit off a man's back as collateral for a loan. His sons, Louis and Saul, would go with their father to collect these suits after school. From this unusual experience, the three developed a love for fine clothing and founded Louis Boston in 1925. Today, the firm is based in the former Museum of Natural History on Newbury Street. Owners Debra Greenberg and Murray Pearlstein use exclusive fabrics, buying only three or four of the same article from designers like Brioni, Kiton and Luciano Barbera.

234 Berkeley Street
Boston, MA 02116
Tel: 617-262-6100

LOWRANCE INTERIORS
Architects and Interior Designers

Focusing on classic elegance and simplicity, this firm uses grade-A materials and furnishings, including many museum-quality antiques. With a precise eye for design and space, the firm creates homes for a tony clientele and is frequently used to design two or three homes owned by the same family. Jack Lowrance, president and owner, and Richard Gaz, senior designer, can transform everything from an estate to a laundry room space; the attention to detail remains the same. This year, the team launched their new line of furniture, already a staple in many fine homes.

707 North Alfred Street
Los Angeles, CA 90069
Tel: 323-655-9713
Fax: 323-655-0359

THE LOWELL
Hotels

Designed by Henry Stern Churchill in 1925, this veritable institution is listed among the National Register of Historic Places. An integral part of the Upper East Side, it boasts its original exterior facade and 1920s architecture. 44 suites and 21 deluxe rooms are decorated with antique furniture, 18th century prints and the finest linens. Chinese porcelain, wood burning fireplaces, marble baths and Bulgari bathroom amenities are some of the other reasons why the Lowell has become a *pied-à-terre* for many CEOs, fashion designers and celebrities.

28 East 63rd Street
New York, NY 10021
Tel: 212-838-1400

LUCHO
Fashion

As Houston's premier menswear retailer, Lucho Florez emphasizes elegance, detail, exquisite fabrics and hand-finishing. To ensure the highest quality, he travels to Italy several times a year, hand-selecting the finest fabrics available. Florez offers a collection of internationally-known European menswear alongside his own designs and has an on-site tailor with more than 30 years experience. Most of Lucho's clientele consists of business executives and he has a strong number of Mexican businessmen who travel to Uptown Park solely for the imported menswear.

5085 Westheimer, #2855
Houston, TX 77056
Tel: 713-961-3577
Fax: 713-961-0971

LONDON LIVERY
Chauffeur Services

In 1987, London was awarded best livery service out of 10 cities on the Papal Tour (quite an imprimatur) and the company was the official Transport of the 1988 World's Fair. In 1994, London took home the Operator of the Year award, granted by the National Limousine Association of America. London Livery is the official transport of Benji the dog, Windsor Court and Maison De Ville Hotels.

771 South Prieur Street
New Orleans, LA 70113
Tel: 504-944-1984
Fax: 504-586-0717

LUCQUES
Restaurants

Caroline Styne and Suzanne Goin (previously of the innovative Campanile restaurant) partnered to open this straightforward, unpretentious space that was once the carriage house of silent movie star Harold Lloyd. Named after a green olive of Provence, Lucques has a rustic feel, with a barn-like ceiling and warm wood cabinetry. Goin's luscious tart of salt cod and brandade garlic is wildly popular, along with the cured pork chop with sweet potatoes, sage and roasted apples. The most talked about restaurant in town, the eatery plays host to a barrage of stars; you might find yourself sitting beside Cameron Diaz or Jodi Foster.

8474 Melrose Avenue
Los Angeles, CA 90069
Tel: 323-655-6277
Fax: 323-655-3925

LUCULLUS
Specialty Shops

When walking into Lucullus, one immediately notices Balthazar, an English bulldog and dear friend to proprietor Patrick Dunne, lying in a heap on the carpet. Next, a barrage of playfully put together culinary antiques stands out, situated on walnut dining and marble coffee tables. This delightful enterprise was founded in 1984 when Dunne, celebrating the Parisian feeling of New Orleans and his love of antiques, began gathering eclectic pieces. Among other treats, he has amassed a particularly strong collection of hand-blown bistro wine glasses.

610 Chartres Street
New Orleans, LA 70130
Tel: 504-528-9620
Fax: 504-561-8030

LUTSKO ASSOCIATES
Architects and Interior Designers

Ron Lutsko is the man behind a number of the country's most beautiful botanical gardens. From coast to coast, Lutsko has worked on a number of highly visible projects. In California alone, his designs have enhanced the Lindsay Natural History Museum in Walnut Creek and the Mill Valley Public Library, while his innovative plans for the French Embassy Garden were exhibited at the Institut Français d'Architecture in Paris. Utilizing many natural elements, including rocks, trees and waterfalls, as well as a host of greenery and flowering plants from all over the world, Lusko creates a variety of environments, each one more inviting than the next.

Pier One 1/2 Embarcadero
San Francisco, CA 94111
Tel: 415-391-0777

LUXURY–REALESTATE.COM
Websites

John Brian Losh, owner of Ewing & Clark, the oldest brokerage firm in Seattle, began the publication *Who's Who in Real Estate* in the 80s, showcasing the best in luxury brokerages worldwide. To give members more exposure, he developed his website in 1995, incorporating photographs of properties. Now the largest, most comprehensive site of its kind in the world, Luxury Real Estate offers over 10,000 properties, all over $1 million each. From elegant winter homes in Vermont to 400 acre farms, the comprehensive network represents 70 of the most reputable brokers in the world.

2110 Western Avenue
Seattle, WA 98121
Tel: 206-695-4836

LUXURYFINDER.COM
Websites

This slick website – which is backed by heavy-hitters like Leonard Stern, Alan Grubman and Fred Seegal – sells everything from designer lipstick to private jets in a brazen monument to conspicuous consumption. But try telling that to Broadway impresario Terry Allen Kramer, who writes a column for the website. She recently begged readers to "throw away the status symbols." "Enough already!" she wrote. "America was built on original ideas by a melting-pot society. The age of monograms reduces us to a copycat culture." Given the venue, her comments seem eccentric, to put it mildly.

55 East 59th Street
New York, NY 10022
Tel: 212-308-8500
Fax: 212-308-8647

LUXURYLINK.COM
Websites   *Rising Star*

From Vermont to Belize, LuxuryLink offers thousands of products of interest to the sophisticated traveler – tours, cruises, specialty travel, hotels, resorts, inns, lodges, yacht charters, villas and spas. The site provides information on weather, time zones, currency conversion, tourist offices, maps and health advisories for the convenience of travelers. A number of packages are offered for auction each week at a fraction of the retail cost.

5200 West Century Blvd., Suite 940
Los Angeles, CA 90045
Tel: 888-297-3299
Fax: 310-215-8279

LYNN JACHNEY CHARTERS
Powerboats & Yachts

Lynn Jachney has always loved traveling by yacht. More than three decades ago she turned that passion into a small sideline, chartering private luxury craft for a select few clients each year. It wasn't long, however, before her reputation for arranging first-class, custom-tailored trips around the globe had won her a number of devoted patrons. A past president and current board member of the American Yacht Charter Association, and a board member of the Charter Yacht Brokers Association, Jachney is now recognized internationally as a leader in her field. Warmly recommended.

Two Market Square
Marblehead, MA 01945
Tel: 800-223-2050
Fax: 617-639-0216

LYMAN PERRY
Architects and Interior Designers

The course that Lyman Perry founded at his alma mater, the University of Pennsylvania, called Design and the Environment, speaks of this award-winning architect's passion for buildings that respect their relationship to a site's environment and history – as well as to the needs of their future inhabitants. For more than 25 years, Perry has been applying this philosophy to everything from small residential additions and historic renovations, to multimillion dollar private homes and major public facilities. Recently, he was recognized for designing The Nantucket Golf Club, which was named The Best Private Golf Club in America by a major golfing publication. It's no wonder that Perry was selected to design three major projects currently underway on Nantucket Island and Martha's Vineyard, locations which rank among this country's most beautiful.

42 Cassatt Avenue
Berwyn, PA 19312
Tel: 610-889-9966
Fax: 610-889-9969

M. FINKEL & DAUGHTER
Antiques

This Philadelphia institution is a leading dealer in antique schoolgirl samplers and silk embroidery. The son of antique dealers, Morris Finkel founded his own business in 1947 and was joined by his daughter, Amy, in 1975. It was then that M. Finkel & Daughter shifted its focus from furniture to silk embroidery samplers, made by young girls aged between nine and sixteen, which depict a variety of images from the alphabet to complex, detailed domestic and pastoral scenes. While the Finkels now do a large part of their business on the internet, this father and daughter team still exhibit at the Philadelphia Antiques Show every April. Recent acquisitions include an extraordinary sampler created by Sally Parker in 1796 from a school in Salem, Massachussetts.

936 Pine Street
Philadelphia, PA 19107
Tel: 215-627-7797   Fax: 215-627-8199

M. S. RAU ANTIQUES
Antiques

Set behind a leaded glass storefront, under a classic wrought-iron balcony, this New Orleans stalwart is an Ali Baba's cave for antique-lovers. It stocks everything from Fancy Pink diamonds (less than one in a billion diamonds qualify) to monumental Sevres porcelain urns, with Tiffany windows and Chippendale armoires thrown in for good measure. M.S. Rau also stocks cut crystal, antique table services, matched sets of Aubusson Louis XVI furniture, as well as historical curiosities like vintage medical cabinets and conquistador Francisco Pizarro's treasure chest.

630 Royal Street
New Orleans, LA 70130
Tel: 504-523-5660   Fax: 504-566-0057

MADISON AVENUE BOOKSHOP
Specialty Shops

Catering to the carriage trade since 1973, this enchanting little bookstore is a haven for authors and readers alike. The walls are covered with photographs of the many writers who have spent time here, whether relaxing or signing books, a tradition which continues to this day (indeed, many of the books for sale are actually signed copies). The staff are genuinely interested in the world of books – an increasingly rare phenomenon – and the obscure gems on offer are enough to keep any bookworm happy for weeks. For a virtual tour visit madisonavenuebookshop.com.

833 Madison Avenue
New York, NY 10021
Tel: 212-535-6130   Fax: 212-794-5231

MAIDSTONE CLUB
Private Clubs

Many of East Hampton's early settlers came from Maidstone, England, a small town in Kent. In 1881, the club was opened by these descendants, in an attempt to revive their heritage. Strictly a bath and tennis house for its first few years of operation, the club soon expanded to include a golf course, designed by Scotsman Willie Tucker. A true country club, the clubhouse is located on sand dunes, overlooking the Atlantic, cooling the relatively treeless terrain. A par 72, 6390-yard course, it receives annual accolades from *Golf Digest* and was recently rated best in the region by *Met Golfer* Magazine. The club has a hefty waiting list; many wait a lifetime.

Old Beach Lane
East Hampton, NY 11937
Tel: 631-324-0510   Fax: 631-324-8821

LA MAISONETTE
Restaurants

Former executive chef at New York's Plaza Athenée, Jean Robert deCavel has been at La Maisonette for the past six years, serving his seasonal French cuisine to Cincinnati's power circle, from ladies who lunch to President Clinton. The formal, elegant restaurant has received the coveted Mobil five-star award for 35 of its 50 years of existence. Try the roasted spring pheasant served with fresh herbs, or the petit lobster tail with white wine sauce. Ask owner Nat Comisar for a seat by the window.

114 East Sixth Street
Cincinnati, OH 45202
Tel: 513-721-2260   Fax: 513-287-7785

MAGNUM MARINE
Powerboats & Yachts

This truly legendary firm came into being in 1967, when the late Don Aronow built two hulls, specifically for the gut-busting offshore circut. The Magnum 27' and the Magnum 35' both went on to become world offshore champions in open class racing. The new Magnum Pininfarinas come in 80' and 90' versions, with the 80' topping out over 70 mph – as fast as many 38' super boats. In 1976, Magnum Marine was bought by Katrin Theodoli and is the only yacht builder in the world owned by a woman. This achievement has brought Theodoli Italian Knighthood and multiple Woman of the Year awards. Magnum Marine has built yachts for the Kings of Spain and Sweden, the Emir of Kuwait and the Saudi Royal Family.

2900 NE 188th Street
Aventura, FL 33180
Tel: 305-931-4292
Fax: 305-931-0088

MALCOLM FRANKLIN

Antiques

Founded in 1947, Malcolm Franklin was one of the first importers of early walnut veneered furniture. Specializing in 17th and 19th century English furniture, its pieces have ended up in locations as diverse as the White House, Colonial Williamsburg, the Art Institute of Chicago and the de Young Museum. The firm is family operated, owned by Malcolm's son, Paul Mark Franklin, and grandchildren, Daniel Sullivan and Susan Gancer.

34 East Oak Street, 2nd Floor

Chicago, IL 60611

Tel: 312-337-0202   Fax: 312-369-0790

MANELE BAY

Hotels

Bill Gates held his wedding reception on Manele Bay's grounds. The lobby of the hotel hangs over the bay's surface, offering a heavenly view. The hotel is in the style of Mediterranean modernism, tastefully decorated in murals and paintings by local artists. Activities include tennis, golf, skeet shooting and scuba diving. Extensive spa and fitness services are also available. The Ihilani restaurant offers fine, local dining, specializing in seafood.

One Manele Bay Road

Lanai, HI 96763

Tel: 808-565-3800   Fax: 808-565-3868

MANHATTAN ANTI-AGING CLINIC

Cosmetic Surgeons

Associated with Yale's College of Medicine, the Manhattan Anti-Aging Clinic has a history of pioneering research in aesthetic surgery. The clinic pioneered the use of Human Growth Hormone, which allows for unusually fast recovery from surgical procedures. Surgery is performed in New Haven, hormonal and antioxidant treatment in New York, ensuring that every procedure is of the highest quality..

330 Orchard Street

New Haven, CT 06511

Tel: 203-787-4647   Fax: 203-777-0759

MANNY SILVERMAN GALLERY

Art Dealers

Manny Silverman started working at a gallery in college, before running a very successful framing business for many years. Since 1987 he has owned an eponymous gallery in a large, ground floor premise in West Hollywood. Silverman specializes in American art of the post-war period, with an emphasis on Abstract Expressionism.

619 North Almont Drive

Los Angeles, CA 90069

Tel: 310-659-8256   Fax: 310-659-1001

MANSION ON TURTLE CREEK

Hotels

This Renaissance–style Mansion retains the intimate ambiance and charm of the private residence it once was. Originally built in the 1920s for a wealthy cotton baron, Turtle Creek is all about meticulously restored interiors, hand-carved fireplaces, marble floors and leaded stained-glass windows. Suites are elegantly appointed with luxurious baths, private balconies and thoughtful amenities, a king-size canopy bed sprinkled with gardenia petals and a separate servant's entrance for room service with discretion. The Mansion Bar is a popular gathering place for both hotel guests and prominent local socialites.

2821 Turtle Creek Boulevard

Dallas, TX 75219

Tel: 214-559-2100   Fax: 214-520-5896

MANSOUR

Specialty Shops

Stocked with a vast selection of antique rugs — many culled from the estate sales of leading Hollywood homes — Mansour is the showroom to go to if you're looking for that rare find. Being situated in Los Angeles makes for some heavy Tinseltown traffic, and yet denizens from other parts of the U.S. and indeed around the world look to Mansour to find that unique sultanabad or Aubusson piece. Mansour also carries tapestries dating as far back as the 16th century.

8600 Melrose Avenue

West Hollywood, CA 90069

Tel: 310-652-9999

MARC FRIEDLAND

Specialty Shops

Marc Friedland's college career prepared him for a life in public healthcare, but by hook or by crook he found himself designing invitations for make-it-or-break-it Hollywood affairs. Today, Oprah Winfrey and Tom Hanks are among his clients; Friedland also does significant work for charities, ensuring major turnouts. Friedland recently launched a line of stationery, which is available at Bergdorf Goodman in New York and Neiman Marcus in Los Angeles.

4988 Venice Boulevard

Los Angeles, CA 90019

Tel: 323-936-9009

Fax: 323-935-8299

MARC MAGNUS

Jewelry and Watches

Swiss craftsmanship is expected in Zurich-based Marc Magnus' jewelry, timepieces and accessories, but the addition of rare jewels and materials hailing from around the world takes the effect to a new level: that of world-class exotic luxury. Jewelry settings are platinum or 18 karat gold, but the stone itself may be a one-of-a-kind green Indian moonstone; lady's handbags are created in ostrich and crocodile, among other materials. Magnus's clientele is as exotic as his materials: his pieces attract attention around the globe.

41 East 78th Street

New York, NY 10021

Tel: 212-585-3976   Fax: 212-327-1861

MARCASSIN

Winemakers

Helen Turley and her husband John Wetlaufer have a winemaking philosophy that is simple yet strict: limit the crops and make sure that the grapes ripen fully, even if it leads to higher sugar levels. Limiting the crops gives the couple total control — resulting in accolades like a 97 point ranking for their 1996 Vineyard Chardonnay. A testament to Turley's talents as a winemaker, she has striking across-the-board success; every wine that she bottles is considered among California's elite. The 1997 Chardonnay Sonoma Coast is particularly recommended, but nearly impossible to get.

1708 A Washington Street

Calistoga, CA 94515

Tel: 707-258-3678   Fax: 707-942-5633

MARGOT JOHNSON
Antiques
Margot Johnson specializes in late 19th century furniture and decorative art, primarily in Victorian cabinetry. Boasting a significant collection of Herter Brothers and RJ Horner pieces, she has helped to complete collections of numerous private collectors and major museums, including The Cleveland, Virginia and Boston museums. A member of the National Art Dealers Association of America and the Victorian Society, she regularly shows her pieces at the International and American Art Dealers Show and in 1996, was elected to serve on the board of the Attingham school, a prestigious decorative arts center in England.
18 East 68th Street, Apt. 1A
New York, NY 10021
Tel: 212-794-2225

MARGUERITE RIORDAN
Antiques
Marguerite Riordan was one of the dealers to capitalize on the revived appeal of Americana: rebelling against the plastic 'department-store' look that dominated the 1950s and 1960s, the redecoration of her own home soon grew into a business, which in turn became a sprawling landmark store. Set on the waterfront in the historic New England town of Stonington, her store now attracts collectors from around the country. The three-story loft space is stuffed with 18th and 19th century furnishings and American Primitive paintings.
Eight Pearl Street
Stonington, CT 06378
Tel: 860-535-2511   Fax: 860-535-0580

MARIO TRICOCI
Spas and Clinics
Clients are pampered into tranquility at Mario Tricoci, where they can have their hair cut and colored, a manicure, pedicure, a facial and a massage in the same day. A favorite among bridal parties and ladies of the social set, the services available are administered by a highly trained staff of professionals who, as Tricoci says, "won't let you go home without feeling beautiful." The pumpkin manicure and pedicure are particularly popular at the moment: a pumpkin peel enzyme mask dissolves away dead skin, leaving the skin fresh, soft and silky. Or try the water therapy massage, where stress is obliterated in a hydrotherapy tub.
900 North Michigan Avenue
Chicago, IL 60611
Tel: 312-915-0960
Fax: 312-204-9910

MARIO BUATTA
Architects and Interior Designers
One of America's premier designers, Mario Buatta, aka the 'prince of chintz,' has long been known for his unmistakable style, both personally and in his work. Buatta uses a maximum of comfort and a balance of contemporary and antique furnishings set against a fabulous sense of color. "A house should grow in the same way an artist's painting takes form," says Buatta, "achieving an undecorated look." Barbara Walters, Henry Ford II and the late Malcolm Forbes, have all used this style star to decorate their homes. Buatta was also responsible for the renovation of Blair House, the White House guest house.
120 East 80th Street
New York, NY 10021
Tel: 212-988-6811   Fax: 212-861-9221

MARIAN GOODMAN GALLERY
Art Dealers
Specializing in contemporary conceptual drawing, installation, mixed media, painting, sculpture and photography, Marian Goodman Gallery is a long-standing 57th Street institution with an international clientele. Artists represented include Tony Cragg, Dan Graham, Rebecca Horn, Thomas Struth and Jeff Wall. Don't miss British artist Steve McQueen's films – at the time of writing, his latest had collectors and admirers flocking in from foreign parts.
24 West 57th Street
New York, NY 10019
Tel: 212-292-8530
Fax: 212-581-5187

MARK SIMMONS
Architects and Interior Designers
Mark Simmons' interiors are so timeless that it's difficult to tell whether they were created yesterday or 20 years ago. Formerly of William Hamilton, one of Nashville's leading design firms, he ventured out on his own early in the 1990s and usually balances a workload of three residential projects at once. A self-confessed traditionalist, Simmons prefers to work alone, dedicating all of his attention to his clients. Equally enamored by color, fabric, texture and accessories, Simmons designs with a restrained eye and prides himself on becoming very good friends with his clients.
1931 21st Avenue South
Nashville, TN 37212
Tel: 615-269-6360

THE MARK
Hotels

Affluent Europeans flock to this chic uptown haven, where former guest's requests and preferences are recorded to ensure their comfort on future stays. A member of *The Leading Hotels of the World*, The Mark was aptly described in a British magazine last year as "discreet enough for the Earl of Snowdon, smart enough for Sharon Stone and hip enough for Bruce Springsteen." It is owned by Monte Carlo-based Georg Rafael. If dropping his name does not get you a good table or open the right doors, ask Giorgio, the Argentinian head concierge.

25 East 77th Street
New York, NY 10021
Tel: 212-744-4300   Fax: 212-744-2749

MARTEL PRODUCTIONS
Party Organizers and Caterers

For the past 11 years Simone Martel has masterminded key social events from charitable fund-raisers to movie premieres and private functions. Martel has worked closely with and orchestrated unforgettable fundraisers for the likes of Steven Spielberg, Arnold Schwarzenegger, Mohammed Ali, Michael Douglas, Lauren Bacall and Ashley Judd. Martel's expertise extends but is not limited to invitation design, supervision of catering, decoration and lighting design, booking entertainment and managing security.

10 East 53rd Street
New York, NY 10022
Tel: 212-753-3999   Fax: 212-753-4329

MARK'S LAS OLAS
Restaurants

With 28 tables in the dining room, five at the bar and eight on the outside patio, it's hard to believe that it's recommended to call a month in advance for a seat. One of the most frequented restaurants in Fort Lauderdale, chef/owner Mark Militello has created a raucous eatery, where the cuisine and the atmosphere battle for attention. Composed of stainless steel, Italian marble, coral, oak and mahogany, the dining room is unmistakably Mark's. Chef Lance Krabel is renowned for his roasted garlic stuffed grilled tenderloin and the wildly popular fresh Florida spiny lobster.

1032 East Las Olas Boulevard
Fort Lauderdale, FL 33301
Tel: 954-463-1000
Fax: 954-463-1887

MARLBOROUGH
Art Dealers

The weekend gallery crawl is now ever-more dispersed – it used to be that you 'did' 57th street or Soho; now you have to include Chelsea as well. In keeping with the general migration of established galleries to the western neighborhood, Marlborough Fine Arts now has a spacious whitewashed outpost there. Reflecting the typical uptown/downtown difference in attitude, the gallery on 57th Street handles established names (Botero, Red Grooms) while the Chelsea branch is home to emerging artists like Keith Sonnier.

40 West 57th Street
New York, NY 10019
Tel: 212-541-4900   Fax: 212-541-4948

MARTHA TURNER PROPERTIES
Property Consultants

Martha Turner takes pride in knowing that her agents find exactly what the discerning buyer wants, in any price range, from a small weekend retreat to a $25 million home or estate. And they do it every time. The leading independent broker of high-end real estate in Houston, Turner is the only Christie's Great Estates affiliate in the area. Founded in 1981, Turner's firm now has 46 full-time agents, dealing in a wide range of properties. They are also affiliated with the national relocation company, RELO.

1902 Westheimer
Houston, TX 77098
Tel: 713-520-1981
Fax: 713-520-8628

MARKS AND DUWAT
Architects and Interior Designers

Growing up in Paris, in a home laden with exquisite, rare antiques, Pascale Duwat seemed destined for interior design – early in life, she developed a natural admiration for fine craftsmanship and style. In 1981, she moved to Palm Beach, joining forces with the mighty David Marks, arguably the biggest name in design in the sunshine state. Commonly described as "better than any architect" regarding use of space, Marks is responsible for beautifying mansions and private estates, often in the style of 18th century France. Duwat travels to Europe four to five times a year, where she satisfies her passion for rare fabrics.

344 Worth Avenue
Palm Beach, FL 33480
Tel: 561-655-1633
Fax: 561-655-1642

MARK'S GARDEN
Florists

With a staff of 50, Mark's Garden is the largest flower shop in Los Angeles, well known for its trendsetting English garden baskets and wedding designs. Located on busy Ventura Boulevard, it is often filled with passersby shopping in the lush garden rooms. For the past seven years, the California gem has created floral designs for the Academy Awards Governors' Ball and has provided the elaborate floral decor that grace the stage of the Dorothy Chandler Pavilion for the Los Angeles Philharmonic. The firm of choice for many motion picture productions, television shows, film premieres and high profile weddings, Mark's has recently introduced a line of garden architecture – handcrafted metal gates, arches and garden screens – all with their typically elegant touch.

13838 Ventura Boulevard
Sherman Oaks, CA 91423
Tel: 818-906-1718   Fax: 818-386-2693

MARTHA ANGUS
Architects and Interior Designers

From ex-New Yorkers seeking the quieter life to internet entrepreneurs with new fortunes and a keen interest in fine art, Martha Angus brings her formidable design career to bear on every type of home, from small beach houses in Hawaii to mansions in the city. Moving west in the 1990s, she brought her New York City sensibility to California and has been in constant demand ever since. Angus studied at the école des Beaux Arts in France and Sotheby's in New York. She admits to being a painter at heart and brings a fine art approach to everything she does. By mixing avant garde contemporary art with high level traditional design and selective antiques, she creates strong structures and bold designs and is influenced by the work of David Hicks and Sills and Huniford. Her impressive background includes extensive work for Ralph Lauren and Estée Lauder, including a handful of Lauder's homes around the world, but Angus' own personal favorite is the interior of Giorgio Armani's current Milan home.

1017 Bush Street
San Francisco, CA 94109
Tel: 415-931-8060   Fax: 415-931-8095

MARTIN KATZ
Jewelry and Watches

A jewelry lover since his undergraduate days in Indiana, Michael Katz was the youngest manager at Laykin et Cie, which was the jewelry salon at I. Magnin in Beverly Hills. In 1988 Katz went into business for himself, working with clients such as Anjelica Huston, Emma Thompson, Nicole Kidman and Angela Bassett to match their unique tastes to exquisite pieces of vintage and contemporary jewelry. His collection focuses primarily on platinum pieces of art deco and Edwardian origin.

P.O. Box 10658
Beverly Hills, CA 90213
Tel: 310-276-7200   Fax: 310-276-3775

MARVIN ALEXANDER
Specialty Shops

Entering the Marvin Alexander store is like walking into a glass menagerie. This lighting specialist and decorative accessories resource has been selling mostly European merchandise for the past 40 years. One-of-a-kind antique furniture, ranging from the late 17th century to the 1920s, vies for space with the shop's ever-growing reproduction line, including copies of antique Louis XIV, Regency, Louis XVI and Second Empire. Don't be surprised to see top international decorators and architects on site.

315 East 62nd Street
New York, NY 10021
Tel: 212-838-2320   Fax: 212-754-0173

ALICE F. MASON
Property Consultants

Alice F. Mason has been working in real estate for over 40 years. One of the top residential brokers in New York, Mason — who is ably assisted by her daughter, Dominique Richard — specializes in the sale of luxury co-ops, condominiums and town houses. This real estate doyenne, who has strong links to the Democratic Party, is also renowned for her aplomb as a hostess.

635 Madison Avenue
New York, NY 10022
Tel: 212-832-8870
Fax: 212-832-7634

MARY BOONE GALLERY
Art Dealers

From its foundation in 1977, this Fifth Avenue gallery has exhibited the work of innovative young artists such as Jean Michel Basquiat, Ross Bleckner, Eric Fischl, Barbara Kruger, Brice Marden and Julian Schnabel, who all came to prominence whilst represented here. Many of those early exhibits greatly influenced the current crop of artists Mary Boone represents, such as Will Cotton, Karin Davie, Leonardo Drew, Inka Essenhigh, Damian Loeb, Tom Sachs and Peter Wegner. With a new Chelsea gallery opening in Fall 2000, Boone looks set to retain its place at the head of the New York gallery scene.

745 Fifth Avenue
New York, NY 10151
Tel: 212-752-2929
Fax: 212-752-3939

MASON & MORSE
Property Consultants

Mason & Morse's grasp extends far beyond the resort town of Aspen to encompass the best properties and ranches in the American West, from Idaho to Texas, Kansas to California. The firm has over 100 years of experience selling premier properties to those who need a little space, whether it's the famous Velvet Ranch (on 472 acres) or on up to a 25,000 acre Sun Ranch in Montana's Madison Valley. 45 agents offer advice on everything from water rights to ranch management.

514 East Hyman Avenue
Aspen, CO 81611
Tel: 970-544-9700
Fax: 970-925-7027

MATTHEW MARKS GALLERY
Art Dealers

New York's Chelsea is threatening to replace SoHo as the neighborhood of choice for established contemporary-art galleries. One of the first to leave the increasingly anonymous SoHo, Matthew Marks snapped up not one but two edge-of-town locations near 10th Avenue. Each gallery shows one artist at a time; recently, Weegee's photographs were shown on 24th Street and Katarina Frisch's sculptures were on 22nd. The gallery currently represents over 20 artists who consistently garner glowing notices. Lucien Freud, Brice Marden, Ellsworth Kelly and Nan Goldin are just some of the artists on the roster.

523 West 24th Street
New York, NY 10011
Tel: 212-243-0200

ALAN MATARASSO, M.D.
Cosmetic Surgeons

We can't tell you who goes to see Dr. Alan Matarasso. In fact, the man dubbed "Surgeon to the Stars" so assiduously guards the privacy of the celebrities and socialites who flock to him for the natural look his plastic surgery provides, that he has a concealed private entry to his well-appointed Park Avenue office. Recognized by his peers, as well as by leaders in the health and fashion industries, for his technologically advanced techniques in cosmetic surgery of the face and body, Matarasso's high-profile clientele also appreciate the individualized treatments he recommends to ease postoperative recovery, which includes homeopathic remedies and massage therapy. Certified by the American Board of Plastic Surgeons, and a member of the American Society for Aesthetic Plastic Surgery and the American Association of Plastic Surgeons, Matarasso also serves as an Associate Professor at Albert Einstein College of Medicine. He is a highly regarded educator, author and surgeon who has given more than 400 lectures to his fellow medical doctors. It's no wonder that Matarasso has been named among the top doctors in his field by seven major publications.

1009 Park Avenue
New York, NY 10028
Tel: 212-249-7500   Fax: 212-628-5000

MARY MAHONEY
Specialty Shops

After having two children and pursuing a Masters degree in Irish studies, Mary Mahoney founded her namesake shop. Spread over 10,000 square-feet, the first floor is dedicated to the finest European crystal, china, silver and table accessories. Clients spend hours on the second floor, smartly laden with D'Porthault bed, bath and table linens along with gift items and fine linens from France, Italy and Germany. The Minneapolis native does not limit her client base solely to her inventory; Mahoney frequently has fabrics woven and researches antique firms to match any idea. During the Palm Beach season, the shop hosts jewelers, art dealers and designers from around the world. This store is not to be missed.

351 Worth Avenue
Palm Beach, FL 33480
Tel: 561-655-8288
Fax: 561-655-8574

MATSUHISA
Restaurants

Chef and owner Nobu Matsuhisa designed this small and intimate seafood restaurant himself. Opened in 1987, it was the precursor to the fabled Nobu empire. Matsuhisa's experience as a Japanese chef who worked for many years in Peru is evident in signature dishes like new style sashimi, cooked slightly in hot olive oil for people who don't eat raw fish; with jalapeños and cilantro it achieves a blend of Caribbean and Japanese flavors. This is the only restaurant in the United States which serves the exquisite Hokusetsu sake, served cold in bamboo bottles.

129 North la Cienega Boulevard
Beverly Hills, CA 90211
Tel: 310-289-4925   Fax: 310-659-0492

THE MAUNA LANI BAY
Hotels

A five Diamond retreat between two white sand beaches on the Kohala Coast of Hawaii's Big Island, Mauna Lani Bay is an exquisite blend of sophisticated luxury and Hawaiian hospitality. Discriminating travelers elect to luxuriate in one of the five bungalows – The Orchid, Plumeria, Hibiscus, Bird of Paradise or The Heliconia. Each offers 4000 square feet, including two master bedroom suites, two master baths and a guest bath – just in case.

68-1400 Mauna Lani Drive
Kohala Coast, HI 96743
Tel: 808-885-6622
Fax: 808-885-1483

MAURICE BADLER FINE JEWELRY
Jewelry and Watches

This unassuming, unpretentious Midtown boutique carries some of the more prestigious jewelry lines available. Designers such as Roberto Coin, Asch-Grossbardt and Rina Limor are represented, in stones from South Sea pearls to classic diamonds. Jeff Badler's small, erudite team specialize in stealth-shopping: customers can have their favorite pieces recorded at the store, alongside the dates of anniversaries or birthdays; husbands are then called before the special day, and an appropriate piece selected.

578 Fifth Avenue
New York, NY 10036
Tel: 800-M-BADLER

MAURICE JENNINGS AND DAVID MCKEE

Architects and Interior Designers

The legendary Fay Jones, who was an apprentice of Frank Lloyd Wright, won the American Institute of Architect's gold medal in 1990. Jones retired in 1997, but his longtime associates Maurice Jennings and David McKee maintain this firm's organic style, utilizing refined, milled woods to create homes of distinction. The firm specializes in chapels and private residences, including the Roy Reed house in Hog Eye, the Edmondson residence in Forrest City and the Thorncrown Chapel in Eureka Springs.

619 West Dickson
Fayetteville, AR 72701
Tel: 501-443-4742   Fax: 501-443-0637

MAXWELL GALLERIES

Art Dealers

Mark and Colleen Hoffman continue Fred Maxwell's work in bringing significant 19th and 20th century American and European paintings and sculpture to the West Coast. The collection has tripled since the gallery was founded in 1940 – today, particular attention is given to early American landscape and genre scenes as well as impressionist and post-impressionist paintings from the American and European schools. Artists represented include Ning Hou, Robert Russin, David Stewart and Mark English, among others.

559 Sutter Street
San Francisco, CA 94102
Tel: 415-421-5193
Fax: 415-421-4858

MAUS & HOFFMAN

Specialty Shops

There is a certain kind of man and woman who personifies the Maus & Hoffman customer. Successful and entrepreneurial certainly, but also confident enough to eschew designer labels in exchange for classic style and enduring quality. The long-established brands found here – Hickey-Freeman, Brioni and Oxxford Clothes to name some of the oldest – have been around since this firm first opened its doors in the Sunshine State in the 1940s, providing the kind of lighter-weight cruisewear, sportswear, and dress clothing its active and well-traveled customers prefer. 2nd and 3rd generation descendants of the firm's founder manage each store along with an outstanding staff, offering gracious and attentive service in Fort Lauderdale, Palm Beach, Boca Raton, Bal Harbour, Naples and Sarasota.

800 East Las Olas Blvd
Fort Lauderdale, FL 00031
Tel: 954-463-1472   Fax: 954-463-1587

THE MAYFLOWER INN

Hotels

Together with designer Mariette Himes Gomez, New Yorkers Adrianna and Robert Mnuchin recreated the Mayflower Inn, a European-style country house, in 1992. The original architecture and decor of the 25 suites has been completely restored, offering Oriental carpets, canopied four-poster beds, damask bedspreads, quirky clocks, toile lamps, Frette linens and Limoges china. The series of public rooms – lobby, parlor, game room and library – are all dramatic and elegant, filled with treasures from France and England.

118 Woodbury Road
Washington, CT 06793
Tel: 860-868-9466   Fax: 860-868-1497

MAXFIELD

Fashion

Maxfield is a fashion oasis housing the world's most illustrious designers. Comme Des Garcons, Gucci, Yohji Yamamoto, Helmut Lang, Giorgio Armani, Jean Paul Gaultier and Dolce & Gabanna can all be found at the store, which was one of the the first in California to introduce the top Japanese and European designers. This 10,000 square foot store is a high-end paradise, with a lavish array of exotic merchandise to complement the home, the best clothing the world has to offer, rare and distinctive artworks, collectible jewelry and watches.

8825 Melrose Avenue
Los Angeles, CA 90069
Tel: 310-274-8800
Fax: 310-657-8880

MCMILLEN

Architects and Interior Designers

Founded in the roaring twenties and serving such clients as the Vanderbilts, Rockefellers, Fords and Kennedys, McMillen was the first American full-service interior design firm. Having introduced eclecticism – the mixing and matching of old and new pieces, with occasional ethnic influence – it soon became the dominant principle in American interior design. As the decades rolled by, projects got bigger and bigger, including the redesign of rooms at the White House and major corporate makeovers for Chemical Bank, Mobil and Morgan Stanley. But the full-time staff of 25 can accomodate more intimate projects as well – yachts and planes are also specialties of the house.

155 East 56th Street
New York, NY 10022
Tel: 212-753-6377

MECOX GARDENS

Specialty Shops

Owner Mac Hoak left a career in banking in 1966, when he decided to make his passion his priority. Influenced by the European tradition of gardens as outdoor rooms, Hoak's emphasis is on simplicity, which is reflected in the elegant and well-constructed pots, dishes and furniture he sells - whether brand-new or centuries old. Hoak works with top name interior designers to enrich clients' homes and gardens with class and sophistication. There is a Mecox branch in Manhattan, which is managed by the indefatigable Britta.

257 County Road, 39A
Southampton, NY 11968
Tel: 631-287-5015
Fax: 631-287-5018

MEADOWOOD NAPA VALLEY
Hotels

For the ultimate in wine country grace and hospitality, look to Meadowood Napa Valley, an exquisite, private property reminiscent of a grand country estate – think West Coast Gatsby. Here you will enjoy the polished service of one of eight personal concierges (guest service managers), attending to the special amenities and prized reservations that make one's sojourn on the estate and exploration of the Napa Valley most memorable. Meadowood offers eighty-five cottages, suites and lodges as well as croquet, tennis, golf, swimming, a complete health spa, a wine center, a cultural affairs program and celebrated fine dining in the The Restaurant at Meadowood. Highly recommended.

900 Meadowood Lane
St. Helena, CA 94574
Tel: 707-963-3646   Fax: 707-963-3532

MEDFITNESS
Fitness

Just off Central Park, MedFitness provides the intimate, one-on-one service synonymous with the pampered Upper East Side. Emphasizing quality over quantity, the gym keeps its clientele small and its staff large; each has his or her own specialization: boxing, karate, body buidling, yoga, and endergmologie (cellulite reduction). Other special services include home training sessions and phone or e-mail consultations for the traveling fitness buff.

12 East 86th Street
New York, NY 10028
Tel: 212-327-4197

MELLON BANK
Wealth Management

While other banks rush to consolidate and grow ever-larger, Mellon remains headquartered in Pittsburgh; as always, it provides detailed, attentive service to its select clients. Asset-specific analysis is the first step of a program tailored to each individual client; a full range of financial planning and investment services is also offered, including trust and estate planning, information management and expert equity and fixed-income management.

1 Mellon Bank Center
Pittsburgh, PA 15258
Tel: 412-234-5000   Fax: 412-236-1662

MERCER HOTEL
Hotels

Equipped with Christian Liaigre's minimalist decor and Andre Balazs' legendary sense of cool, the Mercer is a haven of creature comforts and anonymity. Privacy? The hotel doesn't even have a proper sign – the word Mercer is simply printed on the café window. Guest rooms come with oversized bathrooms, Sony Qbric stereo systems, extensive CD and video libraries and fine linens, including 200-thread Egyptian sheets. Room service is the best way to sample Jean-Georges Vongerichten's goodies from the Mercer Kitchen: the basement restaurant is full of star gazers.

147 Mercer Street
New York, NY 10012
Tel: 212-966-6060

MERCHANT'S HOUSE MUSEUM
Museums

By 1832, New York City had become the pre-eminent port of the United States. In search of a more residential neighborhood, wealthy landowners moved from downtown to the more fashionable Greenwich Village district. Seabury Tredwell moved into the house at 29 East Fourth Street in 1835. When many of his neighbors began moving further uptown (as society dictated), Tredwell, his wife and seven children stayed exactly where they were. Today, the house is one of the finest surviving examples of Greek Revival architecture of the period. It is the only family home in the city to survive intact, inside and out, from the late 1830s.

29 East Fourth Street
New York, NY 10003
Tel: 212-777-1089

MEREDITH LONG GALLERY
Art Dealers

One of the most prestigious gallery owners in America today, Meredith Long has championed the rebirth of interest in 19th and 20th century American Art since 1957. Artists represented include George Inness, Georgia O'Keeffe, Max Weber and Joseph Stella and the estates of Wayman Adams and Charles Umlauf. This year, Long presented *An American Impressionist*, an astonishing retrospective of Childe Hassam's work. On a lighter note, look out for Andy, Meredith Long's Cavalier King Charles Spaniel, who parades up and down the gallery with more vigilance than any security guard could possibly muster!

2323 San Felipe
Houston, TX 77019
Tel: 713-523-6671
Fax: 713-523-2355

METROPOLITAN LIMOUSINE
Chauffeur Services

What a difference details make. This company has been providing the highest quality limousine service available for 28 years. By carefully screening its drivers, Metropolitan ensures they are informed, knowledgeable and prepared with impeccable appearances, personalities and service habits. With affiliates in nearly every major U.S., Canadian and European city, it is a superb way to arrive at any destination. Flight information is broadcast live into the operations office and monitored carefully to ensure the efficient flow of your transportation needs. At the gate, Metropolitan's multilingual greeting personnel handle luggage and take clients through the airport to a waiting Mercedes, Lincoln Town Car sedan or extended limousine. Arriving by private jet? Metropolitan will have a car waiting planeside. The fleet also includes passenger vans and motor coaches. All vehicles are immaculate and all cars have direct-dial telephones, as well as private, sophisticated radio systems allowing the driver to stay in constant communication with his operations office. The National Limousine Association awarded Metropolitan Operator of the Year and Chauffeur of the Year four times in the past ten years.

845 North Michigan Avenue, 1B
Chicago, IL 60611
Tel: 800-437-1700
Fax: 312-808-1786

MERRILL LYNCH FINANCIAL SERVICES
Wealth Management

With roots going back to 1885, Merrill Lynch is one of America's oldest financial-services giants. Its wealth-management services, handling $1.8 trillion in client assets, are distributed over several departments, taking advantage of its full capabilities in investment banking and brokerage, as well as tax and estate-planning, and many others. For the creme de la creme, Merrill Lynch offers a Family Office Group – a full-time crew of experienced lawyers, accountants, and financial mentors – that is, if you make the hurdle of $100 million in investable assets.

250 Vesey Street
New York, NY 10281
Tel: 212-449-1000

METROPOLITAN MUSEUM OF ART
Museums

The Met is truly spectacular in both form and content. Home to a couple of million art works, from all over the world and spanning all the ages, it would take a lifetime to exhaust the comprehensive collection. With ancient art, 11th century Chinese painting, armory from the Middle Ages, Korean ceramics, painting and photography, this powerhouse institution guarantees nothing less than a memorable experience. The Met's collection of art from Southeast Asia is the biggest of its kind in the world.

1000 Fifth Avenue
New York, NY 10028
Tel: 212-650-2911   Fax: 212-650-2170

MEURICE GARMENT CARE
Specialty Shops

The self-styled *Stainmaster*, Meurice Garment Care is the preferred dry cleaner to Armani, Dolce & Gabanna, Prada and Versace. Owner Wayne Edelman is a pro – his father remembers stitching Eleanor Roosevelt's stockings. Meurice routinely receives clothing parcels from Israel, South Africa, Italy and other foreign ports of call. The Long Island native has cleaned one of a kind couture gowns that other cleaners wouldn't dare touch, for fear of ruining them. The only customer ever turned down by the firm was a museum which requested the cleaning of a shrunken African head.

20 Park Avenue
Manhasset, NY 11030
Tel: 800-240-3377   Fax: 516-627-2943

MIA N. WEINER
Art Dealers

Enamored by Renaissance humanity and ideals, Mia Weiner graduated college and immediately began collecting Old Master drawings and oil sketches from the period. Her first client was the British Museum of Art. Since that sale in 1979, Weiner has supplied the Getty, Metropolitan Museum of Art, Chicago and Washington Museums with 16th and 17th century Italian drawings. The New York native prefers drawings to paintings because "in a drawing, one can see exactly what the artist was thinking from beginning to end."

Mountain Road
Norfolk, CT 06058
Tel: 860-542-1893

THE METROPOLITAN OPERA
Events

With its sweeping sets by Zeffirelli and a wealth of glamour, drama and passion, the Met is truly one of the world's great opera companies. Everyone who is anyone has performed here, from Caruso to Pavarotti, from Callas to Fleming. While it may not have the intimacy or charm of Milan's La Scala, Lincoln Center is one of the eccentric jewels of modern architecture. Opening night bonus: New York society on its best behavior.

Lincoln Center for the Performing Arts
New York, NY 10023
Tel: 212-362-6000

MICHAEL GRAVES & ASSOCIATES

Architects and Interior Designers

For over 30 years, this Indiana native has been inspiring others in and out of his field with his accessible, figurative designs. A winner of over 130 prestigious awards for his work in architecture, interiors, products and graphics, Graves enjoys a superb international reputation, which makes a recent remark – to the effect that very few editors of a shelter magazine have a shred of integrity left – all the more interesting. Truly one of the most original voices in contemporary American design.

341 Nassau Street
Princeton, NJ 08540
Tel: 609-924-6409

❧

MICHAEL TAYLOR DESIGNS

Specialty Shops

One of the first top-rank interior decorators to buck the overly plastic futuristic design trend of the 1950s and 60s, Michael Taylor pioneered the neutral-toned, naturalistic California look. His artistry with white slipcovers, beige and khaki colors, and abundant stonework was responsible for much of what we think of today as contemporary interior design. The firm that bears his name is now a maker of fine furniture, best known for its stonework tables, available in 11 showrooms across the country.

1500 17th Street
San Francisco, CA 94103
Tel: 415-558-9940   Fax: 415-558-9770

❧

MICHAEL WERNER GALLERY

Art Dealers

This New York and Cologne-based gallery represents a wide range of the best modern and contemporary artists. The emphasis is on German and European post WWII paintings, drawings, photography and sculpture. One of the most intriguing aspects of Werner exhibitions is the pairing of contemporary artists alongside the work of their major influences, for example, the late Joseph Beuys alongside Wilhelm Lehmbruck.

4 East 77th Street
New York, NY 10021
Tel: 212-988-1623   Fax: 212-988-1774

MICHAEL'S

Restaurants

Michael McCarty founded his namesake restaurant in a renovated house from the 1930s near the beach in Santa Monica. His cuisine encompasses French, Italian, Hispanic, Oriental and American ingredients, techniques, presentations and philosophies – reflecting the New York native's world travels. The dining room is warm and rosy, spacious and dimly-lit. Lunch is best in the open-air sculpture garden, with a view of the contemporary art collection. Try the West Coast Swordfish, served with tomatillos, serranos, cilantro and lime or the amazing carpinteria squab with shitake mushrooms in Pinot Noir.

1147 Third Street
Santa Monica, CA 90403
Tel: 310-451-0843   Fax: 310-394-1830

❧

MIGUEL ADROVER

Fashion   Rising Star

By the time Miguel Adrover had his second show, he was hailed as an instant design guru. The line was made out of donated fabrics and things, well, off the street. An antique Louis Vuitton bag sewn into a miniskirt and sleeves propped up with old baseball caps forced fashionistas to radically reappraise their notions of chic. Adrover's line is now available at Barney's and Neiman Marcus, while the Majorca native, who grew up on an almond farm, still works out of his East Village apartment. He looks set to become one of the more successful young designers in America.

149 Bowery
New York, NY 10002

MILLE FLEURS

Restaurants

Chef Martin Woesle was born in Southern Germany and began cooking at the age of 16. In Germany, aspiring chefs must be at least 24 years old and have eight years of restaurant experience to be admitted to culinary school. The requirements were waived for Woesle, who was admitted at 18 and graduated first in his class. In 1998, he was named one of "the great regional chefs in America" by the James Beard Foundation. Although he prides himself in not having a signature dish, the medallions of venison loin and the smoked, layered salmon are sheer perfection. Ask to be seated in the charming Spanish garden or the fountain room, overlooking the elegant courtyard. Warmly recomended.

6009 Paseo Delicias
Rancho Santa Fe, CA 92067
Tel: 858-756-3085
Fax: 858-756-9945

MILLER & ARNEY

Antiques

Joe Miller opened his firm right after his college graduation in 1973. By that time, he had already amassed a significant collection of 18th and 19th century furniture and accessories, so it seemed entirely logical to open a firm of his own. Located in Georgetown, Miller now offers a vast array of sought-after treasures. At the time of writing, items of interest included a 1790 Georgian sideboard and a Birch Sofa from the same period.

Wisconsin Avenue
Washington, DC 20007
Tel: 202-338-2369   Fax: 202-338-1246

❧

MINARDI SALON

Hair and Beauty

Color and cut have been passions for Beth and Carmine Minardi far longer than their salons' 15-year run would indicate. Husband Carmine has gone from trimming college sorority girls to caring for top models and Hollywood stars, while colorist and wife Beth took her childhood artistic leanings and applied them to her study of color. Now, 30 employees help shape heads and perfect such shades as 'luxury blonde' and 'drop-dead gorgeous red.' Christie Brinkley, Cameron Diaz, Faye Dunaway and Sara Jessica Parker are among the famous manes to have passed through the doors of the townhouse duplex that holds the salon.

29 East 61 Street
New York, NY 10021
Tel: 212-308-1711
Fax: 212-753-6831

MINDY WEISS
PARTY CONSULTANTS

Party Organizers and Caterers

Mindy Weiss is a Beverly Hills-based celebrity wedding planner and trend expert. Credited with organizing dream affairs for clients like André Agassi, Steve Tisch and Billy Crystal, Weiss began her career 15 years ago by creating her own line of wedding invitations. She soon became interested in all aspects of the special day, and began her full service event planning company. Today, working with clients to custom create invitations, favors, room décor and lighting, Weiss is one of the most trusted people in the industry.

232 South Beverly Drive
Beverly Hills, CA 90212
Tel: 310-205-6000   Fax: 310-205-6005

MIRAVAL

Spas and Clinics

Aesthetically and functionally elegant, Miraval is a vacation destination which specializes in reducing the stress of its guests. Appropriately located in the Sonoran desert of southern Arizona, the spa spans 150 acres and offers over 100 casitas, many offering a breathtaking view of the Santa Catalina Mountains. Guests personalize their programs, choosing from 120 activities and treatments including a full line of massage and skin care, meditation, early morning rides on horseback, early morning hiking and aqua aerobics.

5000 E. Vía Estancia Miraval
Catalina, AZ 85739
Tel: 520-825-4000
Fax: 520-825-5199

MITCHELL-INNES AND NASH

Art Consultants

This complementary partnership handles 19th and 20th century fine art from two Madison Avenue galleries. Lucy Mitchell-Innes focuses on masterworks by contemporary artists on the secondary market and David Nash represents impressionist and modern artworks. The inventory includes masters (old and new) like Monet, Renoir, Ellsworth Kelly, Jackson Pollock and Jasper Johns. The consultants co-represent the estate of William de Kooning with the Matthew Marks Gallery and present extensive exhibitions of his work. Other recent shows include the early paintings of Andy Warhol, the Spectrums of Ellsworth Kelly and a survey of Nicholas de Stael.

1018 Madison Avenue
New York, NY 10021
Tel: 212-744-7400
Fax: 212-744-7401

JUAN PABLO MOLYNEUX

Architects and Interior Designers

If you have the good fortune to commission the architectural and design services of Juan Pablo Molyneux, you should plan on keeping your home forever. The average Molyneux client has absolutely everything; coming to him in search of the unattainable, he somehow finds it - a Molyneux interior is the unequivocal Jewel in the Crown. Born in Chile of English heritage and trained in Paris' école des Beaux Arts, Molyneux's career in New York began in 1983. Since then he has been wowing the city with his meticulous and eclectic interiors. An avid lover of the Greco-Roman tradition, he soon rejected the rigors of modernism he was trained in and established a style distinctly his own. Considering Trianon the epitome of the very best of French classicism, Molyneux is equally impressed by Gehry's Guggenheim and incorporates modern touches to his own designs. When he is not studying 18th century France – which itself marks the revival of neo-classical architecture – or creating exquisite interiors, Molyneux can be found heli-skiing in the Canadian Rockies, or motorcycle cruising. But Molyneux still considers interior design a more hazardous occupation.

29 East 69th Street
New York, NY 10021
Tel: 212-628-0097   Fax: 212-737-6126

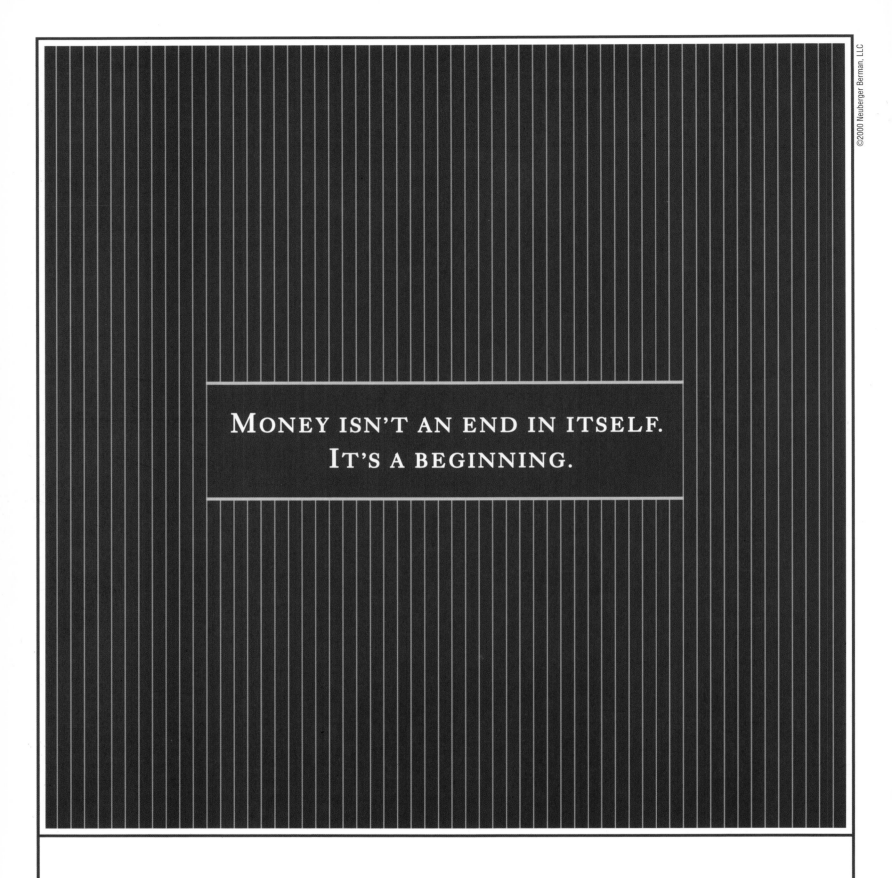

MONEY ISN'T AN END IN ITSELF. IT'S A BEGINNING.

If you have $500,000 to invest, you qualify for customized asset management.
Now you can really get started.

Atlanta • Boston • Chicago • Dallas • Houston • Los Angeles • Miami • New York
Philadelphia • San Francisco • West Palm Beach
Private Asset Management | Trust Company Services

1-877-461-1940   NEUBERGER BERMAN   www.nb.com

MLS LIMOUSINES

Chauffeur Services

California car culture finds its highest expression at MLS Limousines, where clients can select from an enormous range of classic and new cars. Vintage Rolls-Royces, new Bentley convertibles and stretch Rolls limousines are just the beginning of MLS's 60-car fleet, which includes every variety of stretched vehicle imaginable, as well as the 'land yachts' (luxury coaches) increasingly popular with entertainment figures. Luxury car rental is also available for the out-of-towner who knows the California mantra: "You are what you drive."

9641 Sunset Boulevard
Beverly Hills, CA 90210
Tel: 800-310-1980
Fax: 310-271-8979

MOLINA

Jewelry and Watches

The business of declaring one's love never seems to get any cheaper – unless, of course, one enjoys the company of very cheap dates. For the rest of us, companies like Molina ("Exceptional jewels for exceptional people") are a godsend. Top manufacturers of jewelry and watches like Audemars Piguet, Fabergé and Vacheron Constantin are stocked alongside the work of emerging new designers in a showroom which smacks of class. Far and away the finest jeweler in Arizona.

3134 East Camelback
Phoenix, AZ 85016
Tel: 602-955-2055
Fax: 602-955-2606

MONTREUX GOLF & COUNTRY CLUB

Golf Clubs

Located less than 25 minutes away from Lake Tahoe in Nevada's spectacular Sierra mountains, Montreux Golf & Country Club was awarded a PGA tournament, the Reno-Tahoe Open, in just its second year of operation, a rare honor afforded to new courses. Add magnificent estates and cottages with old world, Northern European architecture, and you have one of the finest mountain golf communities in the world. A final seal of approval comes from course designer and golf legend, Jack Nicklaus, who ranks Montreaux "one of my top four or five."

16475 Bordeaux Drive
Reno, NV 89511
Tel: 775-849-9444
Fax: 775-849-3130

MOORE BROTHERS WINE COMPANY

Wine Merchants

A commitment to consistency characterizes this wine emporium. The transfer of wine from vineyard to customer is exquisitely controlled: the store is kept a cool 55 degrees year-round. Specializing in French and Italian vintages, Moore has recently introduced select cognacs and grappas, as well as sake. And a surprising final touch: a children's playroom is available for parents who procrastinate between buying the St.Emilion and the Graves.

7200 North Park Drive
Pennsauken, NJ 08109
Tel: 856-317-1177

THE MORGAN LIBRARY

Museums

The Morgan Library, originally the private library of financier John Pierpont Morgan, one of America's greatest cultural benefactors, hosts one of the finest collections of rare books and manuscripts in the world. Morgan began collecting in 1890, compiling illuminated, literary and historical manuscripts; early printed books and old master drawings. Highlights include Charles Dickens' original manuscript of *A Christmas Carol*, Albrecht Dürer's *Adam and Eve* and original sections of Thoreau's *Walden*. Ranging from preparatory studies and sketches to finished works of art, more than 100,000 drawings and prints span the 14th to 20th centuries. Holdings include works by Blake, Degas, Pollock, Reubens and drawings by Rembrandt and da Vinci. The Gilder Lehrman Collection is the largest and finest collection of historical documents held in private hands.

29 East 36th Street
New York, NY 10016
Tel: 212-685-0610   Fax: 212-481-3484

MORGAN STANLEY DEAN WITTER

Wealth Management

In the explosion of American wealth that has occurred over the last five years, the standards of exclusivity have been raised significantly. Case in point is Morgan Stanley Dean Witter's private wealth management division, where the minimum liquidity has been raised to $10 million (up from an earlier $5 million). If you make the cut, your assets will be looked after by experts with a close knowledge of the various investment markets. And size doesn't hurt: as MSDW is a full-service financial services company, you will have access to a range of top-flight brokerage and investment services from the inside.

1585 Broadway
New York, NY 10036
Tel: 212-761-4000

MORGENTHAL FREDERICS

Specialty Shops

Opticians do not come much better recommended than Morganthal Frederics, a provider of eyewear to the Oscar ceremonies, and winner of *New York* Magazine's award for best optician in the city. Two Madison Avenue stores, a boutique in Soho and another outlet in Bergdorf Goodman ensure that clients like Sean Puffy Combs and Robin Williams don't have to stray too far for comfortable, elegant prescription lenses and sunglasses.

399 West Broadway
New York, NY 10012
Tel: 212-966-0099
Fax: 212-966-8767

MORRISON & FOERSTER

Law Firms

This San Francisco-based firm represents cutting-edge industries as well as more established businesses and individuals. One of the more progressive-minded law firms, Mofo (as it calls itself) has been voted one of the 100 Best Companies to work for by both *Fortune* and *Working Mother* magazines, proving that business acumen does not exclude community values. High-profile mergers and acquisitions (with First Brands and Intel among others) are a speciality. Mofo has 17 offices, scattered over California, South America, Europe and Asia.

425 Market Street
San Francisco, CA 94105
Tel: 415-268-7000

MURAD SPA
Spas and Clinics

Dr. Howard Murad was a pioneer in the development of several skin-care technologies taken for granted today – vitamin C creams, Alpha Hydroxy acids, antioxidants – and the same forward-looking spirit prevails at his day spa in El Segundo. (Don't worry, new products are not tested on guests). Murad tends to the inner person as well as the outer; in addition to vitamin C infusion treatments, hydrotherapy and a full variety of traditional deep cleansings and massage, nutritional profiling and stress relief are offered. Named as one of the best day spas in the country by *Allure* magazine, Murad also sells its own line of upscale nutraceuticals and beauty products.

2141 Rosecrans Avenue
El Segundo, CA 90245
Tel: 310-726-0470   Fax: 310-726-3216

MUSEUM OF CONTEMPORARY ART, CHICAGO
Museums

One of the nation's largest facilities devoted to art of our time, this museum has been offering exhibitions of provocative and innovative contemporary art since 1945. Documenting visual culture through painting, sculpture, photography, video, film and performance, this year's exhibits have included works by Judy Fox, Lisa Yuskavage, Nicky Hoberman and Van Lamsweerde among others. Located near the historic water tower in downtown Chicago, the MCA boasts a gift shop, bookstore, restaurant, 300-seat theater and a terraced sculpture garden with a serene view of Lake Michigan.

220 East Chicago Avenue
Chicago, IL 60611
Tel: 312-280-2660

MUSEUM OF CONTEMPORARY ART, SAN DIEGO
Museums

When the San Diego Museum of Art opened its doors in 1926, a collection of Arthur Putnam's small bronzes, a half-dozen minor paintings and some decorative arts constituted the entire permanent collection. Today, the small but influential Museum hosts 3000 works from 1950 to the present. The late Lele and Rea Axline gave a significant boost when they left it $30 million, placing MCA's endowment among the top five for contemporary art museums in the country. The collection boasts an elaborate array of Chinese bronze sculpture and a world-renowned collection of painting and related works from India.

1001 Kettner Boulevard
San Diego, CA 92101
Tel: 619-234-1001

Mrs. Fiske Warren and her daughter Rachel, by John Singer Sargent

MUSEUM OF FINE ARTS, BOSTON
Museums

Boston's venerable museum of Fine Arts is renowned for its 19th century European paintings, Japanese art collection, and its John Singer Sargent murals. With masterpieces from all over the world, this world class collection is housed in two impressive buildings, the 1918 Evans Wing and the West Wing, designed by I.M. Pei. Permanent exhibitions include a comprehensive collection of Nubian art, European painting, art of ancient Americas and a fine collection of Egyptian art.

465 Huntington Avenue
Boston, MA 02115
Tel: 617-267-9300

MUSEUM OF FINE ARTS, HOUSTON
Museums

The largest and most significant cultural presence in the southwest was founded in 1900 as the first art museum in the state of Texas. Last year it was joined by a handsome new addition, in the Audrey Jones Beck building. The $83 million, 192,447 square foot addition will house the museum's European Art - including impressionist and post-impressionist work by Monet, Renoir and Seurat. The Beck Building includes a restaurant, museum store and galleries for major special exhibitions.

1001 Bissonnet Street
Houston, TX 77005
Tel: 713-639-7300

MUSEUM OF MODERN ART
Museums

MoMA has the foremost collection of 20th century art in the world. From an initial bequest of eight prints and one drawing in 1929, the collection has grown to include more than 100,000 paintings, sculptures, prints, photographs, architectural models, drawings and design objects. Innovative and forward thinking, the museum owns some 14,000 films and four million film stills, making it a world leader in film archiving. Visited by 1.5 million people each year, its permanent collection is popular but special events draw visitors in just as frequently.

11 West 53rd Street
New York, NY 10019
Tel: 212-708-9400

NAMBÉ
Specialty Shops

Both company and product name, Nambé contains no silver or lead and is the safest metal that can be used for cooking. In 1999 Nambé introduced a new line of full-lead crystal. Award-winning designers collaborated with master European glass blowers to create a collection which smacks of inspired simplicity. Fans include Oprah Winfrey.

104 West San Francisco Street
Sante Fe, NM 87501
Tel: 505-471-2912   Fax: 505-437-9355

NANCY GOSLEE POWER & ASSOCIATES
Architects and Interior Designers

Formerly an interior designer, Nancy Goslee Power now concentrates on designing exteriors. She has worked closely with architects like Frank Gehry and Steve Ehrlich. Having traveled extensively, Power's various influences mixed with her design sense and horticultural knowledge invariably bring landscapes and gardens to exuberant life. Her work has been published in Breaking Ground: Portraits of Ten Garden Designers and she has written a book, The Garden of California.

1660 Stanford Street
Santa Monica, CA 90404
Tel: 310-264-0266   Fax: 310-264-0268

NAOMI LEFF & ASSOCIATES
Architects and Interior Designers

Naomi Leff is widely acclaimed for her diverse sense of style, her creative use of color and texture and her ability to create a winning ambiance. Leff's extensive client list includes stores for Ralph Lauren, Giorgio Armani and the homes of Tom Cruise and Nicole Kidman and Kate Capshaw – she is one of the most sought after designers working in the United States today.

12 West 27th Street
New York, NY 10001
Tel: 212-686-6300

HOTEL NASH
Hotels   Rising Star

Located one block behind the infamous Versace mansion in the heart of the Art Deco district, Hotel Nash was destined for style. An object lesson in 1930s Deco after it's recent $11 million renovation, its 55 rooms are decorated in sage and soothing ivory; three pools (saltwater, mineral and freshwater) occupy the lavish courtyard garden. The better views, surprisingly, are not over the city, but behind, where a clear view of the Versaces' observatory battles the stretch of blooming gardens. Incidentally, the Hotel's restaurant, Mark's, serves seafood fit for gods.

1120 Collins Avenue
Miami Beach, FL 33139
Tel: 305-674-7800   Fax: 305-538-8288

NATHAN LIVERANT AND SON
Antiques

In 1920, Nathan Liverant arrived in Colchester with the intention of making a life for himself and his family; little did he know that he'd put the unassuming town of Colchester on the map. After three generations, the Liverant family still controls the business, which deals in fine examples of American furniture, silver, porcelain, paintings and accessories, including mirrors, baskets and other decorative items. According to the owners, "there's probably no reason in the world to come here except to see us—oh, and a world-famous hot dog stand."

168 South Main Street
Colchester, CT 06415
Tel: 860-537-2409
Fax: 860-537-0577

NATIONAL GALLERY OF ART
Museums

The National Gallery of Art was founded in 1937, on acceptance of a bequest by Andrew W. Mellon. The paintings and works of sculpture donated by the financier formed a nucleus of high quality around which the collections have grown. American, British, Dutch, Flemish, Spanish and assorted 20th century art make up the permanent collection. The American collections are particularly extensive, boasting works by artists as diverse as Gilbert Stuart, John Singleton Copley and Andy Warhol. Recent highlights include an ambitious retrospective of the work of John Singer Sargent and a much-publicized exhibition of van Gogh oils.

4th Street and Constitution Avenue NW
Washington, DC 20565
Tel: 202-737-4215

NATIONAL GOLF LINKS OF AMERICA
Golf Clubs

The Club was founded in 1908 under the leadership of Charles B. McDonald. Having grown up in Scotland, he studied courses and set out to build a first-class course in the U.S. which would incorporate many of the better qualities of courses in the British Isles. Among the famous holes represented are the Road Hole and Eden from St. Andrews, Alps from Prestwick, Redan from North Berwick and Sahara from Sandwich. Golf architects make frequent visits to the course to study some of its challenging and enduring features. Deceased members' name plates, including those of Henry Clay Frick and Dwight Eisenhower, are kept on the lockers. The 18th hole provides an especially dramatic view of the Taconic Bay.

Sebonac Inlet Road
Southampton, NY 11968
Tel: 631-283-0410
Fax: 631-283-0424

NEAL AUCTION COMPANY
Auction Houses

John Neal, a collector of 19th-century Americana, founded Neal Auction Company in 1984. The South's preeminent antique auction gallery, located in New Orleans' prestigious Uptown neighborhood, is a mecca for fine arts, decorative arts, paintings, furniture, silver porcelain, sculpture, jewelry and Oriental rugs. Bidding may be executed in person or by phone, if presale arrangements are made. The October Louisiana Purchase Sale is highly regarded. Neal has secured record prices for a Louisiana armoire.

4038 Magazine Street
New Orleans, LA 70115
Tel: 504-899-5329

Gare Saint-Lazare, by Edouard Manet

ENTICE.

PAUL MORELLI

COME EXPLORE THE MANY TREASURES NEIMAN MARCUS HAS TO OFFER. FROM THE FINEST IN FASHION TO HEIRLOOM JEWELRY, YOU'LL FIND OUR SELECTION IS UNSURPASSED. AND, AS ALWAYS, WE OFFER LEGENDARY PERSONAL SERVICE AND ATTENTION TO DETAIL. WE INVITE YOU TO SEE FOR YOURSELF WHY IT'S A SHOPPING EXPERIENCE LIKE NO OTHER.

PAUL MORELLI
JEAN MAHIE
CYNTHIA BACH
BVLGARI
PIAGET
ROBERTO COIN
MANOLO BLAHNIK
GIORGIO ARMANI
CHANEL®
KIESELSTEIN-CORD
GUCCI
DOLCE & GABBANA
PRADA
ERMENEGILDO ZEGNA
DAVID YURMAN
VALENTINO
BADGLEY MISCHKA

NEIMAN MARCUS
Fashion

For more than 90 years, Neiman Marcus has served the needs and desires of countless celebrities and society members, including Grace Kelly, Sophia Loren and Gloria Vanderbilt. The preeminent retailer in the country is synonymous with high fashion, good taste, and singular gifts. With 31 stores in 17 states across the country, it is easier than ever to access the world's ultimate wish book. Signature services include the September debut of *The Christmas Book* and the unveiling of the *His and Hers* gifts, both of which are eagerly awaited each year. The famous *His and Hers* retailing phenomenon was born in 1960 with the first gift of a pair of Beechcraft single-engine airplanes. Now a much-loved tradition, each year heralds a new, sometimes whimsical, but always interesting gift, such as *His and Hers* hot-air balloons, Chinese junks, submarines, camels, Egyptian mummy cases, Chinese shar-pei puppies, ermine bathrobes, robots, windmills, and ostriches. During the 1970 recession, however, the firm did not receive any orders for its modern day *Noah's Ark for Pessimists*. Only $500,000, it came complete with a French chef, Swedish masseur, German hairstylist, English valet and Italian couturier. With any luck, they'll bring that one back.

1618 Main Street
Dallas, TX 75201
Tel: 214-741-6911   Fax: 214-742-4904

NEMATI COLLECTION
Antiques

For 40 years, the Nemati name has been recognized for expertise in 16th through 19th century oriental rugs and tapestries. A must-see for the design community, collectors and connoisseurs, the pieces are on display in a spacious, well-lit gallery, featuring a custom-built sliding wall system with 1500 square feet of tapestry viewing area – an industry first. The $8 million collection of art lies at your feet, but staff can arrange for selected pieces to be hung on the walls for viewing.

1059 Third Avenue
New York, NY 10021
Tel: 212-486-6900
Fax: 212-755-8428

NETJETS
Airplanes

In 1986, Richard Santulli, the chairman of Executive Jet, introduced the concept of fractional aircraft ownership. Now owned by Berkshire Hathaway (whose chairman, Warren Buffett, has a plane called 'The Indefensible') NetJets has a corporate clientele that includes Dow Chemical, General Electric, Prudential, Seagram and Texaco. In the last three years, the firm has ordered 632 new aircraft (totaling more than $10 billion) from Boeing, Cessna, Dassault Falcon, Gulfstream and Raytheon. Clients include Michael Mondavi, Pete Sampras and Tiger Woods – three young men in a hurry.

625 North Hamilton Road
Columbus, OH 43219
Tel: 800-821-2299

NEW ORLEANS JAZZ & HERITAGE FESTIVAL
Events

Running from late April until early May, this 10-day jam session has reached beyond its roots to embrace every form of popular music – from Big Band to Zydeco. Recent performers include Sting and Lenny Kravitz as well as stalwarts such as Wynton Marsalis and Chick Corea. The scope of the offerings is unparalleled: thousands of artists play over the course of the festival, and the odd Hollywood celebrity or rock and roller will often jump onstage to help liven things up. The gospel tent is the only place to be if you need Bayou-soul awakening.

336 Camp Street, Suite 250
New Orleans, LA 70130
Tel: 504-522-4786
Fax: 504-558-6121

NEUBERGER BERMAN
Wealth Management

This premier independent investment advisory firm has been helping individuals, families and institutions build wealth, earn income and preserve capital since 1939. In addition to private asset management, the firm also offers clients estate planning and trust services. They have over $55 billion under management (as of May 2000). Legendary investor and art aficionado Roy Neuberger founded the firm in 1939. Since then, Mr. Neuberger has donated over 700 pieces from his personal art collection to the Neuberger Museum at the State University of New York at the Purchase campus.

605 Third Avenue
New York, NY 10158
Tel: 212-476-9000

NEVADA WINE CELLAR & SPIRITS
Wine Merchants

This is the only firm that carries California cult wines in Nevada: the enviable collection includes Cakebread, Hartwell and multiple auction-worthy vintages of Talbott. Caviar, truffles, cigars and some 300 types of beer are also stocked at the store, which is down the road from André Agassi's Vegas base. Partner Sonny Ahuja is known for his "follow-ups" – calling customers to see if they've enjoyed their purchase and scouring the earth for just one more bottle. Clients include entertainer Wayne Newton and boxer Mike Tyson.

8665 West Flamingo Road
Las Vegas, NV 89147
Tel: 702-222-9463   Fax: 702-222-9763

NEW ORLEANS AUCTION GALLERIES

Auction Houses

At New Orleans Auction Galleries, one can arrive empty handed and leave with anything from an American Rococo Revival laminated rosewood sofa to a pair of 19th century painted Paris porcelain jardinieres. This auction house draws in people from around the globe and offers a huge variety of goodies for sale in all shapes and sizes. Jean Vidos owns and runs the operation with flair and passion; an impressive ambassador for the business, she is very enthusiastic about the future of auctions and the role her ambitious company will play.

801 Magazine Street
New Orleans, LA 70130
Tel: 504-566-1849
Fax: 504-566-1851

NEW ORLEANS MUSEUM OF ART

Museums

In 1910, local businessman Isaac Delgado offered $150,000 to the City Park Commission to create a "temple of art for rich and poor alike." Today, visitors find Delgado's dream thriving with 46 galleries housing 40,000 works, valued at over $300 million. NOMA boasts a fine selection of European art including 17th century Dutch, 18th century French and impressionist paintings. Among the Museum's more unusual holdings are beautiful jewel-like watercolor miniature portraits, a stunning Fabergé collection of imperial Easter eggs and a gallery devoted to the works of African-American and Louisiana artists.

One Diboll Circle
New Orleans, LA 70124
Tel: 504-488-2631   Fax: 504-484-6662

NEW YORK CITY BALLET

Events

The New York City Ballet was the idea of Lincoln Kirstein. He envisioned an American ballet where young native dancers could be trained and schooled under the guidance of the world's greatest ballet masters to perform a new, modern repertoire – rather than relying on touring groups of imported artists. Now one of the foremost companies in the world, it has 90 dancers, making it the largest dance organization in America. With an active repertoire of over 150 works, principally choreographed by George Balanchine, Jerome Robbins and Peter Martins, the company has toured to great acclaim all over the world.

20 Lincoln Center
New York, NY 10023
Tel: 212-870-5690   Fax: 212-870-4280

THE NEW YORK BOTANICAL GARDEN

Museums

Delighting all five senses with 250 acres and 27 outdoor gardens, the garden is rightfully described by *Preservation* magazine as "Eden with no end." Only twenty minutes from the center of Manhattan, it provides respite from urban life with its landscaped gardens, virgin forests, ponds and parade of blossoming colors. In 1997, the historic Enid A. Haupt Conservatory opened after a four-year restoration – now offering tropical rain forests, desert galleries and Palms of the Americas Gallery, the largest collection of palm trees under glass in the US. An historical landmark, the Botanical Garden invariably hosts rotating attractions alongside permanent treasures such as the Peggy Rockefeller Rose Garden and the Plant Studies Center, a comprehensive museum of plant life.

200th Street
Bronx, NY 10458-5126
Tel: 718-817-8616   Fax: 718-562-8474

NEW YORK AVIATION

Airplanes

New York Aviation recently celebrated its 23rd year serving the industry. Jack Gentile's chartered planes are used by the Saudi Arabian Royal family and many top dogs in film, music and Wall Street. New York Aviation maintains a world-wide network in over 48 countries – they can have a jet or piston powered aircraft or helicopter anywhere on the globe within a few hours to serve customers in very short order. As Gentile says, "Money is not a concern for our clients; speed, service, and quality are."

La Guardia Airport
Flushing, NY 11371
Tel: 718-279-4000
Fax: 718-279-3814

NEW YORK PALACE HOTEL

Hotels

During the Gilded Age, Henry Villard was one of Manhattan's most celebrated architects. Today, his landmark mansion houses Le Cirque 2000. Next door, a sleek 55 story tower is home to one of the finest hotels in the city. Try the Triplex Suites, each with a top-tier terrace, solarium, private roof garden and circular staircase. At the 7000 square-foot fitness center, cross-training sneakers, personal TV monitors and cordless phones are complimentary – proof that everyone loves a bargain!

455 Madison Avenue
New York, NY 10022
Tel: 212-888-7000

NEW YORK YACHT CLUB

Private Clubs

The preeminent yacht club in the United States accepts reciprocity from only two clubs: the St. Francis in San Francisco and the Royal Thames in London. Yachts are kept in Newport, Rhode Island. The historically listed building is a prominent feature on club row. Its facade is carved to resemble the front side of a galleon; the walls and ceiling of the dining room create the effect of dining in the hull of a boat, with their dark curved oak. The club now admits lady members despite the loud protest of some of the older, saltier members who lived out their last days in the upstairs bedrooms and enjoyed coming down for drinks dressed only in robe and slippers.

37 West 44th Street
New York, NY 10036
Tel: 212-382-1000   Fax: 212-302-1295

NEWHOUSE GALLERIES

Antiques

Newhouse Galleries was established in St. Louis in 1878. The Gallery moved to New York in the 1920s and to its present location on East 66th Street in 1970. Meg Newhouse Kirkpatric is the fourth generation of her family to own the gallery. It specializes in Old Master paintings but has recently hosted more contemporary work, particularly the sporting paintings of Henry Koehler and top quality botanical art.

19 East 66th Street
New York, NY 10021
Tel: 212-879-2700

NICHOLAS VARNEY JEWELS

Jewelry and Watches   *Rising Star*

Nicholas Varney creates jewelry to suit the needs, and charm the imagination, of the world's most elegant and active women. Inspired by nature, Varney's jewels are sumptuous and elegant, yet spontaneous and whimsical. Soft pink pearls, brilliant diamonds, cobalt sapphires and stones with hues rarely seen in nature are used to create these veritable works of art. Whether brooch or necklace, each piece is crafted by the finest hands in the world with great attention paid to both quality and style. Born into a family with sophisticated taste in design, a young Nicholas Varney dreamed of one day creating such extraordinary works – indeed, the dream has come true.

2400 Presidential Way, Suite 1702
West Palm Beach, FL 33401
Tel: 561-242-0532   Fax: 212-759-0739

NEWTON VINEYARDS

Winemakers

As if the beautiful St. Helena setting wasn't enough, the wine making facilities at this 560 acre estate are housed in a pagoda within formal Japanese gardens. Newton's unfiltered Chardonnay is among the top five Chardonnays produced in California, and their Merlot and Viognier are both excellent.

2555 Madrona Avenue
St. Helena, CA 94574
Tel: 707-963-9000

NICK AND TONI'S

Restaurants

Husband and wife team Jeff Salaway and Toni Ross opened this Hamptons institution in 1988. Its enduring popularity is due in large part to the upscale Mediterranean cooking, fueled by an organic garden out back. A high celebrity quotient has certainly done no harm either; don't be surprised to see Tom Hanks and Steven Spielberg discussing an upcoming film project here.

136 North Main Street
East Hampton, NY 11937
Tel: 631-324-3550   Fax: 631-324-7001

FREDERICK A. NEWMAN, M.D.

Cosmetic Surgeons

Trained at Yale, Harvard and the Institute of Reconstructive Plastic Surgery at New York University Medical Center, Dr. Frederick A. Newman offers his patients an extensive menu of surgical options. He specializes in facial and breast cosmetic and reconstructive surgery, and was one of the first physicians in the country to perform liposuction. Certified by the American Board of Plastic Surgery, he is also a member of the American Society for Aesthetic Plastic Surgery.

Two Overhill Road
Scarsdale, NY 10583
Tel: 914-723-0400   Fax: 914-723-0404

NEWPORT ART MUSEUM

Museums

Since 1916, the Newport Art Museum has collected, preserved, exhibited and interpreted historic and contemporary art of the highest quality. Former home of railroad mogul John Griswold, the Griswold House contains six galleries and is a work of art in itself, designed by Richard Morris Hunt. Highlights in the collection include works by Fitz Hugh Lane, George Innes and Howard Gardiner Cushing. At the annual Summer Gala and Artists' Ball every spring, artists donate a work of art in lieu of purchasing a ticket and the works are sold at a silent auction during the ball.

76 Bellevue Avenue
Newport, RI 02840
Tel: 401-848-8200
Fax: 401-848-8205

NEWPORT MUSIC FESTIVAL

Events

Set in a town transformed by the great robber barons of the 19th century, Rhode Island's Newport Music Festival has made use of the former palaces of the Vanderbilts and their friends, turning them into elegant concert halls, for more than 30 years. The two-and-a-half-week festival, held in mid-July, is renowned for launching international artists. Director Mark Malkovich researches unusual music, planning each of the 60 classical programs.

P.O. Box 3300
Newport, RI 02840
Tel: 401-846-1133   Fax: 401-849-1857

NEWSEUM

Museums

Experience breaking news as it happens on a 126-foot-long video monitor. Compare how 70 newspaper front pages report today's top stories. Try your hand at being a TV news correspondent for the fictitious newspaper, *The Daily Miracle*. Trace the evolution of news from the spoken stories of ancient times to today's worldwide information explosion. Newseum showcases a remarkable display of historic newspapers, magazines and broadcasts from around the globe. The flagship center in Virginia includes a theater and a cyber café. The New York branch offers an outstanding series of talks, exhibitions and seminars throughout the year.

1101 Wilson Boulevard
Arlington, VA 22209
Tel: 888-NEWSEUM
Fax: 703-284-3777

NIEBAUM COPPOLA

Winemakers

When Oakville Estates went bankrupt in 1975 moviemaker Francis Ford Coppola made the sellers an offer they couldn't refuse; he wanted to make "just enough wine to drink." With the legendary André Telitscheff as advisor, Coppola created a red with a blend of Cabernet Sauvignon, Merlot and Cabernet Franc. Called Rubicon, it is aged 6 years (3 years in oak barrels, 3 years in the bottle) before release. Back in the 1980s it was rather rustic, although the 1994 has 14% alcohol and is full, well-rounded with a spicy finish.

1991 St. Helena Highway
Rutherford, CA 84573
Tel: 707-968-1100

NOBU

Restaurants

Nobu's eponymous restaurant, owned in partnership with Robert DeNiro and Drew Nieporent, opened in New York to wide acclaim in 1994, where it has been dishing up Nobu Matsuhisa's innovative Japanese food ever since. Where else can you sit amidst 50,000 black river stones, birch tree trunks and countless celebrities while enjoying the creations of the most celebrated Japanese chef in America?

105 Hudson Street
New York, NY 10013
Tel: 212-219-0500   Fax: 212-219-1441

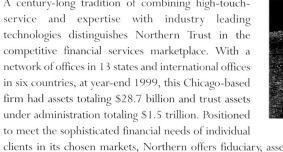

NORTON MUSEUM OF ART
Museums

Ralph and Caroline Norton opened their eponymous museum with hopes of sharing their extensive personal collection of painting and sculpture with the public. At the time of his death in 1953, Mr. Norton had collected over 500 significant works of art. With further acquisitions and donations, the museum now has over 4500 works, concentrated in French Impressionist, Post-Impressionist and American art from the early 1900s to the present. The collection includes works by Monet, Picasso, Gauguin and O'Keeffe. The museum is also renowned for its distinguished collection of Chinese bronze, jade, ceramics and Buddhist sculpture – the finest collection of Oriental art in the United States.

1451 S. Olive Avenue
West Palm Beach, FL 33401
Tel: 561-832-5196

NO. 9 PARK
Restaurants

Nationally known Chef/owner Barbara Lynch offers a menu of European classic country fare featuring cuisine from southern France and Italy. Located on Boston's historic Beacon Hill (across from the Massachusetts State House,) No. 9 Park is casually elegant with 1940's décor and rich tones of green, blues and browns. No. 9 Park also offers a full service bar and a café area with a separate menu. See why No. 9 Park was recently named one of the "Top 25 New Restaurants in America" by *Bon Appétit*, "Top 50 Restaurants in America" by *Travel and Leisure* and "Best New Restaurant, 1999" in Boston by *Food & Wine* magazine.

9 Park Street
Boston, MA 02108
Tel: 617-742-9991   Fax: 617-742-9993

NORTHERN TRUST
Wealth Management

A century-long tradition of combining high-touch-service and expertise with industry leading technologies distinguishes Northern Trust in the competitive financial services marketplace. With a network of offices in 13 states and international offices in six countries, at year-end 1999, this Chicago-based firm had assets totaling $28.7 billion and trust assets under administration totaling $1.5 trillion. Positioned to meet the sophisticated financial needs of individual clients in its chosen markets, Northern offers fiduciary, asset custody, investment management, tax and estate planning, brokerage and private banking services. Northern's Wealth Management Group meets the complex financial needs of 226 high net worth families in the U.S. and worldwide – each typically with more than $100 million in assets – who often employ multiple money managers for global investment. In 1999, Wealth Management administered assets in excess of $52 billion, $14.5 billion of which was under Northern's management. *Worth* magazine's 1999 Reader's Choice Survey named Northern Trust the best private bank in the country, "because it makes a practice of delivering on its promises."

50 South La Salle Street
Chicago, IL 60675
Tel: 312-630 6000   Fax: 312-630-1512

NOVA LIMOUSINE SERVICE
Chauffeur Services

If you don't like cinnamon on your cappuccino, Nova knows. Prefer *The Wall Street Journal* to local papers? You've got it. Almost like a concierge service, president Anthony Brusdelins handles special requests such as fresh flowers and dinner reservations with grace. His firm offers the finest automobiles and every luxury amenity imagined.

15201 Dallas Parkway
Dallas TX, 75001
Tel: 972-490-3333
Fax: 972-233-8125

NURSERY LINES
Specialty Shops

The fashionable baby can find his or her complete wardrobe as well as nursery furnishings at this Lexington Avenue outpost. The store is no stranger to supermoms: Madonna and model Vendela, as well as the Bronfman family, come here for the classic infantwear, much of it with a dash of Italian style. Handknit items are also available, as well as custom nursery design by appointment.

1034 Lexington Avenue
New York, NY 10021
Tel: 212-396-4445   Fax: 212-396-4870

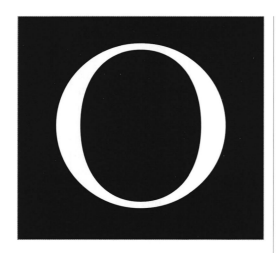

O'HARA GALLERY

Art Dealers

Ruth O'Hara's love for art has become a family affair. Along with her husband Barney (the "secret weapon") and her two sons, she collects contemporary masters and impressionist works, including major works by Chagall, Calder and Miró. Formerly of the FAR gallery on Madison Avenue, the New York native boasts 40 years of experience and expertise. Recent shows have included work by Jean Michel Basquiat, Roy Lichtenstein, Pablo Picasso and Andy Warhol.

41 East 57th Street, Suite 1302
New York, NY 10022
Tel: 212-355-3330

OAKLAND HILLS COUNTRY CLUB

Golf Clubs

Even the most competitive professionals regard Oaklands with awe. After capturing the 1951 U.S. Open with a final round of 67 on the South Course, Ben Hogan uttered his famous line, "I am glad I brought this course, the monster, to its knees." The gently rolling (if treacherous) hills include a North Course and a clubhouse modeled after George Washington's Mt. Vernon Estate.

3951 West Maple Road
Bloomfield Hills, MI 48301
Tel: 248-258-1698

OAKMONT COUNTRY CLUB

Golf Clubs

Oakmont has hosted more championships than any other course in the country – a figure that includes seven U.S. Opens. Distinguishing features of the course include a 9th green so large that it doubles as the practice green, and the infamous Church Pew bunkers, which attract errant shots on the 3rd and 4th holes. In fact, the course originally featured over 350 bunkers.

1233 Hulton Road
Oakmont, PA 15139
Tel: 412-661-2360

OCEAN REEF CLUB

Hotels

If you have a face that everyone in the world recognizes, you vacation at Ocean Reef Club. The only guests at the resort are members and their invitees, which makes it feel like a pleasant family reunion. It is very difficult to secure a membership here, but once you're in you will never know how you survived before – there are two golf courses, 11 tennis courts, indoor and outdoor pools, a marina and a private airstrip.

31 Ocean Reef Drive
Key Largo, FL 33037
Tel: 305-367-2611   Fax: 305-367-2224

THE OLD HOUSE

Restaurants

Originally from Guadalajara, Chef Martin Ramos was named Santa Fe's Chef of the Year for 2000 and his restaurant, located in the acclaimed Eldorado Hotel, has zealous locals and visitors clamoring for more. The menu is sophisticated and fearless – from pan-seared crab cakes with a lemon-tomato remoulade and green papaya to Venison enchiladas, Ramos incorporates fresh ingredients throughout. A veteran of New York's Le Cirque, Ramos looks set to prosper for many years in Santa Fe.

309 West San Francisco
Santa Fe, NM 87501
Tel: 505-988-4455   Fax: 505-995-4555

OLD LOUISVILLE INN

Hotels

A private residence until 1960, this lovely old inn still has the charm of a wealthy friend's country home. Each of the 10 bedrooms is adorned in antique quilts, Victorian furniture, bay windows and working fireplaces. The Celebration suite has a king sized canopy bed and oversized whirlpool. Many of the bathrooms still have their original fixtures.

1359 South Third Street
Louisville, KY 40208
Tel: 502-635-1574   Fax: 502-637-5892

OLDE HOPE ANTIQUES

Antiques

Founded on July 4, 1976, Olde Hope Antiques occupies a carriage house in the quaint Bucks County town of New Hope. This is not a cosmopolitan emporium of Chippendale and Saxony, but rather a treasure trove of 'sophisticated country' Americana. Painted 18th and 19th century furniture and folk art are the main draws - also quilts, hooked rugs and portraits.

6465 Lower York Road
New Hope, PA 18938
Tel: 215-862-5055   Fax: 215-862-0550

THE OLDE PINK HOUSE

Restaurants

Built in 1771, the Habersham House was renamed the Olde Pink House when the soft, native brick began to bleed through the plastered walls and changed the color of the Mansion from white to bright pink. In 1992, the William Balish Family completely renovated the property, restoring it to its original grandeur. Today, Olde Pink House offers the pleasure of top class southern cuisine in a space which smacks of history. Ask to sit by the fireplace.

23 Abercorn Street
Savannah, GA 31401
Tel: 912-232-4286   Fax: 912-231-1931

L'OLIVIER FLORAL ATELIER

Florists

As the name indicates, Olivier Giugni's Upper East Side shop is not simply a florist, but a real workshop. Sculptural principles govern the arrangements, which are based on a 'frame' of exotic greens to which flowers are added. Having trained under Pierre Cardin (think space and structure), Giugni established his New York store five years ago and has since acquired a significant clientele: the yearly Colbert Gala employs Giugni's talents, as does the neighboring Restaurant Daniel. Specialty of the house: landscaped orchid gardens.

19 East 76th Street
New York, NY 10021
Tel: 212-774-7676   Fax: 212-774-0058

OBER, ONET & ASSOCIATES

Party Organizers and Caterers

Polly Onet is one of the more successful young event planners in New York, but one rarely reads about the glittering soirées she organizes in the gossip columns. Why? Because most of her customers are in the mega-wealthy category. They are the sort of people who would prefer to be in the front line of a nuclear war than the dizzy heights of *Page Six*. Onet's more visible clients include John Kluge, George and Susan Soros, and David and Julia Koch. Her new office in Southampton coordinates event needs on Long Island's East End.

205 East 95th Street
New York, NY 10128
Tel: 212-876-6775

OSTERIA DEL CIRCO
Restaurants

The Maccioni family have created another legend with this restaurant just south of Central Park. As the name implies, Osteria del Circo is like dining under a sophisticated European big top – with owners and brothers, Mario, Marco and Mauro as ringmasters, father Sirio, proprietor of Le Cirque and his wife Egidiana, the supervising chef. Executive Chef Alessandro Giuntoli's menu is as creative as the setting – combining the traditional home-cooking styles of Mrs. Maccioni with his own Tuscan traditions. Giuntoli describes his dishes as "real Tuscan food with a New York dress." Like its younger namesake in Las Vegas, Circo is playfully designed by Adam Tihany. The colorful decor is innovative, whimsical and vibrant. But unlike a circus, the interior is comfortable, the fabrics are luxurious and the custom-designed Italian chairs are deep and seductive. Incidentally, Circo received *Wine Spectator's* 2000 "Award for Excellence" for its outstanding wine list, compiled by wine director, Philip Bohorfoush.
120 West 55th Street
New York, NY 10019
Tel: 212-265-3636

ONE PICO
Restaurants

Located in Shutters on the Beach, the most luxurious hotel in Santa Monica, this waterfront dining room is open, airy, formal but soothing – a floor to ceiling limestone fireplace, amber-colored wood floors, clean, contemporary lines and a tall beamed ceiling provide a stunning backdrop for Desi Szonntagh's impressive California-American cooking. Formerly of Le Cirque in New York, his Chilean sea bass (served with black risotto) is sublime. Ask for an oceanfront view.
1 Pico Boulevard
Santa Monica, CA 90405
Tel: 310-587-1717

ONVIEW.COM
Websites

Onview.com has brought together over 190 of the most prestigious galleries and dealers in the world to list works of art for sale online. Dealer members include: Newhouse Galleries, Matthew Marks Gallery and Meridian Fine Art, among other bold names who belong to exclusive fine art associations. The site features works by artists like Gary Windogram, William Wegman and contemporary artist Marina Abramovic. Each work purchased from the website is certified authentic and just in case the Picasso doesn't suit the dining room, there is a 15 day return policy.
20 West 20th Street, Suite 904
New York, NY 10011
Tel: 212-337-8500

OPUS ONE
Winemakers

Opus One was the brainchild of Robert Mondavi and Philippe de Rothschild. Its emergence (and, at the time, stunning expense) paved the way for the ultra-premium Napa Valley wines that now command prices equal to their pedigreed French counterparts. A recent $26 million facility that combines elegant simplicity with cutting-edge technology has updated the winery without abandoning the fundamentals: the grapes are still harvested with utmost care, grown in small clusters and selected according to stringent criteria.
7900 St. Helena Highway
Oakville, CA 94562
Tel: 707-944-9442

L'ORANGERIE
Restaurants

If you're looking for wealth, power and beauty, you're in the right place. Just 6000 miles from Paris, Gerard Ferry's L'Orangerie does its best to dispel that geographic reality. Amidst a sea of moguls and movie stars, Chef Ludovic Lefebvre's menu offers haute cuisine that smacks of simplicity, freshness and flavor – the same sort of qualities that Hollywood bigshots are looking for in the blockbuster scripts they discuss over lunch.
903 North La Cienega Boulevard
Los Angeles, CA 90069
Tel: 310-652-9770   Fax: 310-652-8870

ORCHID AT MAUNA LANI
Hotels

Water, water, everywhere – the Orchid at Mauna Lani may be on the desert side of Hawaii's Big Island, but its beachfront location and 10,000 square-foot pool tend to dispel that impression. (By the way, the desert can be a good thing: the other side of the island receives rain almost every day of the year). Built to Ritz-Carlton standards but Hawaiianized by new management, the hotel marries Italian marble bathrooms with Polynesian flair. The Presidential Suite wraps around the entire top floor and features its own baby grand piano.
1 North Kaniku Drive
Big Island Kaholi, HI 96743
Tel: 808-885-2000   Fax: 808-885-1064

OREGON BACH FESTIVAL
Events

Described by the *Los Angeles Times* as "a musical experience virtually without equal in America," the Oregon Bach Festival has provided the Pacific Northwest with its Bach fix for 31 years. Presided over by conductor and artistic director Helmuth Rilling, the three-week festival combines works by Bach with other baroque and classical pieces, as well as modern and contemporary work by artists both established and new. Set on the rolling campus of the University of Oregon, this is one of summer's musical highlights.
1257 University of Oregon
Eugene, OR 97403
Tel: 541-346-5666

THE PACIFIC-UNION CLUB
Private Clubs

In 1889, the Pacific Club and the Union Club consolidated to form the Pacific-Union Club, which is now the fifth oldest city club in the United States. After the earthquake and fire of 1906, this distinctly private entity purchased what remained of the Flood Mansion on Nob Hill for its clubhouse. Fully renovated in 1999, today the club houses a dining room, bar, reading rooms, private dining rooms, a formal library, squash courts, a swimming pool, Masseur's station, dry sauna and 29 bedrooms. Purely social, the Pacific-Union Club has 950 members.

1000 California Street
San Francisco, CA 94108
Tel: 415-775-1234   Fax: 415-673-0104

PACE WILDENSTEIN
Art Dealers

This super-power of the modern and contemporary art world, which celebrated its 40th anniversary in 2000, is known for presenting highly-acclaimed exhibitions on a monthly basis in its two New York venues. Artists such as Jim Dine, Agnes Martin, Elizabeth Murray, Claes Oldenburg and Coosje van Bruggen are among those represented, as well as the estates of Alexander Calder, Henry Moore, Pablo Picasso and Mark Rothko.

32 East 57th Street
New York, NY 10022
Tel: 212-421-3292

PAHLMEYER
Winemakers

Pahlmeyer was catapulted to stardom in 1991 when its Chardonnay was ranked best in the nation. Its popularity soared higher still after a supporting role in the movie *Disclosure*, opposite Michael Douglas and Demi Moore. Colorful owner Jayson Pahlmeyer (a qualified attorney) describes the wines as "industrial strength" to convey their abundance of viscous fruit flavors, creamy oak and intense aromas. The red Bordeaux Blend is incredibly concentrated. Pahlmeyer is planting a further 75 acres of vines in the new year – good news for wine lovers.

PO Box 2410
Napa, CA 94558
Tel: 707-255-2321
Fax: 707-255-6786

LE PALAIS
Restaurants

Casinos can certainly help you test your luck in the seaside town of Atlantic City, but cunning visitors head straight to The Resorts (the city's first gaming establishment) to sample the culinary delights of Le Palais, where nothing is left to chance. Critics adore this French restaurant and various publications have cited it among the best in town. The menu has evolved from strictly French to accommodate more continental flavors. Meanwhile, it still offers some of the finest cuisine, service and ambiance along the Jersey shore.

1133 Boardwalk
Atlantic City, NJ 08401
Tel: 609-340-6400
Fax: 609-340-7919

PALM BEACH INTERNATIONAL ART & ANTIQUE FAIR
Events

The Palm Beach International Art & Antique Fair has rapidly become an important fixture in the world of arts and antiques. This year the fair will run from February 1st through to February 11th with 77 world class dealers exhibiting furniture, paintings, Asian art, jewelry, carpets, tapestries and books in the International Pavilion. Popular local exhibitors include Greenleaf & Crosby and Richter of Palm Beach. Those coming from further afield include Stockinger of Munich and Lily Beer, who hails from Buenos Aires.

3725 South East Ocean Boulevard
Sewalls Point, FL 34996
Tel: 561-220-2690
Fax: 561-220-3180

PALM BEACH POLO AND COUNTRY CLUB
Polo Clubs

This winter headquarters for international high-goal players—all 14 polo fields of it—also offers one of the finest golf courses in the area. The polo club regularly hosts the prestigious U.S. Open Championship, and equestrians enjoy a world-class winter festival that attracts sponsorship from heavyweights like Revlon, Cadillac and Ralph Lauren. The club has a high social cachet–Prince Charles has played in a Rolex Gold Cup tournament here, and regular spectators include Jimmy Buffett and fashion designer Calvin Klein.

11199 Polo Club Road
Wellington, FL 33414
Tel: 561-798-7110
Fax: 561-798-7125

PALMER JOHNSON YACHTS
Powerboats & Yachts

Palmer Johnson has manufactured more than 350 luxury mega-yachts over the last eight decades. From its headquarters in the Great lakes at Sturgeon Bay, the firm has emerged as one of the most innovative high-end, private yacht builders in the world. All-aluminum hulled boats are strong as steel and as light as fiberglass – their shallow draft and hull strength allow them to carry additional fuel and navigate shallow waters. The 195-foot Baronessa, commissioned by a high-profile Asian businessman, demonstrates the firm's ability to produce luxurious, seaworthy mega-yachts on budget and on schedule.

61 Michigan Street
Sturgeon Bay, WI, 54235
Tel: 920-743-4412
Fax: 920-743-3381

PASCAL
Restaurants

Reminiscent of the finest restaurants in Cote d'Azur, Pascal Olhats' eponymous eatery is elegant and warm, decorated with an abundance of multicolored roses and rich mahogany. His contemporary French cuisine reflects the perfectionist behind it. The sautéed foie gras and a traditional crab soufflé are particularly sublime. Superb cuisine coupled with razor sharp service justifies the long wait for a weekend reservation.

1000 North Bristol Street
Newport Beach, CA 92660
Tel: 949-752-0107
Fax: 949-752-4942

THE PENINSULA BEVERLY HILLS
Hotels

The only AAA Five Diamond and Mobil Five Star hotel in Southern California (for the seventh year), the Peninsula Beverly Hills consistently strives to maintain its reputation for unsurpassed service. 16 private villas nestled among award-winning, lush tropical gardens, and the recently expanded, incredible spa make this hotel a luxurious oasis in the heart of Beverly Hills. The Belvedere was named the best hotel restaurant in Southern California by the 1999 *Zagat* survey. Guests staying in one of the hotel's premier suites or villas – the California Villa, the Peninsula Villa, the Grand Deluxe Suite, the Patio Suite, or the Peninsula Suite – are extended the use of their own personal 2000 Audi A8, for the duration of their stay, at no additional charge.

9882 Little Santa Monica Boulevard
Beverly Hills, CA 90212
Tel: 310-551-2888   Fax: 310-788-2319

PAUL, HASTINGS, JANOFSKY & WALKER
Law Firms

This Los Angeles-based firm has 600 attorneys in nine offices around the world. It specializes in cross-border transactions and disputes in East Asia. Media and telecommunications work is also high on the list of specialties, while business and employment law, real estate, tax and litigation are solid strengths, as expected. The firm closed out the 90s with the second-largest high-yield debt issue of the decade, Charter Communications' $3.6 billion bond.

555 South Flower Street
Los Angeles, CA 90071
Tel: 213-683-6000

PAUL KASMIN GALLERY
Art Dealers

Last October, Paul Kasmin moved into a brand new gallery in New York's Chelsea District. Son of the London art dealer John Kasmin, Paul has carved out a niche for himself in New York City. With a celebrated roster of artists including Alessandro Twombly, Nancy Rubins and Aaron Rose, the 38 year old's clients include Emily Fisher Landau and music mogul Gil Friesen.

293 10th Avenue
New York, NY 10001
Tel: 212-563-4474

PATINA
Restaurants

Chef Walter Manzke serves French-Californian cuisine in this award-winning restaurant, which remains popular among Hollywood's notoriously fickle hotshots. Post-renovation it now seats 115, smartly spread throughout four dining rooms. Owned by Joachim and Christine Splichal, their catering offshoot, Patina Catering, offers a full party-planning service for everything from dinner for two to lavish film premieres.

5955 Melrose Avenue
Los Angeles, CA 90038
Tel: 323-960-1760   Fax: 323-467-0215

PASTIS
Restaurants   *Rising Star*

Before it opened, this modest café in New York's Meatpacking District was subject to the sort of hysteria which accompanies a pop star's arrest for indecent exposure. Owner Keith McNally has become something of a celebrity in New York – principally, one suspects, because Balthazar survived the cruel winds of change to emerge as stylish, not just fashionable. Quite an achievement, really. This affable Englishman in New York certainly knows how to play the Pied Piper: Pastis is no better than dozens of New York bistros, but McNally's manicured masses just keep coming.

9 Ninth Avenue
New York, NY 10014
Tel: 212-929-4844

PEABODY MUSEUM OF NATURAL HISTORY
Museums

Yale's Peabody Museum is a leading paleontology and geology research museum. Workshops and laboratories in the fields of paleontology, archaeology, zoology, and evolutionary biology make Peabody a working museum and a major source of science education for New Haven. Other permanent displays include exhibits on Ancient Egypt, Native Americans, Pacific cultures and a full-scale, mounted Brontosaurus.

170 Whitney Avenue
New Haven, CT 06520
Tel: 203-432-5050
Fax: 203-432-9816

PAVILLION AGENCY
Employment Agencies

For 38 years, co-owners Keith & Clifford Greenhouse have served the needs of the influential and high profile, providing sevices from nannies, housekeepers and chefs, to butlers, chauffeurs and personal assistants. Whether it's a nanny for the kids or a butler for your good self, this small family-run company is all about discretion.

15 East 40th Street, Suite 900
New York, NY 10016
Tel: 212-889-6609

PAUL STUART

Fashion

Since 1938, this family-owned firm has been providing high quality tailored clothing for discerning men and women. The style has changed little (but then, style never goes out of fashion). You might describe it as *Town & Country* meets the best of Europe, or as new world aesthetics and old world tailoring. Designers scour the globe in search of fine fabrics to create garments worthy of pampered, upscale clients, like the Time Warner honcho who wanted boxing glove cufflinks custom-made in honor of a title fight.

Madison Avenue & 45th Street
New York, NY 10017
Tel: 212-682-0320   Fax: 212-983-5871

THE PEAKS RESORT AND GOLDEN DOOR SPA

Spas and Clinics

The ski town of Telluride is home to The Peaks Resort, a luxurious getaway in the heart of the Rockies. With 42,000 square feet of spa over five levels, its Golden Door spa offers 44 treatment rooms, an Olympic size lap pool, squash, racquetball and a climbing wall. Sybarites who aren't interested in saunas or jacuzzis will be pleased to learn that each weekend the town of Telluride is popular with balloonists during the summer months; the lodge affords a superb vantage point for viewing these magnificent contraptions.

136 Country Club Drive
Telluride, CO 81435
Tel: 970-728-6800   Fax: 970-728-6175

PEBBLE BEACH RESORTS

Golf Clubs

For golfers, there are few places that compare to Pebble Beach. Site of the AT&T Pro-Am, in which Samuel L. Jackson, Clint Eastwood and President George Bush have all participated, the famous Links course is considered among the top five in the world. Jack Nicklaus, Tom Kite and Tom Watkins have all made history here. Reputations are made on the par three 17th and par five 18th holes. Almost as famous as the course, the pub at Pebble Beach, the Tap Room, has won various awards for its French cuisine.

2700 Seventeen Mile Drive
Pebble Beach, CA 93953
Tel: 800-654-9300
Fax: 831-644-7960

THE PENINSULA NEW YORK

Hotels

The Peninsula adds an elegant Belle Époque touch to the cosmopolitan flair of Fifth Avenue. Travelers and savvy New Yorkers alike flock to the hotel's outdoor roof-terraces to admire the impressive vistas up and down the avenue, while relaxing with a perfectly prepared cocktail. The hotel's tri-level spa and fitness center provide additional stress relief in the form of numerous beauty treatments and alternative healing therapies. Back in 1998, a $45 million renovation restored the property's original architecture and added a classic contemporary feel to each of its 55 suites, which are now brighter and grander than ever. The Peninsula Suite, with its spectacular views and large parlor is, without a doubt, the loveliest of them all. Of the hotel's three restaurants and bars, Adrienne's is the most intimate; Swiss chef Oliver Dudler serves fantastic French dishes to hotel guests and locals six nights a week.

700 Fifth Avenue
New York, NY 10019
Tel: 212-956-2888   Fax: 212-903-3949

JON PERLMAN, M.D.

Cosmetic Surgeons

Specializing in breast augmentation, implants, lifts, reductions, tummy tucks, liposuction, and face-lifts, Dr. Jon Perlman is a leading member of the American Society for Aesthetic Plastic Surgeons. The New York City native is known for practically invisible incisions and exceptional follow-up care (all post-op visits are included in the price of the surgery). A clinical professor of plastic surgery at UCLA, Perlman serves primarily a celebrity clientele, offering private waiting rooms for those who need to dodge the press. Call about a month in advance; the office is always busy but tries to accommodate patients at short notice.

414 North Camden Drive, Suite 800
Beverly Hills, CA 90210
Tel: 310-854-0031
Fax: 310-275-5079

PERNA LUXURY REAL ESTATE

Property Consultants

For the last five years now, discerning clients have been counseled by 27 hand picked national real estate brokers from Perna Luxury Real Estate, who work in conjunction with 11 different international brokerage firms. Lou and Jane Perna, the company's owners, have a wealth of experience, both in the real estate industry and in Lou's case as a *Fortune 500* Executive. Both are avid golfers who reside in Desert Mountain, not far from John Wayne's old ranch in Nogolas, which is one among many palatial properties they have brokered the sale of.

8787 East Pinnacle Peak Road
Scottsdale, AZ 85225
Tel: 480-515-0100
Fax: 480-515-0200

PERSONAL CONCIERGE INTERNATIONAL

Specialty Shops   *Rising Star*

Pascal Riffaud founded PCI in 1994 after spending many years as a concierge himself – at the St. Regis in New York, the Ritz in Paris and the Four Seasons in Hamburg. No stranger to unique requests, Riffaud once found a five foot tall Tweety bird for a client's daughter's fifth birthday. Later that day he procured sold-out VIP, court side basketball tickets for the same client. A network of exclusive restaurant contacts allows Riffaud to secure reservations at the hottest restaurants – don't be surprised if you end up sitting at the best table too. That's the sort of service which Riffaud will provide as a matter of course.

575 Lexington Avenue, 4th Floor
New York, NY 10022
Tel: 212-527-7575
Fax: 212-527-7576

PETE DYE GOLF CLUB

Golf Clubs

This six-year old course was built on the site of a former coal mine. The legendary Pete Dye transformed it into a 7248 yard par 72 course which includes teemarkers built from the coal railroad and a trip through an underground coal mine between the 6th and 7th holes. If, as some members claim, walking the course is a religious experience, then approaching the tough par 4399-yard 17th hole is like coming face-to-face with the creator.

Aaron Smith Drive
Bridgeport, WV 26330
Tel: 304-842-2801
Fax:304-842-4323

PETER COPPOLA SALON

Hair and Beauty

Peter Coppola's philosophy has changed little since he opened his first salon on Long Island in 1970: "I love making women look beautiful." That's quite a claim, but then, satisfied clients include Julia Roberts, Elle McPherson, Meg Ryan and Cindy Crawford. Christopher John, Madonna's exclusive colorist for the past 6 years, works at the salon five days a week and Barbra Streisand's stylist, Burton, flies in for two weeks a month from Los Angeles. Coppola's team includes 31 stylists and colorists, two nail technicians and a waxing specialist. He also has two salons in Boca Raton, and one in Westport.

746 Madison Avenue
New York, NY 10021
Tel: 212-988-9404   Fax: 212-988-9691

PERFORMANCE SKI

Specialty Shops

Energetic young husband and wife team, Lee Keating and Tom Bowers (he is a former skiing champion), run this small shop adjacent to the Gondola in the heart of Aspen. Popular with visiting luminaries like media magnate Rupert Murdoch, it is packed to the rafters with all the top names in skiwear. Incidentally, Lee's brother, Michael, is equally at home with designer comfort – he runs the town's Gucci store.

408 South Hunter Street
Aspen, CO 81611
Tel: 970-925-8657
Fax: 970-920-3911

PETER MARINO & ASSOCIATES

Architects and Interior Designers

Peter Marino creates super-opulent interiors for discerning clients (Gianni Agnelli, Ron Perelman, Bernard Arnault) often mixing antiques and artworks from several different centuries. Marino made his name as an architect, working on big retail projects like Barney's in Los Angeles, and the Giorgio Armani store on Madison Avenue. With its headquarters on Gotham's Upper East Side, the firm also maintains offices in London, Philadelphia and East Hampton.

150 East 58th Street,
New York, NY 10022
Tel: 212-752-5444   Fax: 212-759-3727

PETER CUMMIN & ASSOCIATES

Architects and Interior Designers

In addition to the landscape architect's duty to harmonize horticulture with architecture, Peter Cummin's design philsophy raises the ante: the landscape must look "as if it's always been there." This does not mean, of course, that trees and vines must run wild; formal Italianate gardens are a specialty. Indeed, classical influence abounds in the ten-year-old firm's work, although projects as diverse as adobes and New England shingle houses have also been executed with great success.

39 Prentice Williams Road
Stonington, CT 06378
Tel: 860-572-4111   Fax: 860-535-3624

PETER MICHAEL

Winemakers

After a lifetime in international business, Briton Sir Peter Michael bought 600 acres in the hills north of Knights Valley. "You need to return to the soil" says Sir Peter, "It's a pretty basic human feeling." Michael's Chardonnay and Cabernet Sauvignon are both world class. Ralph Hersom, Wine Director at Le Cirque 2000, says that his Sauvignon Blanc, L'Après Midi, is often overlooked, but "clearly outstanding." As the gallant Sir Peter puts it, "Of the many businesses I have founded, this is the only one that carries my family name. I hope it will remain a legacy for generations to come."

12400 Ida Clayton Road
Calistoga, CA 94515
Tel: 707-942-4459

PETERSEN AVIATION

Airplanes   *Best Kept Secret*

If you're in the Los Angeles area and have a sudden need to be whisked to Tokyo or London in a Gulfstream G4SP, this full-service aviation company will accommodate you with little notice. On board you are treated to important passenger amenities like Krug champagne and beluga-and-buckwheat blinis! With twin-engine jet helicopters for local service, light jets for transcontinental jaunts and a 1998 *Pilots Choice Award*, Petersen also sells and manages personal aircraft for private clients.

7155 Valjean Avenue
Van Nuys, CA 91406
Tel: 800-451-7270   Fax: 818-902-9386

THE PHOENICIAN
Hotels
With one of the most spectacular natural settings in the world as a backdrop, The Phoenician is a 250 acre luxury resort that has just about everything, including an award-winning French restaurant, a cactus garden and a $6 million art collection representing European, Asian and American artists. Manager Mark Hodgdon claims that the hotel epitomizes "European elegance with a unique Southwestern flair." Amenities include an oversized chess board, water volleyball, a championship golf course, a dozen tennis courts, nine swimming pools and a massive fully equipped spa offering everything from herbal body treatments to something called "energy therapies."
6000 E. Camelback Road
Scottsdale, AZ 85251
Tel: 480-941-8200   Fax: 480-947-4311

PGA CHAMPIONSHIP
Events
A ticket to the PGA Championship is worth its weight in social gold. Only 30,000 tickets are offered for the final championship and holders always include celebrities, socialites and household names from around the world. Ticket types include 'The Wanamaker,' which offers the most luxurious seats in the house. Inside the Wanamaker Club, guests enjoy fine dining, comfortable furnishings and oversized television monitors. Golf enthusiasts can recline while they watch the finalists compete for over $3 million in prize money.
100 Avenue of the Champions
Palm Beach, FL 33410
Tel: 561-624-8497   Fax: 800-477-6465

PHILADELPHIA MUSEUM OF ART
Museums
Housed in a spectacular neo-classical building which was fashioned after the Champs Elysée, the third largest museum in the U.S. has a permanent collection of over 400,000 works. Among the 200 galleries, some 25 are devoted to Medieval and early Renaissance art, including a Romanesque cloister and a Gothic chapel. The Ceremonial Japanese Tea Garden is a highlight, as is van Gogh's *Sunflowers*.
26th Street & Benjamin Franklin Parkway
Philadelphia, PA 19130
Tel: 215-684-7500   Fax: 215-235-0050

PHILIP BALOUN
Florists
For many moons now Philip Baloun has been wowing us with spectacular displays from mother nature. The Chicagoan has worked for some of the most prestigious public institutions in the country, from gala dinners at the Metropolitan Museum of Modern Art to showers of flowers at the New York State Theater's 25th Anniversary. Baloun also caters weddings, providing everything from lighting to sound, in salubrious settings all over the east coast.
340 West 55th Street
New York, NY 10019
Tel: 212-307-1675   Fax: 212-582-1152

PHILIP COLLECK
Antiques
Owned and directed by Mark and Diana Jacoby since 1988, this firm deals in fine 18th century English furniture, works of art, English lacquer, Chinese export furniture and mirrors. Colleck occupies an 1857 landmark brick house and caters to private collectors and interior designers. Wares are exhibited on three floors in elaborate period settings.
311 East 58th Street
New York, NY 10022
Tel: 212-505-2500
Fax: 212-529-1836

PHILIP H. BRADLEY
Antiques
After 65 years in the business, Philip H. Bradley has become an icon in the world of American antiques. His sprawling shop attracts seasoned buyers and professional dealers alike, all eager to explore his unrivaled inventory of late 18th and early 19th century American furniture and decorative arts. Renowned for his vast collection of fireplace tools and andirons (the White House recently purchased a pair), Bradley's selection of tall-case American clocks also entice antique lovers to Downington.
1101 East Lancaster Avenue
Downingtown, PA 19335
Tel: 610-269-0427

PIERRE HOTEL
Hotels
Located across the street from Central Park, the Pierre Hotel offers the best classic luxury in New York City. Conveniently located beside Fifth Avenue, home to the finest shopping, the hotel is lavishly decorated in fine antiques and collectibles. Afternoon tea is served in the famous, muraled rotunda. The Pierre offers weekend dancing and nightly entertainment. Julian Bonpard, executive chef of Café Pierre, prepares a delectable rack of lamb and a sublime pan-seared bass.
2 East 51st Street
New York, NY, 10021
Tel: 212-838-8000   Fax: 212-826-0319

PINEHURST RESORT & COUNTRY CLUB
Golf Clubs
For over 100 years, Pinehurst has been a jewel of the genteel south. Boasting world class accomodations, innovative cuisine and lavish guest facilities, the resort is justly acclaimed as a tried and tested winner. And the club? Host of the 1999 and 2005 U.S. Open Championships, it has had a seminal influence on the game of golf. Steeped in a century-old tradition of excellence and ageless beauty, Pinehurst is a gem.
Carolina Vista Drive
Pinehurst, NC 28374
Tel: 910-295-6811

PINEHURST POLO CLUB

Polo Clubs

This small, casual club boasts only a dozen members, who have from two to eight ponies a piece. Spectators are always welcome and matches can turn into 100-strong social gatherings. Because the players are all amateurs, there are no high-goal egos here. Pinehurst is managed by Octogenarian Bob Johnson; he has been playing the game since 1934. The club's motto is "play for the fun of it."

56 Pinelake Drive
Whispering Pines, NC 28327
Tel: 910-949-4650

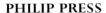

PHILIP PRESS

Jewelry and Watches

Philip Press works principally in platinum, creating extraordinary jewelry that is emboldened by the medium. Press designs each piece himself, blending the old world tradition of hand made jewelry with new age technology to create ornate art deco rings, brooches and necklaces. Press, who originally comes from New York, does a lot of work with young guns in the music and film industry. His opulent line of wedding and engagement rings are particularly coveted — encased in handmade lacy metal work, engraved and fitted with the finest diamonds, they are carried in more than a hundred stores across the United States.

8601 Sunset Boulevard
Los Angeles, CA 90069
Tel: 310-360-1180
Fax: 310-360-1185

PHILIP JOHNSON/ ALAN RITCHIE ARCHITECTS

Architects and Interior Designers

When Philip Johnson, the 94 year-old grandfather of modern American architecture, was asked last year how he would be spending the millennium, his response was simple. "There is no millennium to me," he said. "I just go on working faster and faster. I have no more time." Obviously Johnson is not content to rest on his considerable laurels as a guiding force in the key architectural movements of the modern era – the International Style and Postmodernism. With credits that include the famous New Canaan Glass House, the AT&T Building, the Lipstick Building and the legendary Grill Room at the Four Seasons, he would certainly be entitled to do just that.

375 Park Avenue
New York, NY 10152
Tel: 212-319-5880   Fax: 212-319-5881

PLANTATION

Specialty Shops

When the notoriously particular movie director James Cameron needed a new custom-designed entertainment system, and Sharon Stone wanted an updated look for her San Francisco mansion, both turned to Plantation, the three-year-old furniture and accessory gallery that has become known among Los Angeles' sophisticated shoppers as the most innovative home boutique in town. The store carries an exceptional variety of furniture, from traditional pieces to classics of mid-century modern, unified by an emphasis on timeless design and a love of the sensual. The store's engaging owners, Mark Cole and Craig Olsen, will even work one-on-one with their clientele to help create furniture that meets their exact specifications. Fusing together varying elements is their forte – wood, stone, glass and tile meet an amazing array of tactile leathers and fabrics for a look that is unique, yet undoubtedly masculine. Always on the cutting-edge, the two garner their creative inspiration from many sources, including the world of high fashion. But a recent visit to the store by a very enthusiastic Giorgio Armani suggests to us that such inspiration may indeed be a two way street.

144 South La Brea Avenue
Los Angeles, CA 90036
Tel: 323-932-0511   Fax: 323-932-0485

THE PITCHER INN

Hotels

Young bucks in the entertainment industry are particularly fond of this Relais et Chateaux property, which is located in the picturesque village of Warren, Vermont. Each of the eight rooms and two suites are appointed with original art and antiques, wood burning fireplaces and steam showers. Try to snag the Trout Room, which is furnished with a king-size bed set in a custom frame made of untouched birch, a private porch, wood burning fireplace and standing trees. The School Room features an original slate blackboard with chalk and erasers, a period school desk with an old-time globe and dioramas of the Vermont seasons. Dine privately in the wine cellar, which boasts 3500 varietals.

275 Main Street
Warren, VT 05674
Tel: 802-496-6350   Fax: 802-496-6345

PLANTERS INN

Hotels

A beacon of Southern civility, Planters Inn overlooks the Old Market — a collection of antique shops, art galleries, the theater district and Charleston's best restaurants and bistros. Innkeeper Larry Spelts treats guests with extraordinary warmth and courtesy. Rooms and suites are spacious, with high ceilings, canopied four-poster beds, museum quality furnishings, original art and piazzas overlooking the garden courtyard. Reserve the Proprietor's Suite, which offers two bedrooms, a large living room, two bathrooms with floor to ceiling créme marsil and a private veranda entrance. Call at least six weeks in advance for a spring or fall reservation.

112 North Market Street
Charleston, SC 29401
Tel: 843-722-2345
Fax: 843-577-2125

PLAZA ATHÉNÉE
Hotels
Majestic and luxurious, the Plaze Athénée is fashionably located on Manhattan's Upper East Side. Guests are a stone's throw from Central Park, designer boutiques, art galleries and New York's finest department stores. The elegant lobby has Italian marble floors and delicate French antique furnishings. Of the 36 suites, eight include dining rooms and private terraces. Bathrooms offer Frette bathrobes, Rose Aurora marble and fresh flowers. Among many other accolades, the Plaza Athénée was named "One of the Ten Best Hotels in the World" by the International Association of Travel Editors in 1998.

37 East 64th Street
New York, NY 10021
Tel: 212-734-9100   Fax: 212-772-0958

THE POINT
Hotels   Rising Star
Grand and fanciful, the great log mansions at The Point personify the 19th century notion of roughing it in great style. Former home of the Rockefeller's, the resort, nestled in the heart of the Adirondack mountains, is the hideaway that all others are measured by. 11 distinctive guest quarters are spread among four buildings – each with lake views and spacious private baths. At the Great Hall's round tables, each dish is prepared under the culinary guidance of one of the world's preeminent chefs, Albert Roux of Le Gavroche in London.

Beaverwood Road
Saranac Lake, NY 12983
Tel: 800-255-3530   Fax: 518-891-1152

POST RANCH INN
Hotels
The Post Ranch Inn sits on 98 acres of prime California hinterland. Surrounded by California redwoods, and nestled close to the cliff edge, a spectacular wood-and-glass design affords breathtaking views of the Pacific ocean. The Sierra Mar Restaurant, which is situated on the grounds, boasts an award-winning wine list and is very popular among guests who hail from all over the world. The ranch is particularly popular with couples who come to celebrate a special occasion, or those in need of some rest and relaxation.

P.O. Box 219, Highway One
Big Sur, CA 93920
Tel: 831-667-2200
Fax: 831-667-2512

PNC ADVISORS
Wealth Management
PNC Advisors is the fourth largest money manager for the high net worth market, and part of the 11th largest bank in the United States. They offer financial solutions through a one-on-one version of traditional and investment banking, tailored to clients' specific investing history. Since acquiring the 145-year-old Hilliard Lyons in 1998, PNC Advisors has been operating in 19 states, serving over 400,000 clients and managing over $65 billion.

3305 Flamingo Drive
Vero Beach, FL 32963
Tel: 561-231-6300
Fax: 561-231-4016

PRIMAVERA
Specialty Shops
Specializing in French and Italian glass, furniture and objets d'art of the 1920s through the 1950s, Audrey Friedman and husband Haim Manishevitz have been a staple in New York elegance since 1968. A fervent collector, Friedman fell into business through her own love for art deco and unique, signed jewelry. The New York native often becomes firm friends with her clients, and she has a sharply discerning eye (and a flair for botany and landscaping.) At the time of writing, the couple were preparing to go to auction in London, for the sixth time this year.

808 Madison Avenue
New York, NY 10021
Tel: 212-288-1569

PRINCE MICHEL VINEYARD
Restaurants
One of 52 French master chefs in the United States, Jean Leduce offers a true *haute cuisine* experience at Prince Michel. Upon entering, guests are brought into the Lafayette room, where silhouettes of Revolutionary soldiers adorn the walls and Virginia's social superstars smoke cigars over martinis at the stately cherry bar. The Jefferson room (a bust of the great man and his original drawings line the walls) overlooks the vineyard. Try the fillet of bison, served with fresh tomato and zucchini.

Route 29
Leon, VA 22725
Tel: 540-547-9720
Fax: 540-328-1185

PRESCRIPTIVES
Hair and Beauty
Prescriptives makes foundation to measure. This cosmetics house, known as the foundation authority, specializes in Custom Blend couture foundation, powder and concealer. With exclusive technologies, Custom Blend is created to suit individual skintone. Special additives and treatments pamper, please and perfect the skin. This superlative service is completed in minutes. Exclusively at Bergdorf Goodman, Prescriptives offers Custom Blend Lipstick. Designed according to whim or with the expertise of Prescriptives Color Analysts, Custom Blend Lipstick allows infinite interpretation. Whether opalescent, golden-hued or as a simple pink nuance, Custom Blend Lipstick is created to satisfy the most epicurean desire.

767 Fifth Avenue
New York, NY 10022
Tel: 212-572-4400   Fax: 212-572-6725

PRIVATE CHEFS, INC.
Employment Agencies
The world's elite turn to Private Chefs, Inc. to find the perfect chef to satisfy their culinary needs. Acclaimed Austrian-born Chef Christian Paier chooses only the highest caliber chefs to cater to PCI's discerning clientele; which includes Tina Turner, Will Smith, John Travolta and the Royal Family of Saudi Arabia. Whether hiring a live-in or -out chef for your summer home, private yacht or the executive dining room of your corporate headquarters, you will always have a master of international cuisine at your disposal through Private Chefs, Inc.

204 South Beverly Drive, Suite 105
Beverly Hills, CA 90211
Tel: 310-278-4707   Website: www.privatechefsinc.comm

PRINCETON UNIVERSITY
Colleges
It is, as they used to say, top-flight. The muted Gothic campus frames a vibrant intellectual community stocked with gifted students of every nationality and background. The new football stadium is praised as an architectural marvel, the money flows and the professors are talking heads for television news. And yet F. Scott Fitzgerald would certainly recognize the place: the best eating clubs – Tiger Inn, Cottage and Ivy – are still the bastions of Prospect Street and a witty *bonhomie* remains the preferred mode of social discourse. The most culturally "southern" of the Ivy League universities, Princeton is for those who combine their intellectual rigor with a certain civility.

Stanhope Hall
Princeton, NJ 08544
Tel: 609-258-3000   Fax: 609-258-1301

≈

PRIVÉ
Hair and Beauty
Laurent Dufourg's Privé offers fine hair care and make up at its locations in Los Angeles and New York. The Manhattan space (at the SoHo Grand) is cozy and stylish, while the brand new LA flagship is a more ambitious salon, offering a full range of services from color and cut to pedicure. Laurent's wife, Fabienne, played an important role in designing the interiors. Both salons are a favorite of the younger celebrity set, including Uma Thurman and Gwyneth Paltrow.

7373 Beverly Boulevard
Los Angeles, CA 90069
Tel: 323-651-5045   Fax: 323-651-0509

PROFESSIONAL NANNIES INSTITUTE
Employment Agencies
The capable Denise Kapelus, former director of the Mother and Child Center, is at the helm of this well-regarded firm. A meticulous screening and placement process ensures that the nannies selected are genuine kid lovers and competent care givers. Little princes and princesses of the silver spoon variety are doted upon; support is also provided for long suffering families and nannies alike.

501 Fifth Avenue, Suite 908
New York, NY 10017
Tel: 212-692-9510
Fax: 212-692-9835

≈

PUCCI
Fashion   Best Kept Secret
Brutally against mass production, Pucci seems like a charming relic of the 1920s and 30s, when the production of a custom made suit involved hands, a good eye and impeccable taste. These "architects of design" offer the finest woolens, silk linings and antelope horn buttons, while seasoned craftsmen (who make individual paper patterns) construct the entire suit on premises and sew only by hand. While handmade suits at Pucci are mostly traditional, orders have included such oddities as refined zoot suits. Dean Martin and Jerry Lewis are among the clients who have visited this image-maker over the years.

333 North Michigan Avenue
Chicago, IL 60601
Tel: 312-332-3759

PUENTE & PILA
Architects and Interior Designers
Martha Puente and Beatrice Pila-Gonzalez joined forces in 1988. Both are trained interior designers, but while Puente's strengths lie in budget management, finishes and antique furniture, her partner's skills lie in concepts and contemporary furniture design. Known for a classy, "clean" style (and a healthy disregard for frivolous trends) the Florida-based firm designs private residences, medical offices, research laboratories, apartments and the occasional bar – recently, the duo designed a brasserie for Oscar winner Michael Caine.

224 Valencia Drive
Coral Gables, FL 32124
Tel: 305-443-2227

LA QUINTA
Golf Clubs
Palm Springs may be home to over one hundred golf courses, but the three gems found at LaQuinta stand apart from the crowd in the Coachella Valley. Resort guests can take advantage of the Dunes and Mountain courses while Citrus is open to members only. Stand on the tee box at the Mountain's par three 16th and enjoy a panoramic view of the Santa Rosa mountains and the surrounding valley. Seclusion and privacy have attracted celebrities to this resort since the 1930s — not to mention the great golf.

49-499 Eisenhower Drive
La Quinta, CA 92253
Tel: 800-598-3828

RANDOLPH DUKE
Fashion

Having shed all his ties with Halston (where his former assistant, Kevan Hall, is now ensconced as head designer) Randolph Duke has emerged as one of the most exciting young designers in America today. His sophisticated, unashamedly glamorous eveningwear is adored by actresses like Hilary Swank, Angelina Jolie and Charlize Theron. Having masterfully resurrected an icon of American fashion, Duke is well on his way to acquiring similar stature.
260 West 39th Street,
New York, NY 10018
Tel: 212-768-1730

R.H. LOVE GALLERIES
Art Dealers

Flanking Chicago's Magnificent Mile, R.H. Love Galleries is housed in an opulent Italianate mansion built for Samuel M. Nickerson, President of the First National Bank. Since 1970, art historian and dealer Richard H. Love has used the house to showcase American art from 1785-1940, an intriguing and diverse period that encompasses portraiture, the Hudson River School, romanticism, tonalism, impressionism, post-impressionism and even early modernism: art for just about everyone.
40 East Erie Street
Chicago, IL 60611
Tel: 312-640-1300   Fax: 312-640-5435

RABBIT RIDGE VINEYARDS
Winemakers

In his school days, Eric Russell was a long distance runner known as 'The Rabbit.' When he and partner Darryl Simmons bought this property in 1979, choosing a name did not pose a problem. Today, Russell and Simmons have 35 acres under vine and with purchased grapes in the Dry Creek and Carneros, Rabbit Ridge turn out roughly 70,000 cases of wine a year. Their single vineyard Zinfandels are particularly worth hunting for.
3291 Westside Road
Healdsburg, CA 95448
Tel: 707-431-7128   Fax: 707-431-8018

RACQUET & TENNIS CLUB
Private Clubs

Housed in a brick and limestone Florentine Renaissance style building with a loggia on the second floor, where afternoon tea and muffins are served in the warmer months, the Racquet & Tennis club is a dramatic architectural outpost amidst its glass and steel neighbors. Founded in 1890, the club moved to its current residence in 1916 when members complained that larger buildings were blocking sunlight from the skylight-lit indoor courts. Traditionally an institution for Ivy League members of the New York Stock Exchange, this gentlemen-only club now attracts, above all, sportsmen: this is where George Plimpton keeps fit and up to date. The club also houses a world class collection of sports paintings and sculpture as well as a sports library decorated with portraits of former members, such as Charles Scribner, who published, among other sportsmen, one Ernest Hemingway.
370 Park Avenue
New York, NY 10022
Tel: 212-753-9700

RADU PHYSICAL CULTURE
Fitness

Radu was named by the *Guinness Book of World Records* as one of the most successful fitness trainers in history. His method, developed over 30 years ago, guarantees improvements in coordination, strength and agility. The combination of athletic training, gymnastics, track and field, karate, soccer, muscle physiology and weight training comprise the workout. In his second book, *Radu Simply Fit*, the guru describes his philosophy on health and wellness and showcases his regimens. Radu is often called "the toughest trainer in town." He has helped to craft the bodies of Jennifer Lopez, Cindy Crawford and Matthew Broderick.
24 West 57th Street
New York, NY 10019
Tel: 212-581-1995

RALPH LAUREN
Fashion

"I believe in design that has integrity, design that lasts. Whatever it is, it must be part of the lifestyle and become more personal with time." With this credo as his guide, Ralph Lauren has gone from manufacturing neckties (in 1967) to overseeing a lifestyle empire which incorporates everything from elegant clothing and fragrances to home accessories, furniture, linens and paint. It's a global brand so successful that $8 billion worth of Polo products were purchased in 1999 alone, spreading Lauren's sporty take on old-school style around the world. And, to his credit, Mr. Lauren is a patriot too: after years of using the American flag as a marketing tool, he spent $13 million restoring the original Star Spangled Banner.
867 Madison Avenue
New York, NY 10021
Tel: 212-606-2100

RALPH M. CHAIT GALLERIES
Antiques

Like his father and grandfather before him, Allan Chait served as President of the National Antique and Art Dealer's Association. His ultra-distinguished family firm is the oldest dealer in Chinese Art in the United States. Since 1962 its Manhattan gallery has been an opulent showcase for top-notch porcelain, sculpture and Chinese export silver, which can also be viewed at prestigious fairs like the Ellis Memorial Show in Boston and the Los Angeles Antique Show in Santa Monica. Incidentally, Chait predicts a resurgence of interest in later porcelains (from the 17th century onward) due to new export restrictions.
12 East 56th Street
New York, NY 10022
Tel: 212-758-0937   Fax: 212-319-0471

RANCHO VALENCIA RESORT
Hotels
Nestled into the rolling hills of a private canyon overlooking the Dieguito Valley, Rancho Valencia's setting is reminiscent of the hills of southern France. Each of the beautifully constructed *casitas* boast Berber carpets, cathedral ceilings and French doors leading to a private patio. One of the top tennis resorts in the country, other amenities include a comprehensive spa and fitness center. A Relais et Chateaux property, Rancho Valencia is owned and managed by the same firm which runs Auberge du Soleil and San Ysidro Ranch – both *Elite 1000* members.
5921 Valencia Circle
Rancho Santa Fe, CA 92067
Tel: 858-756-1123

RAYTHEON TRAVEL AIR
Airplanes
Our readers and advisors claim that this fractional airline program – a subsidiary of the giant Raytheon Corporation – is one of the best in the industry. Like all fractional programs, Raytheon operates on the premise that not all businesses or individuals can justify buying entire airplanes, yet they would greatly benefit from private air travel. So the firm sells shares (part ownership) in individual aircraft, enabling clients to conduct business travel according to their own schedules. As CEO Arthur Wegner puts it, "With a business aircraft, you can visit four cities in a day and return home in time for dinner. This freedom affords you the ultimate commodity: more time to effectively manage your business."
101 South Webb Road
Wichita, KS 67201
Tel: 888-824-6359
Fax: 316-676-7603

REBECCA MOSS
Specialty Shops
In the age of the impersonal word-processor, if you're going to write it out, you might as well do it in style. Sam Zagoori founded this center for pen-and-paper fans 11 years ago, naming it after his late grandmother (an aficionado herself). Try the Chelsea pen, a single ball point with a wire wound clip. Its aluminum body is often called futuristic but it's the smoothest pen in the inventory, well-balanced and light. Looking for the perfect plume for your favorite poet? Ask Amanda, the erudite manager, to show you the limited edition collection and a line of fine leather pen cases.
510 Madison Avenue
New York, NY 10022
Tel: 800-INK-PENS

THE REGENT BEVERLY WILSHIRE
Hotels
Some of the world's most influential people insist on staying in the Regent's Penthouse suite while in California. The 5000 square-foot space has three bedrooms and baths, a living room, dining room, den, large-screen television and deluxe sound system. Pets (under 15 pounds) are fed liver paté and Evian water from a silver tray. The Wilshire wing, built in 1928, is traditional in decor with dark wood and rich mahogany walls. The Beverly wing, built in 1973, has a more continental feel. Guests always prefer one over the other; concierge John Thompson will happily fax you photos of both. Managed by the mighty Four Seasons Group, the Regent offers the high standards one expects of that veritable superpower of the hotel world.
9500 Wilshire Boulevard
Beverly Hills, CA 90212
Tel: 310-275-5200   Fax: 310-275-5986

THE REDFERN GALLERY
Art Dealers
Ray Redfern established his Laguna Beach gallery after purchasing the Donna Schuster estate in 1975. For the past 25 years he has researched and exhibited California *plein air* impressionists, active during the years 1890-1940. The quality and variety of these painters, some trained in Europe and some locally, is a Californian secret that the rest of the world has just started to discover. Artists represented include William Wendt, Mark Rossi and Granville Redmond.
1540 South Coast Highway
Laguna Beach, CA 92651
Tel: 949-497-3356   Fax: 949-497-1324

REEBOK SPORTS CLUB
Fitness   *Rising Star*
Spread over 6 floors, spanning 140,000 square feet, Reebok may be New York's finest fitness club. Every trainer is required to have a degree in physical science. Many of the classes offered are exclusive to the club, including Fluidity, which combines yoga and ballet to create an intensive stretching body and mind workout. For those tired of typical workouts, the club offers Forza, an Italian sword class which offers an intense cardio workout. After training, hit the full-service salon and day spa for a massage, pedicure or an oxygenating facial.
160 Columbus Avenue
New York, NY 10023
Tel: 212-362-6800

REGEN-LEIGH ANTIQUES
Antiques
Color, patina and proportion are always above reproach in Regen-Leigh's collection of English and Continental furniture and *objets d'art* from 1700 to 1840. Owner Barbara Culbreath, who trained at London's Royal Society of Arts and Christie's, works with leading interior designers, building neoclassical collections for luminaries like Elton John and the Turner family. Culbreath has long-standing access to prestigious European collections, affording clients a valuable guarantee of provenance.
3140 East Shadowlawn Avenue NE
Atlanta, GA 30305
Tel: 404-262-9303
Fax: 404-816-6463

JOHN REILLY
Portrait Painters and Photographers
It was while teaching European history at the University of Illinois 25 years ago that John Reilly began pottering around with a camera; he soon realized that his true place in life was behind a lens. His gentle nature and gift for making subjects feel at ease has led Reilly to become one of America's foremost portrait photographers, with Chicago's more prominent individuals, families and institutions among his clients.
358 West Ontario
Chicago, IL 60610
Tel: 312-266-2550   Fax: 312-266-2519

RENNY
Florists

Legend has it that the designer Mickie Minardos in Dominick Dunne's *People Like Us* is based on Renny. That seems unlikely, although he is one of the more celebrated characters on the American floral scene. The Missouri native's first professional job was designing the terrace of Bill Blass's penthouse, whom he met at a party. He then began working for clients of major interior designers like Mario Buatta and Albert Hadley. More a party designer than a mere florist, Renny has planned White House dinners for Presidents Nixon, Ford, Reagan and Clinton. His signature designs feature tight, English-style floral arrangements and suspended candle balls.

505 Park Avenue
New York, NY 10022
Tel: 212-593-3688

REVEL
Restaurants   *Rising Star*

A law school graduate, chef Maurizio Marfolgia has worked in the kitchens of Barolo and I Tremerli. Owner Philip Danisi also took a circuitous route to his present position: he left a successful career in broking derivatives in order to create "an elegant restaurant committed to the highest quality food and ambiance." The result, Revel, is certainly elegant (thanks to designer Daniel O'Connor) and the ambience is civilized. In summer, ask for a seat on the garden patio. The seasonal Italian cuisine has some way to go.

24 East 81st Street
New York, NY 10021
Tel: 212-249-5720   Fax: 212-249-5695

HOTEL REX
Hotels

Redesigned by the Joie de Vivre group in 1996, the former Orchard Hotel is billed as the West Coast's answer to the famous Algonquin Hotel of the 1920s. The hotel has a library, complete with first-edition, leather bound titles and monogrammed club chairs (savor that moody, bookish atmosphere). Quotes from literary giants cover the corridor walls, while elevator doors are decorated with collages made from 1920s Social Registers. Rooms at the Rex are masculine, clad in bold, Ivy-league color and polished timber furniture. Located on prime Sutter Street, Rex is around the corner from the best of San Francisco's galleries and antique shops.

562 Sutter Street
San Francisco, CA 94102
Tel: 415-433-4434
Fax: 415-433-3695

RIALTO
Restaurants   *Best Kept Secret*

Only the second restaurant in Boston to receive *Boston Globe* restaurant critic Allison Arnett's four-star rating, Rialto offers warm ambiance, affable staff and delectable food. Executive chef Jody Adams has garnered national acclaim for her slow-roasted Long Island duck, served with braised escarole. Drawing in the Harvard Square crowd for the past five years, the dining room also hosts traveling celebrities like Elizabeth Shue and Marisa Tomei. Newly renovated, Rialto is now adorned in classic rust colors and vibrant, collegiate greens, lending to its candlelit intimacy. Ask maitre'd Gary Sullivan for a table by one of the large panel windows.

1 Bennett Street
Cambridge, MA 02138
Tel: 617-661-5050   Fax: 617-661-5053

RICE UNIVERSITY
Colleges

Rice University is a private, nonsectarian research university enrolling 4000 students a year. 98% of the faculty hold Ph.Ds in their fields — two Nobel Prize winners in chemistry have spent their entire academic careers teaching at Rice. This year, 28 students won coveted National Science Foundation Fellowships for graduate study in science and engineering, the largest number of any school in the country. Famous alumni include nature writer John Graves, venture capitalist John Doerr, Pulitzer Prize-winner Larry McMurty and Congressman Bill Archer.

PO Box 1892
Houston, TX 77252
Tel: 713-348-4036

RICHARD GOULD ANTIQUES
Antiques

For over 40 years Richard Gould Antiques has offered the finest in 18th and early 19th century English and American furniture and decorative arts. His inventory consists of pottery, porcelain, needlework, glass, period boxes, tea caddies and metalwork. There is also a large collection of Chinese export porcelain on display. Many pieces have been placed in international collections and prominent museums.

808 North La Cienega Boulevard
Los Angeles, CA 90069
Tel: 310-657-9416
Fax: 310-657-9416

RICHARD GRAY GALLERY
Art Dealers

Richard Gray, one of the most respected figures in the art world, was elected President of the Art Dealer's Association of America in 1998. His Chicago and New York galleries, which deal primarily in impressionist, modernist and contemporary paintings, are currently preparing for exhibitions of work by Picasso and Giacometti. Recent hits include Frank Stella's *Recent Paintings and Sculpture* and *The Edge* by Sam Francis. The importance of the Gray Gallery is reflected in its association with modern masters such as Matisse, Rothko, Warhol — and is solidified by Gray's exclusive clientele.

875 North Michigan Avenue
Chicago, IL 60611
Tel: 312-642-8877
Fax: 312-642-8488

RENAISSANCE
Restaurants

All-American comfort food gets the gourmet treatment at this hot Aspen eatery. Citing his mantra that "elegance should be simple," chef/owner Charles Dale (formerly at Le Cirque) creates the ultimate après ski dishes, including a sublime duck cassoulet and a black bean shepherd's pie prepared with a distinctly Southwestern twist. Call early for reservations: with only 45 seats, Renaissance fills up fast. Request a table near the window for stunning views of the Aspen Mountains.

304 East Hopkins Avenue
Aspen, CO 81611
Tel: 970-925-2402

RICHARD KEITH LANGHAM
Architects and Interior Designers

The late Jackie Onassis was the quintessential Richard Langham client – someone who appreciates understated, classic style, but with a bit of playfulness and perhaps an evocative twist or two. In demand with private clients across the county, Langham and company are currently readying a new showroom to feature their signature upholstered pieces and antiques, all designed in the old-world English tradition of comfort and enduring quality.

153 East 60th Street
New York, NY 10022
Tel: 212-759-1212
Fax: 212-759-5151

RICHARD L. FEIGEN & COMPANY
Art Dealers

Inaugurating his first gallery in Chicago in 1957, Richard Feigen exhibited 20th century masters, concentrating on German Expressionism and Surrealism. He was an early champion of Francis Bacon, Jean Dubuffet, Joseph Cornell, Claes Oldenburg, Ray Johnson and James Rosenquist. Today, the company he founded deals in paintings, drawings and sculpture from the 13th through the 20th centuries. Look for Feigen's recently published book, *Tales From The Art Crypt*, where he reveals the fate of Gertrude Stein's collection and other art world secrets.

49 East 68th Street
New York, NY 10021
Tel: 212-628-0700
Fax: 212-249-4574

RICHARD MEIER
Architects and Interior Designers

Name any architectural award you can think of and chances are good that Richard Meier has won it, probably more than once. Now in his mid-sixties, Meier is one of the true giants of the field. His buildings are unmistakable. Whether we are talking about innovative private residences – the stunning Neugebauer House in Naples, Florida, is one recent example – or his groundbreaking public projects, such as the Getty Center in Los Angeles, all feature a glorious interplay of natural light and open space, with sun rays bouncing off white walls and glinting through transparent glass surfaces. His latest big commission is the Church of the Year 2000 in Vatican City.

1001 Gayley Avenue 3rd Floor
Los Angeles, CA 90024
Tel: 310-208-6464
Fax: 310-824-2294

RICHARD NORTON
Antiques

Richard Norton describes his clients as "intelligent and discerning, looking for pieces that are lifelong treasures." In 1933, his father founded the firm with his personal array of 18th and 19th century French and English antiques. Today, the collection spans over 5000 pieces, showcasing a particularly impressive selection of French armoires and English country tables. Norton couldn't see himself involved in any other sort of business; he describes his life as a "working vacation."

612 Merchandise Mart Plaza
Chicago, IL 60654
Tel: 312-644-9359   Fax: 312-644-8771

RICHARD YORK GALLERY
Art Dealers

Having rapidly expanded since its opening in 1981, the Richard York Gallery has become a significant fixture on the art scene. Maintaining active links with major institutions, including the Metropolitan Museum of Art and the Amon Carter Museum, the gallery specializes in American paintings, drawings and sculpture from the last 300 years. An extensive body of work by artists such as Copley, Peale and Cassatt reflects the gallery's commitment to outstanding American art.

21 East 65th Street
New York, NY 10021
Tel: 212-772-9155

THE RITTENHOUSE HOTEL
Hotels

In Philadelphia, the city of brotherly love, visitors to the AAA Five-Diamond Award winning Rittenhouse Hotel are greeted by the 'Welcome Statue,' a beautiful woman who extends the 'Rittenhouse Rose.' The cordial and hospitable air continues throughout this 98 room boutique hotel, which to many of its discerning guests – like Oprah Winfrey, Luciano Pavarotti and President Bush – is considered an elegant home away from home. This landmark of Philadelphia style is the perfect combination of intimate service and world-class amenities. Located in the heart of exclusive Rittenhouse Square, the hotel is central to the area's finest cultural attractions, dining and an outstanding array of shops along the famous Rittenhouse Row. Regally appointed guest rooms are enhanced by lavish marble baths and luxury suites with their own whirlpool tubs. Weary travelers can loll the day away at the Adolf Biecker Spa and Salon, which offers state-of-the-art fitness equipment, an indoor pool, sauna, aromatherapy and massage. If you feel the need to unwind further, the Cassatt Tea Garden is the perfect antidote to life's little traumas, or simply the place for a professional or not-so professional meeting. The exquisite Treetops Restaurant features the innovative creations of executive chef, Jim Coleman – well known for his national television program, *Flavors of America*. The Rittenhouse is additionally complemented by a Smith & Wollensky Restaurant; according to *The New York Times* it is "a steakhouse to end all arguments." That goes for the hotel as well.

210 West Rittenhouse Square
Philadelphia, PA 19103
Tel: 215-546-9000   Fax: 215-546-9858

RITZ-CARLTON, BUCKHEAD
Restaurants

Growing up with his grandparents in the South of France, Chef Joel Antunes helped tend to the family vegetable garden. He fed the chickens and would carefully water his grandfather's herbs. This seminal introduction to *haute cuisine* led the Frenchman on a journey to Atlanta, where his menu draws equally from his French training and travels in Thailand. Try the soft-shell crab with Tom Yum sauce, the seared rare tuna with mango-star anise chutney, or the chicken consommé with chestnut cream and white truffles.

3434 Peachtree Road
Atlanta, GA 30326
Tel: 404-237-2700   Fax: 404-239-0078

RIDGE VINEYARDS
Winemakers

In the late 1950s, three Stanford research scientists bought this property in the Santa Cruz Mountains for recreational purposes – before discovering the three-tier Monte Bello Winery, which had been shut down during Prohibition. The temptation to make wine proved irresistible. The fruits of their labor are a Cabernet Sauvignon of First-Growth quality and an unusual Zinfandel. Incidentally, if you have a chance to taste their Santa Cruz Mountain Chardonnay, do not miss it.

17100 Monte Bello Road
Cupertino, CA 95014
Tel: 408-867-3233

RITA BUCHEIT
Antiques   Best Kept Secret

Of Viennese origin, Rita Bucheit has been sharing her passion and knowledge for fine antiques with Chicagoans since 1987. Offering an extensive collection of authentic Empire, Biedermeier, Vienna Secession antiques and decorative arts, the gallery is a regular stomping ground for savvy curators and private collectors from around the world. This year, Bucheit has added Art Deco chairs, benches, tables, desks and mirrors to her museum-quality inventory.

449 North Wells Street
Chicago, IL 60610
Tel: 312-527-4080
Fax: 312-527-3316

RITZ-CARLTON, LAGUNA NIGUEL
Hotels

Halfway between Los Angeles and San Diego, perched high atop a 150-foot bluff overlooking the Pacific, sits the Ritz-Carlton Laguna Niguel. Built in the style of a classic Mediterranean villa, the hotel is consistently cited as one of the most romantic in the world. Guest rooms open onto private balconies overlooking tiled courtyards that feature ornate fountains, landscaped gardens and spectacular ocean views. Call well in advance to book a corner suite, which boasts fabulous views of both the Pacific and, at night, the twinkling lights of the California coastline.

1 Ritz Carlton Drive
Dana Point, CA 92629
Tel: 949-240-2000
Fax: 949-240-0829

ROBERT MONDAVI
Winemakers

With the founding of his namesake flagship in the heart of Napa Valley in 1966, Robert Mondavi laid the foundation for the California wine industry and established a reputation as its leading innovator. Under the aegis of his sons, Michael, CEO, and Timothy, Winegrower, the company is now producing wines on three continents and fulfilling the bold vision of its founder on a global basis. The winery produces over 650,000 cases of wine a year – mostly of Chardonnay and Cabernet Sauvignon, but it also produces a variety of others, including a Fumé Blanc, a term invented by Mondavi to describe dry, oak-aged Sauvignon Blancs. Don't miss the Coastal Zinfandel.

7801 St. Helena Highway
Oakville, CA 94562
Tel: 800-228-1395

RITZ-CARLTON HOTEL
Hotels

San Francisco's Ritz-Carlton is consistently rated among the best hotels in the world. Set in a 1909 Nob Hill landmark, high above America's favorite city, its name has long been synonymous with luxury (if you need proof, look at the museum-quality collection of 18th and 19th century art and antiques in the lobby). Check out the Ritz-Carlton Club, a hotel within a hotel, with huge, super-deluxe rooms and suites – plus complimentary cocktails, *hors d'oeuvres*, champagne and caviar. If none of that whets your palate, tuck into the largest single malt Scotch collection in the United States.

600 Stockton Street
San Francisco, CA 94108
Tel: 415-296-7465   Fax: 415-291-0147

THE RIVER CAFÉ
Restaurants

For the visitor from across the world or across the Bridge, the River Cafe offers an unforgettable experience. The dazzling view of the Manhattan skyline and New York Harbor, with the Statue of Liberty off to the right, is the calling card for Buzz O'Keeffe's waterfront restaurant. Often used as a location for major films, it is also the stage for many a marriage proposal because of its romantic setting. With a history of producing outstanding chefs, the restaurant has been tagged as the culinary world's answer to Harvard Business School.

One Water Street
Brooklyn, NY 11201
Tel: 718-522-5200   Fax: 718-875-0037

ROBERT LONG FLORA DESIGN
Florists

The name Robert Long is synonymous with beautiful flowers and white-glove service. The shop delivers daily signature arrangements to the area's most prestigious families and businesses. Designs tend to range from simple elegance – peonies en masse – to sophisticated botanical studies – lady slipper orchids, persimmon branches and blackberry vines. New for this fall is the "White Autumn Collection," featuring white flowers with autumnal textures. Discerning clients rave about their novel approach to weddings and other celebrations. Notably, a strength of Long and his staff is to comfortably blend period menus, music, decor with flowers for an authentic and festive event. Whether it is a simple floral thank you or a fete royale, Robert Long Flora Design stands alone.

3181 Roswell Road
Atlanta, GA 30305
Tel: 404-365-0500
Fax: 404-365-0507

ROCIADA
Restaurants   *Rising Star*

Formerly of New York's Zucca, chef Eric Stapleton is stirring up New Mexican dust with his country-French cuisine at Rociada. Hailed as Santa Fe's best new restaurant in years, it occupies a handsomely renovated 19th century house. Adhering to the philosophy that good art speaks for itself, the menu is simple, yet packed with flavor and texture. Try the shrimp, escargot and parsley cream pastry or the chévre dumplings, served with smoked tomato and onion consommé. Finish with the delectable lavender créme brûlée.

304 Johnson Street
Santa Fe, NM 87501
Tel: 505-983-3800
Fax: 505-983-8306

～

THE ROCKWELL GROUP
Architects and Interior Designers

If you can imagine a cross between a classic, old-world architect and an avant-garde theatrical designer, then you have some idea of the creative genius of the design world's man of the moment, David Rockwell. His firm, the Rockwell Group, is behind many of the most talked about restaurants in New York City, including the delightful Monkey Bar, the sleek new W Hotel and Robert DeNiro's ever-popular Nobu. While such high-profile commercial spaces are the firm's forte, Rockwell is sometimes persuaded to take on private assignments of particular interest.

5 Union Square West
New York, NY 10003
Tel: 212-463-0334
Fax: 212-463-0335

～

RIVIERA COUNTRY CLUB
Golf Clubs

With legendary champions such as Hogan, Nelson, Snead, Watson, Miller and Couples, and celebrity members like Tom Cruise, Sylvester Stallone, Arnold Schwarzenegger and Michael Keaton, you will certainly find yourself in good company here at Santa Monica's smartest country club. Longtime home of the PGA Tour's Los Angeles Open, Riviera's magnificent clubhouse overlooks a panoramic amphitheater surrounding the 18th green.

1250 Capri Drive
Pacific Palisades, CA 90272
Tel: 310-454-6591
Fax: 310-454-8351

～

ROBERT A.M. STERN ARCHITECTS
Architects and Interior Designers

This prestigious firm currently has projects underway in 20 states as well as in the Netherlands, Canada, Spain, Japan and Mexico. Stern is a practicing architect, teacher and writer as well as founder and senior partner in the firm. He is well-known for the shingle style that he developed in designing homes on the east coast. He is also a Fellow of the American Institute of Architects and received the Medal of Honor from its New York Chapter in 1984.

460 West 34th Street
New York, NY 10001
Tel: 212-967-5100
Fax: 212-244-2054

ROBERT ISABELL
Florists

"Oh, so and so is the Robert Isabell of Pasadena…" Isabell has become *the* point of reference in a hugely competitive business. He famously creates entire environments with linens, lighting, sets, entertainment, floral designs and anything else an event may need. Isabell has designed weddings for Caroline Kennedy, Whitney Houston and the Miller sisters.

410 West 13th Street
New York, NY 10014
Tel: 212-645-7767

～

ROBERT TALBOTT SHIRTS
Fashion

America's pre-eminent manufacturer of upscale neckwear and shirts has outlets in Pebble Beach and Carmel, as well as a Madison Avenue showcase in New York City. Talbott's commitment to using only the finest fabric and design is evident in its immaculately produced dress and sport shirts. We particularly like the limited edition hand craftsmanship of the Estate shirt (ranging from $295-$500), which honors the unapologetically masculine style of matinée idols like Clark Gable, Cary Grant, Spencer Tracy and Rudolph Valentino.

Talbott Studio
Carmel Valley, CA 93924
Tel: 831-624-6604
Fax: 831-649-4244

RON HERMAN
LANDSCAPE ARCHITECT
Architects and Interior Designers

At the time of writing, Ron Herman is engaged in planning and implementing thirty-six gardens across the country, reflecting a total construction cost of more than $400 million. Known as one of the world's foremost practitioners of residential landscape architecture and design, he has designed gardens for Oracle's CEO Larry Ellison and a host of other corporate bigwigs. Keeping close ties to Japan, where he pursued graduate coursework, a lot of Herman's designs use a Japanese approach.

261 Joaquin Avenue
San Leandro, CA 94577
Tel: 510-352-4920
Fax: 510-352-4922

RONIN SERVICES INTERNATIONAL
Security Consultants

If you suspect that someone is ripping you off, talk to Richard Haynes. Together with a large network of experts, he provides a comprehensive, state of the art security service. Clients include affluent individuals and companies in fields as varied as petrochemicals, mining, banking and retail – as well as government organizations. Through security surveys, awareness training programs and security management, investigators review the operations of the company (or premises) to identify key areas of vulnerability and weakness.

1021 Temple Street
Charleston, WV 25312
Tel: 304-346-6228

ROSE TARLOW–MELROSE HOUSE
Architects and Interior Designers

When she was six years old, little Rose Khedouri insisted her bedroom be painted pink. Not long afterwards, the future interior designer successfully prevailed upon her mother to paint all the fine antiques in her room to match. The lifetime collector of exquisite objects has said that she became a decorator because she needed venues in which to place her finds. In the 1970s, long before Aaron Spelling discovered Melrose Place, Tarlow opened her stuff-of-dreams antiques shop there. The store, Rose Tarlow–Melrose House, sells both the real thing (mainly pricey 19th century antiques) and her own designs, including a rustic Tuscan walnut table, a gorgeous ebony lamp and a Louis XVI-style desk.

8454 Melrose Place
Los Angeles, CA 90069
Tel: 323-651-2202
Fax: 323-658-6548

ROSENBERG & STIEBEL
Art Dealers

In the wide range of European art handled by Rosenberg & Stiebel, there is a pronounced emphasis on 18th century France. The gallery has sold Old Master paintings, drawings, sculpture and furniture to private collectors and museums worldwide. In New York's Metropolitan Museum of Art alone there are over 300 works that came from the gallery, including the Merode altarpiece, Chardin's *Soupiere d'Argent* and a red lacquer desk made for Louis XV. Established in 1870, this family enterprise is run by Eric Stiebel and his son Gerald.

32 East 57th Street
New York, NY 10022
Tel: 212-753-4368
Fax: 212-935-5736

ROUGH CREEK LODGE
Hotels   Best Kept Secret

Surrounded by rolling Texas hill country, Rough Creek resort features the architectural design of Larry Speck; the exterior is carved from limestone, indigenous to the region. Each room has a scenic, panoramic view of surrounding lakes, trees and hills. The interiors reflect vintage Texas elements, with native stone, wrought iron, 60-foot ceilings and supple leather accents. Rough Creek Lodge is a rustic playground (with a modern approach to comfort and convenience) for nature lovers, hunters and breast beating tycoons.

Route 1 Box 261
Iredell, TX 76649
Tel: 800-864-4705   Fax: 254-918-2570

ROY'S
Restaurants

It's hard to tell which is more popular, the restaurant's eclectic Eurasian style menu or chef/owner Roy Yamaguchi. Frequently cited as "the godfather of Pacific Rim cuisine," Roy offers authentic tropical cuisine – so authentic that the dining room is packed every night. On weekdays, reserve a table in the downstairs bar area for a quieter, more comfortable evening.

6600 Kalanianaole Highway
Honolulu, HI 96825
Tel: 808-396-7697   Fax: 808-396-8706

ROYAL GARDEN AT WAIKIKI
Hotels

Guests are treated like royalty at the Garden, nestled between the mountains and the ocean in Waikiki. Lush, terraced gardens surrounding crystal clear swimming pools provide a heavenly setting for sunbathing. Bedrooms boast closets big enough for kings, marble bathrooms, wet bars and panoramic views of the paradise landscape. The Shizu restaurant offers top-notch authentic Japanese cuisine.

440 Olohana Street
Honolulu, HI 96815
Tel: 808-943-0202

THE RYLAND INN
Restaurants

Trained by "Chef of the Century" Joel Rubochon, Craig Shelton then became David Bouley's sous chef for three years before opening the Ryland Inn, the pinnacle of French dining in the Garden State. The charming, 200-year old country house is dramatic but elegant, boasting rich mahogany, leather banquettes and a bluestone garden patio. With a wine list that offers 900 selections (and a superb cigar menu), the biophysics degree from Yale has clearly taught Shelton perfect balance.

Route 22 West
Whitehouse, NJ 08888
Tel: 908-534-4011   Fax: 908-534-6592

ROYAL FIESTA CATERERS
Party Organizers and Caterers

The most important thing we can say about Royal Fiesta Caterers is that when this Florida company takes on a function, they make sure that function is perfect. Period. Unlike hotels or country clubs, making a party perfect is their only business. Such dedication to quality explains how Royal Fiesta has garnered its reputation as the place to hold a wedding or corporate event in the Boca, Palm Beach area. No request is too difficult for the friendly, accommodating staff, many of whom, including the company's multitalented chef (formerly of the Boca Hotel) have been with the firm since it's beginning over a dozen years ago. To make one recent party a night to remember they transformed the posh, Royal Fiesta Ballroom into a winter wonderland, complete with artificial snow reflecting the light of the room's breathtaking Czechoslovakian-crystal chandeliers. With numerous amenities available, including the elegant Fountain Room, which accommodates 200, and the cozy Tiffany Room, where up to 40 guests can meet in more intimate surroundings, it's no wonder that such a diverse group of luminaries as Mohammed Ali, football star Larry Csonka, Florence Henderson and the Count and Countess de Hoernle have booked the firm's beautiful Intracoastal Waterway site. For select clients who prefer to do their entertaining at home, Royal Fiesta will also make their legendary service available for elite private parties.

1680 South East Third Court
Deerfield Beach, FL 33441
Tel: 954-570-9422   Fax: 954-570-9833

S. BERNSTEIN & CO.
Antiques

Fine Chinese jade antiquities, from the Neolithic period through the 18th century, are the specialty at this gem of a gallery. Sam Bernstein draws upon more than 20 years of expertise and his associations with scholars, curators and art historians worldwide, as well as an extensive art reference library.

Bernstein applies a methodology for dating objects and develops a dossier on each work. His Chinese jade collection can be found in museum and private collections around the world.

950 Mason Street
San Francisco, CA 94108
Tel: 415-421-3434   Fax: 415-421-3435

S.J. SHRUBSOLE
Antiques

Established on 57th Street in 1936 — the oldest antique store on the street — after operating in London since 1912, this lavish gallery boasts New York's largest selection of antique silver. The inventory is dominated by Paul Revere, Paul de Lamerie and Paul Storr pieces. Owner Tim Martin's collection includes a George II Irish silver bowl, circa 1750 with a most unusual grape vine decoration and a pair of old Sheffield plate claret jugs, circa 1825. S.J. Shrubsole possesses what may be the only silver Scottish toilet service in the world, circa 1703.

104 East 57th Street
New York, NY 10022
Tel: 212-753-8920   Fax: 212-754-5192

~

SAFRA BANK
Wealth Management

A major international provider of private banking and related financial services, Safra Bank has total assets in excess of $4 billion. Underlying its success are both the Safra banking philosophy and a commitment to protecting and prudently growing its clients' capital. The bank's face-to-face service and customer-oriented business methods differentiate it from other institutions.

546 Fifth Avenue
New York, NY 10036
Tel: 212-704-5500

~

SAKS FIFTH AVENUE
Fashion

The Saks empire may now encompass 61 department stores across America, but it's the flagship Fifth Avenue store (opened by Horace Saks and Bernard Gimbel back in 1924) that truly remains synonymous with genteel, high-end retailing. The store's luxurious environment caters to the sophisticated shopper, offering merchandise from top designers like Gucci, Chanel, Prada, Ralph Lauren, Donna Karen and Versace for women; plus Zegna, Brioni, Armani, Hugo Boss, John Bartlett and more for men. Many designers — Calvin Klein for instance — are featured in their own intimate boutiques. Amenities are important at Saks; Café SFA offers gourmet refreshments, information services help visitors navigate the store's many departments with ease, and personal shoppers are available for more comprehensive advice. A complimentary hotel package delivery service even assures that your packages make it home in first-class style.

611 Fifth Avenue
New York, NY 10022
Tel: 212-753-4000   Fax: 212-940-4239

SALANDER-O'REILLY GALLERIES
Art Dealers

This prestigious gallery exhibits and deals in works of art from the Renaissance to the present, including examples of modernism in America, 19th century European and contemporary art. Of the modernists, the gallery represents the estates of Leland Bell, Stuart Davis, Willem De Kooning and Robert DeNiro, Sr., as well as the estate of French-born Gaston Lachaise. This impressive partnership also boasts an unusual collection of work by German Expressionists — from Emil Nolde to Gustav Klimt, Max Beckman to Egon Schiele.

20 East 79th Street
New York, NY 10021
Tel: 212-879-6606
Fax: 212-744-0655

~

SALLEA ANTIQUES
Antiques

Former interior designer Sally Kaltman used to buy antique furniture and small accessories for her design clients — that is, until her fascination with antiques took center stage. Kaltman now sells a fine selection of mostly English furniture from the 18th century, and she also has this country's most extensive collection of antique boxes. "We are known as the box people," says the charming owner, before she lists a mind-boggling inventory of wooden, fruit-shaped tea caddies, tortoiseshell stamp boxes, ivory snuff containers and spectacle cases.

66 Elm Street
New Canaan, CT 06480
Tel: 203-972-1050
Fax: 203-972-1567

~

SALLY HERSHBERGER
AT JOHN FRIEDA
Hair and Beauty

Born in Kansas and raised in California, Sally Hershberger began styling hair at eighteen, landing an apprenticeship at Arthur Johns, the well-known Hollywood salon, while still in beauty school. Here, she began to establish relationships with the biggest names in entertainment, including Cindy Crawford, Brad Pitt, Meg Ryan and Steven Spielberg. A gift from veteran stylist John Frieda, her Melrose Place salon is a feast for the eyes — the waiting room boasts a pool, floor to ceiling windows, bushels of fresh flowers and bleached wood.

8440 Melrose Place
Los Angeles, CA 90069
Tel: 323-653-4040
Fax: 323-653-1377

SALON CRISTOPHE
Hair and Beauty

This full-service salon has valet parking, an espresso bar and a high celeb quotient. Most clients stop by for the wash, haircut, color and styling treatments but many add body wraps and makeup lessons once they have seen the extensive list of services offered. Enjoy a little privacy? Home appointments are no problem. Don't miss the seaweed wrap, lash tinting, or the *Sur Le Pouce*: 90 minutes with an expert hairdresser and a quick stop at the manicurist's table — all while you enjoy a spot of lunch.

348 North Beverly Drive
Beverly Hills, CA 90210
Tel: 310-274-0851

SAN DIEGO MUSEUM OF ART
Museums

The Museum of Art is the city's largest, receiving over 500,000 visitors annually. Holdings include Italian Renaissance and Spanish Baroque works, American art, 19th century European art, and an extensive Asian collection, including Chinese, Japanese, and Korean decorative arts, sculpture and paintings. This year, highlights included *Norman Rockwell: Pictures for the American People*, featuring works spanning more than 60 years of the artist's career, including 70 oil paintings and 322 covers for the *Saturday Evening Post*. In addition to the permanent collection and annual shows, the museum hosts international traveling exhibitions as well as lectures, performances and classes for children and adults.

1450 El Prado, Balboa Park
San Diego, CA 92112
Tel: 619-232-7931   Fax: 619-232-9367

SANDI MILLER BURROWS - PEGGY PICKMAN REINER DESIGNS
Jewelry and Watches

For over twenty years the team of Sandi Miller Burrows and Peggy Pickman Reiner have specialized in custom-made couture precious jewelry for women and men. The duo's imaginative workings are complemented by their materials; brilliant diamonds, natural fancy color diamonds and semi-precious stones set in platinum or 18k gold. Working alongside clients, the designers entice them with a variety of creative renderings and limited edition pieces – they are particularly adept at incorporating clients' own stones into exciting new pieces.

New York, NY
Tel: 800-711-2760   Fax: 212-996-6217

SALON D'ARTISTE
Spas and Clinics

Taking full-service to the extreme, Salon d'Artiste offers every act of pampering imaginable – waxing, body wraps, manicure, pedicure, hair cut and color, tweezing services and a full menu of not so run-of-the-mill services. Try a cleansing facial with an eye zone treatment designed to soothe fine lines, an algae facial exfoliation treatment or a Murad Environmental Shield Vitamin C treatment for a really unique experience. For utter relaxation, try the Swedish massage.

503 West Lancaster Avenue
Strafford, PA 19087
Tel: 610-687-2020

SALTS
Restaurants   *Rising Star*

In only three years of operation, proprietors Lisa-Mandy and Steve Rosen have decorated the walls of Salts with accolades usually awarded to longtime veterans. Jerry Shriver awarded the new venture with "One of the Most Memorable Eats of 1999" and the same year, Steve was named "One of the Best New Chefs in America." The New England hot spot has appeared in *USA Today*, *The Wall Street Journal*, and *Food and Wine*. The menu glitters with delectable entrées; most popular is the pan roasted brook trout, served with a nasturtium vinaigrette. The restaurant is a welcome haven for MIT and Harvard dignitaries, as well as local celebrities. For those who rarely get to Massachusetts, the Rosens have begun working on their first cookbook, *The Heirloom Pantry*.

798 Main Street
Cambridge, MA 02139
Tel: 617-876-8444   Fax: 617-876-8569

SAN DIEGO POLO CLUB
Polo Clubs

Located 25 miles north of San Diego, in Rancho Santa Fe, The San Diego Polo Club is spread across 78 acres of rural California countryside, with five playing fields and a training ground. Membership is limited to 35 founding members, each of whom can recommend one sponsored member. While all of these slots are currently filled, polo enthusiasts new to the area may take solace in the fact that there are an unlimited number of social memberships. The 70 founding and sponsored members keep approximately 650 thoroughbreds at the club, each with a private staff of groomers and trainers. Tommy Lee Jones and Sylvester Stallone have been known to drop in for a game.

14555 El Camino Real
Rancho Santa Fe, CA 92067
Tel: 858-481-9217   Fax: 858-481-2247

SAN FRANCISCO BAY CLUB
Fitness

Since 1977, the San Francisco Bay Club has defined the group exercise experience by providing cutting-edge classes such as the New York City Ballet workout, led by veteran ballerina Rebecca Metzger, and Cardiosamba, an aerobic class blended with Latin and African rhythms. With 33 personal trainers and over 100 classes per week, the 75,000 square-foot facility features an award winning aquatic center, sun deck, whirlpools, saunas and steam room. Post work-out massages, facials and manicures come with the package as well as nutrition courses and lectures on prenatal care.

150 Greenwich Street
San Francisco, CA 94111
Tel: 415-433-2550   Fax: 415-433-7161

SANTA BARBARA POLO AND RACQUET CLUB

Polo Clubs

The late 20s and 30s was a golden era for the Santa Barbara Polo Club. Spectators dressed in the finest fashions and picnicked on cashmere blankets, while servants presented a constant diet of gin, tonic and whatever you're having yourself. Today, you can almost smell this ancient glamour at the picturesque club, which keeps stabling facilities for eight full teams. Glen Holden, Sr., the Jamaican Ambassador, keeps his Gehacag team at the club, and Andrew Busch of the Budweiser family keeps his Grants Farm Manor team here as well. The Polo Black Tie Gala is the social highlight of the year.

3375 Foothill Road
Carpinteria, CA 93013
Tel: 805-684-6683

~

SAN FRANCISCO GOLF CLUB

Golf Clubs

Serious golfers aren't generally known as an effusive lot, but all that changes when they talk about the San Francisco Golf Club, famed for its rolling, tree-lined terrain and outstanding greens. "This course is a must play," raved one recent visitor. "It would be world famous if they hosted a tournament, but members want to keep this secret to themselves." Another asserts that the Tillinghast-designed course's "atmosphere is thrilling, anyone who plays there feels as if they own the place." A member of the PGA tour agrees: "Each hole is memorable in its routing, bunkers and green contours... it's a pure golf experience."

Junipero Serra Blvd. & Brotherhood Way
San Francisco, CA 94132
Tel: 415-469-4100

SAN YSIDRO RANCH

Hotels

Vivien Leigh and Laurence Olivier got married here. Since then, thousands of honeymooning couples have followed in their wake. Why? The answer lies in the serenity of San Ysidro Ranch, the panoramic views and the luxury of its many private cottages, richly-appointed rooms and suites. Its wooded grounds are set against the gracious backdrop of the Santa Ynez Mountains, overlooking the Pacific Ocean and Channel Islands. The explorer of the San Ysidro's gently rolling 500 acres will discover lush, blossoming gardens, in which fruits, vegetables and herbs are cultivated for use in the ranch restaurants.

900 San Ysidro Lane
Santa Barbara, CA 93108
Tel: 805-969-5046
Fax: 805-565-1995

~

SANTA FE HORSE PARK AND POLO CLUB

Polo Clubs

On the edge of New Mexico's adobe city, amid the harsh desert terrain, the Santa Fe Horse Park and Polo Club houses two full-size polo fields and one training arena on 27 acres of Kentucky bluegrass, not to mention a state-of-the-art hunter, jumper, and dressage facility. The polo grounds are maintained for 50 playing members.

460 St. Michael's Drive, Building 1000
Santa Fe, NM 87501
Tel: 505-424-7400

SARATOGA

Events

Located on 350 acres, Saratoga Racecourse is the oldest track in America. Its first thoroughbred meet, staged by gambler, casino-owner, ex-boxing champ and future congressman John 'Old Smoke' Morrissey was run in August of 1863. Today, Saratoga still takes pride in its Victorian heritage, although it is a good deal more cosmopolitan than of old. Each year, Saratoga Springs hosts a 36-day race meet between late July and early September. Saratoga was awarded the "Great Place Award" in 1997 by *American Heritage* Magazine.

2150 Hampstead Turnpike
Elmont, NY 11003
Tel: 516-488-6000   Fax: 516-488-4185

~

SCHWARZ GALLERY

Art Dealers

Frank Schwarz founded this gallery in 1930, originally showcasing his collection of antique furniture and silver. When his son Robert took over the firm in the late 60s, the gallery's focus switched to 18th, 19th and 20th-century American paintings and works on paper — specifically works by Philadelphia artists. The firm has one of the most comprehensive collections of such art in the world, including major pieces from the Peale and Xanthus Smith families. Director Renée Gross is an erudite guide.

1806 Chestnut Street
Philadelphia, PA 19103
Tel: 215-563-4887   Fax: 215-561-5621

SANTA FE OPERA

Events

One of the Southwest's premier opera houses, the Santa Fe has an unusual geographical situation: it is nestled amongst the Sangre de Cristo Mountains seven miles north of Santa Fe proper. The stunning opera house was an open-air amphitheater until 1997, at which point it gained a roof and adobe walls. A tradition of nurturing and launching young international talent continues here, guided by director John Crosby, who established the house in 1957. A more dramatic setting to hear classic and modern opera could hardly be imagined.

Taos Highway
Santa Fe, NM 87500
Tel: 505-986-5900   Fax: 505-986-5999

SCHRAMSBERG VINEYARDS

Winemakers

America's premier producer of *Methode Champenoise* sparking wines, Schramsberg got a jump start in 1972 when Richard Nixon took a bottle of its champagne with him on a visit to China. New vintages offered by the firm include the popular Blanc de Blancs, Cremant, Brut Rose and Mirabelle. Schramsberg incorporates barrel fermentation and extended bottle aging, using grapes from California's finest vineyards. Each Schramsberg cuvée shows unique character and flavors, making the wines a perfect match for a wide variety of foods.

1400 Schramsberg Road
Calistoga, CA 94515
Tel: 942-6668   Fax: 707-942-5943

THE SCHWEBEL COMPANY

Architects and Interior Designers

Todd Schwebel is a renaissance man of sorts. His unique Chicago-based architecture and design firm provides what he likes to call "couture for the house," a focus on every aspect of a building's design, from its architectural structure and gardens, to the subtlest element of its interior design. No detail is too small for his attention, so it's no wonder that his firm is the first one many people – including descendants of some of America's founding families – turn to when the historic homes they treasure need restoration, or when they want to be certain that a new addition will be sympathetic to the original structure. Though well-known as an expert on 19th century American furnishings, Schwebel's passion for integrated design is legendary, whether his project is an 18th century Virginia manor house or a more recent Chicago classic of the modernist era. Working with fine artisans the world over to craft a home's details, he's been known to select an exquisite architectural motif, then repeat that design on hand-blocked wallpapers and custom-embroidered velvet drapery panels to create a truly unforgettable effect. Next for the meticulous designer is the restoration of the venerable Quadrangle Club in Chicago, designed by Howard Van Doren Shaw in Chicago.

311 West Superior Street
Chicago, IL 60610
Tel: 312-280-1998   Fax: 312-280- 2290

SCOTT SNYDER

Architects and Interior Designers

Maintaining offices in Palm Beach and New York, Scott Snyder's work combines classic and timeless interiors with an enduring sense of style. A graduate of a progressive school of the arts in Pennsylvania, he began his career as the owner of an upscale home furnishings store in 1979. Since then he has been offering his expert interior design services to a variety of discerning clients worldwide. Recent projects include a mountain retreat in the Colorado Rocky Mountains, a Texas ranch and a resort in Antigua, British West Indies.

42 Via Mivner
Palm Beach, FL 33480
Tel: 561-659-6255   Fax: 561-832-5946

SCOTTSDALE MUSEUM OF CONTEMPORARY ART

Museums

Local philanthropists Gerard Cafesjian, Virginia Ullman and Ellie and Michael Ziegler each contributed over $1 million to establish this exemplary institution. Upcoming highlights include Donald Sultan's striking pop-influenced still lifes and a retrospective of works by German sculptor Wolfgang Laib. The museum hosts an Art-rageous Ball each February.

7374 East Second Street
Scottsdale, AZ 85251
Tel: 480-994-2787

SCULLY AND SCULLY
Specialty Shops

New York society has long used Scully & Scully as a one-stop-shop for distinguished gifts and home furnishings. Founded in 1934, the store specializes in English and American reproduction antique furniture, Herend porcelain, Lynn Chase china, Halcyon Days English enamels, crystal, silver, leather goods, lamps, and many more of the finest accessories for the home. Its interior design department has done exceptional work in many of New York's more elegant homes and its bridal registry attracts couples from throughout the United States.

504 Park Avenue
New York, NY 10022
Tel: 212-755-2590

SEA ISLAND
Golf Clubs

Built on an 18th century cotton plantation, Sea Island is home to two superb championship golf courses along the coast of Georgia on St. Simons Island. The Plantation Course was redone in 1998 by Rees Jones, while the Seaside, a favorite of golf legend Bobby Jones, was enhanced in 1999 by Tom Fazio. When he's not touring, Davis Love III lives at the club, which has hosted seven USGA championships in its history and hosted the U.S. Women's Senior Amateur Tournament in September 2000. Golfers staying at The Cloister Hotel may use the course, but the club is not currently taking new members.

100 Hudson Place
Sea Island, GA 31561
Tel: 912-638-3611

SEAMAN SCHEPPS
Jewelry and Watches

Seamen Schepps' imagination and chutzpah served him well on both coasts: his witty and flattering jewelry has long been coveted by lady lunchers and movie stars alike. Today, the company Schepps founded in 1904 continues to approach jewelry making with precision and flair, specializing in dressy, design-oriented pieces—even though the Schepps family no longer owns the business. Look out for the trademark shell earrings, a stunning combination of 18-karat gold and beautiful gemstones. Schepps' clients – past and present – have included the Duchess of Windsor, Andy Warhol, Blanche Knopf and Eileen Ford. No wonder he was called 'America's Court Jeweler.'

485 Park Avenue
New York, NY 10022
Tel: 212-753-9520   Fax: 212-753-9531

SEATTLE ART MUSEUM
Museums

When the Seattle Art Museum opened its doors in Volunteer Park in 1933, the collection focused primarily on Asian art. Today, the new, five-story property, designed by Pritzker Prize-winner Robert Venturi, has matured into a world-class arts institution with a global perspective. The collection numbers over 21,000 objects, including early Thai ceramics and over 200 Native American masks, sculpture, textiles and household objects from the Pacific Northwest, British Columbia and Alaska.

100 University Street
Seattle, WA 98101
Tel: 206-625-8900

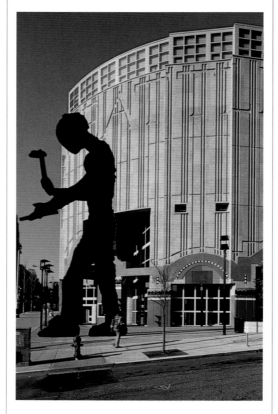

SEMINOLE GOLF CLUB
Golf Clubs

Only a lucky few have had the privilege of playing golf at Seminole, one of the most exclusive clubs in the country. Palm-tree lined fairways and 200 bunkers of brilliant white sand await, not to mention the par 4, 390-yard 6th hole, one of member Ben Hogan's favorites. In fact, Hogan often prepared for The Masters by playing here. The course, located just north of Palm Beach, was designed by Donald Ross and completed in 1929.

901 Seminole Boulevard
North Palm Beach, FL 33408
Tel: 561-626-1222

77 MAIDEN LANE
Spas and Clinics

For an exhilarating personal experience for both men and women, spend an hour or an entire day in the hands of San Francisco's most respected professionals. Sherlee Rhine's team offers an assortment of services ranging from mud baths, wraps, deep-cleansing facials, aromatic pedicures and makeup lessons in addition to hair coloring and styling. The 'Perfect Half Day' package is the ultimate in luxury, guaranteed to de-stress and rejuvenate. If your time is short, you can relax with a Swedish or deep tissue massage in as little as 25 minutes, or pamper your feet with foot reflexology, or your hands with a paraffin treatment in just 15 minutes. The all-inclusive 'Belle of the Ball' package is a perfect gift for any woman and the 'Tune Up for Men' will make the man in your life very happy.

77 Maiden Lane
San Francisco, CA 94108
Tel: 415-440-5063   Fax: 415-391-0877

SHADOW CREEK
Golf Clubs

At first glance, you may think the lush green fairways of Shadow Creek's 7239 yard par 72 course are a mirage rising out of the Las Vegas desert. But they're not, even though the $1000 green fee does include one night's stay at the nearby Mirage Hotel (sorry) and a limo ride to the course. Throw in 18 holes of eminently playable golf with incomparable hospitality, and you have one of the safest bets yet in this gambling Mecca.

3400 Las Vegas Boulevard
Las Vegas, NV 89109
Tel: 888-778-3387   Fax: 702-692-8193

SHARON SACKS PRODUCTIONS

Party Organizers and Caterers

President of this Los-Angeles based event production company, Sharon Sacks has staged events for princes and presidents, for the Three Tenors and countless Hollywood elite. Her creations have been set against the glamour of Beverly Hills and the excitement of World Cup soccer in Paris. And while she's executed large scale events – everywhere from L.A.'s Memorial Coliseum to New York's Times Square - her flawless sensibilities may be best glimpsed, more intimately, near the altar of romance. Among those fiancés who have turned to Sacks are Norman Lear, Bud Yorkin, Alan Horn and Billy Gerber. And Sacks' much publicized wedding of John Stamos to Rebecca Romijn, featured on *Oprah*, was lauded as one of the top weddings in recent years. On the world stage, Sacks Productions has worked on behalf of President Clinton, Al Gore, Senator Barbara Boxer, Hillary Rodham Clinton and Britain's Prince Andrew. Her services include budget management, event design, invitations and guest list management, catering, floral design, transportation and security

6934 Canby Avenue, Suite 103
Reseda, CA 91335
Tel: 818-996-9655   Fax: 818-996-9654

SHAFER

Winemakers

In 1972 John Shafer left a long career in publishing and moved to the Napa Valley to realize a dream. After purchasing a 209-acre estate in the Stags Leap District, the Shafer family crushed their first Cabernet grapes. That first Cabernet became a benchmark, winning the acclaimed San Francisco Vintners Club taste-off upon release. Over a decade later, it took first place in an international blind tasting in Germany, where it outranked Château Margaux, Château Latour and Château Palmer. From a modest beginning of 1000 cases in 1978, the winery has grown steadily; today it produces some 30,000 cases of Cabernet Sauvignon, Merlot, Chardonnay and Sangiovese.

6154 Silverado Trail
Napa, CA 94558
Tel: 707-944-2877

SHAPUR MOZAFFARIAN

Jewelry and Watches

Shapur Mozaffarian's jewelry store on Post Street in San Francisco houses a wealth of traditional and unique artistry. Each of Shapur's one-of-a-kind pieces carries the mark of generations of expertise and superior craftsmanship. The business originated in Persia in 1883, but his family's tradition of jewelry-making dates back even further.

245 Post Street
San Francisco, CA 94108
Tel: 415-392-1200
Fax: 415-392-6660

SHEARMAN & STERLING

Law Firms

Shearman and Sterling came of age in the golden era of frontier capitalism and the birth of American financial markets. Andrew Carnegie and J.P. Morgan were early clients; their railroads, banks and insurance companies helped grow S & S into the international powerhouse it is today. The firm is now the top legal representative for IPOs, one of the most lucrative of legal fields. S & S is also among the more 'wired' law firms – its internal and external computer and communications systems are second to none.

599 Lexington Avenue
New York, NY 10022
Tel: 212-848-4000

SHELLY ZEGART QUILTS

Specialty Shops

The best American quilts are found at this Kentucky institution. Proprietor Shelly Zegart, the author of *American Quilt Collections: Antique Quilt Masterpieces*, consults with clients to help them understand and collect this uniquely American art form. The pure homespun Americana evoked by these quilts is unmatched by any other folk art form, and clients from around the world have come to depend on Zegart to supply expert advice and supreme quality quilts. There is no actual shop; call for an appointment.

300 Penruth Avenue
Louisville, KY 40207
Tel: 502-897-7566   Fax: 502-897-3819

SHERRY-LEHMANN

Wine Merchants

Jack Aaron and his brother Sam founded Sherry-Lehmann in 1934, immediately after the end of prohibition. From day one, the Manhattan-based wine merchants have had a reputation for quality and innovation. Responsible for introducing many of the top French chateaux to the U.S., the firm's collection of claret and port is one of the finest in the world. Sherry-Lehmann also does great justice to the wine regions of Australia, New Zealand, South Africa and California. Warmly recommended.

679 Madison Avenue
New York, NY 10021
Tel: 212-838-7500   Fax: 212-838-9285

SHUTTERS ON THE BEACH
Hotels
This sumptuous yet unpretentious beach hotel has the lived-in feel of a private residence. Guest rooms are elegant in every detail – a complimentary copy of Ernest Hemingway's *Old Man and The Sea*, CDs, potted plants and framed antique pictures of beach goers from the 1920s and 30s – and many boast sunset views over the Pacific. Bathrooms have separate chambers for the shower and the sink, two sinks in the vanity and double-size whirlpool tubs. Warmly recommended.

One Pico Boulevard
Santa Monica, CA 90405
Tel: 310-458-0030   Fax: 310-458-4589

SHINNECOCK HILLS
Golf Clubs
A traditional links-style golf course with tall grasses lining its narrow fairways, Shinnecock Hills is one of the five founding clubs of the United States Golf Association. Redesigned by Stanford White in 1931, the course is a classic of natural beauty and tradition. It has hosted the U.S. Open three times in the last century and has been chosen to host again in 2004. With 325 members, the club is full to capacity, although it does have a 10 year waiting list.

200 Tuckahoe Road
Southampton, NY 11968
Tel: 631-283-1310

SHIPMAN HOUSE
Hotels   Best Kept Secret
As quoted by his wife Charmain, Jack London said "To me, Mother Shipman is the First Lady of Hawaii." A Hawaiian of high rank, Mary Kahiwaaialii Johnson Shipman received the house as a gift from her husband Willie, a cattle rancher. Mary threw elegant soirées at the House – today, the 1912 Steinway Grand Piano that Hawaii's last Queen, Liliuokalani, played at those parties still stands. A very private, five-room inn owned and operated by Barbara Ann Anderson (Mary and Willie's great-granddaughter), Shipman House allows travelers to see Hawaii without the crowded fuss of a major resort. Stay in Auntie Carrie's room, which encompasses one third of the original ballroom; it overlooks a lush backyard.

131 Kaiulani St.
Hilo, HI 96720
Tel: 800-627-8447

SHREVE & CO.
Jewelry and Watches
Founded in 1852 by the brothers Shreve, this is San Francisco's oldest jeweler and one of the nine oldest in the nation. Shreve carries a full range of jewelry, including diamonds, watches and precious stones but it is best known for its Mikimoto boutique, showcasing large black Tahitian South Sea pearls and cold-water akoyas. The firm also boasts a Suna Boutique, where a pink diamond set in platinum glistens from its showcase.

200 Post Street
San Francisco, CA 94108
Tel: 415-421-2600
Fax: 415-296-8187

SHREVE, CRUMP & LOW
Antiques
In 1796, silversmith and watchmaker John McFarlane founded Shreve, Crump & Low, named after its most generous investors. At the time, the firm was only selling jewelry; the antiques department wasn't launched until just before the Civil War. The oldest dealer in America is steeped in tradition: advertisements from the 1800s are remarkably similar to those used today (with the exception of the gas lighting department). Featuring 18th and 19th century English and American furniture, decorative arts, prints, paintings and estate jewelry, many of the better pieces relate to New England's history, primarily the China Trade period.

330 Boylston Street
Boston, MA 02116
Tel: 617-267-9100

SIDLEY & AUSTIN
Law Firms
Even when conducting billion-dollar cases, Sidley & Austin focuses on cost-effective service and high ethical standards in its legal practice. Its 900 attorneys represent many of the largest American corporations and most powerful citizens on three continents. Several of its most important cases have been argued before the U.S. Supreme Court, proving that corporate law does sometimes come out of the boardroom.

One First National Plaza
Chicago, IL 60603
Tel: 312-853-7000   Fax: 312-853-7036

SILVER OAK CELLARS
Winemakers
In 1972 Justin Meyer and Raymond Duncan became partners. Their goal was to plant a vineyard and manage 750 acres of land that Duncan owned. Today Silver Oak specializes in the production of Cabernet Sauvignon, making two appellations from

its integrated wineries in Alexander and Napa Valley. An extensive aging program (and a great deal of patience) contributes to the legendary finesse and complexity of Silver Oak. The 1992 is particularly good.

915 Oakville Cross Road
Oakville, CA 94562
Tel: 800-273-8809

SOOLIP PAPERIE & PRESS
Specialty Shops

Soolip Paperie and Press is a paper boutique featuring a vast array of handmade papers and cards, photo albums, journals, ribbons, stationery and writing accouterments. A haven for those who appreciate the art of gift wrapping and the subtleties of presentation, Wanda Wen, Grant Forsberg and their team will also design and print one-of-a-kind wedding and party invitations, birth announcements and personal stationery in their custom letterpress printing department. For household accessories and furniture, visit Soolip Bungalow, which houses an eclectic mix of treasures, such as 18th century Chinese antiques and a distinctively luxurious women's clothing collection.

8646 Melrose Avenue
West Hollywood, CA 90069
Tel: 310-360-0545   Fax: 310-360-0548

SILVERADO VINEYARDS
Winemakers

Walt Disney's widow Lillian, daughter Diane and her husband first purchased land in Napa Valley in the mid-1970s. After realizing that the grapes they were selling were too good to part with, they decided to build their own winery, and in 1982 they produced the first wine under the Silverado moniker. Today they farm over 350 acres and produce a superb Cabernet Sauvignon in addition to Merlot, Sangiovese and Sauvignon Blanc.

6121 Silverado Trail
Napa, CA 94558
Tel: 707-257-1770   Fax: 707-257-1538

VICTOR SKREBNESKI
Portrait Painters and Photographers

John Malkovich, Bette Davis and Vanessa Redgrave have all been photographed by this gifted photographer, who has long been celebrated as one of America's best. He chooses the image and you choose the size, which might be a 6-by-6 foot print, like the one a power couple from Chicago requested. Skrebneski has worked with everyone from Lacroix to St. Laurent and has recently published a book, *Skrebneski: The First 50 Years.*

1350 North Lasalle
Chicago, IL 60610
Tel: 312-944-1339

SKADDEN, ARPS, SLATE, MEAGHER & FLOM
Law Firms

From its new base in Times Square, Skadden Arps attorneys rule over a legal empire with 21 offices worldwide. A wide variety of casework and clients are represented, from start-up high-tech companies to *Fortune 500* organizations, from government entities to wealthy investors. But Skadden is no triumph of quantity over quality: 37 of the firm's partners were listed in the 2000 edition of *The Best Lawyers in America.* Of course, visitors to the Times Square HQ can also get a gander at the mini-skirted Condé Nast editorial staff, with whom the firm shares a building.

4 Times Square
New York, NY 10036
Tel: 212-735-3000   Fax: 212-735-2000

SOLE BY SOLEDAD TWOMBLY
Fashion

In the autumn of 1997 Soledad Twombly and Maria Pia Bascilico met in New York City. Today, their line of eastern-inspired women's wear is

cherished by fashion insiders. Recently Twombly created a couture maternity line only available at Barneys. The Buenos Aires native's main inspiration for this came from her son Caio, whose father (and Soledad's husband) is the talented artist Alessandro Twombly.

611 Broadway, Suite 841
New York, NY 10012
Tel: 212-477-2005
Fax: 212-674-8617

SOKOLIN WINES
Wine Merchants
Bill and Dave Sokolin, a father and son team, are among the largest importers of Bordeaux wines. They also control a chunk of the nation's supply of Dom Perignon. Recently moved from Manhattan to the East End of Long Island, they are looking with keen interest at the rapid developments in the neighborhood: Bill devoted a section of his last book, *The Complete Wine Investor*, to the investment potential of Long Island wine. Incidentally, besides being one of the great characters of the American wine business, Bill once played baseball for the Brooklyn Dodgers.

25 North Sea Road
Southampton, NY 11968
Tel: 631-283-0505   Fax: 631-287-3739

SONIAT HOUSE
Hotels   Best Kept Secret
Located in the heart of the French Quarter, Soniat House is one of New Orleans' best-kept secrets. Rodney and Frances Smith have turned their 1830 Creole-style townhouse into a gem of a hotel. Each one of its 33 rooms is unique, individually decorated with French and American antiques by the couple, whose passion for collecting is evident in every detail. In fact, so many guests wanted to purchase the furniture they found in their luxurious rooms and suites that the Smiths happily opened two antique galleries to meet their requests.

1133 Chartres Street
New Orleans, LA 70116
Tel: 504-522-0570   Fax: 504-522-0570

SOTHEBY'S
Auction Houses
Samuel Baker, who founded Sotheby's in London in 1744, would hardly recognize his old firm today. The company that once auctioned the books Napoleon took into exile with him is today offering goodies as diverse as Russian space capsules, Tyrannosaurus Rex fossils and a 60-year-old slice of wedding cake (don't ask). Recent triumphs include the personal estates of Jacqueline Kennedy Onassis and the Duchess of Windsor, which both sold for staggering figures, and Cézanne's *Rideau, Cruchon et Compotier*, which made a record breaking $60.5 million. A few months ago, owner Alfred Taubman made history again, when Sotheby's became the first international auction house to hold auctions on the internet. That wasn't, of course, the only time that Sotheby's made headlines in the last year. What would Samuel Baker say?

1334 York Avenue
New York, NY 10021
Tel: 212-606-7000

STAG'S LEAP WINE CELLARS
Winemakers
Warren Winiarski left a teaching career at the University of Chicago in 1964 to follow the destiny in his name: in Polish Winiarski means "Son of a Winemaker." Winiarski's 1973 S.L.V. Cabernet won first place in the 1976 Paris Tasting, beating Chateau Mouton Rothschild and other premier crus, putting California on the world wine map. This family-owned and operated winery (not to be confused with neighboring Stags' Leap Winery) produces other varietal wines, but its Cabernet is still the star attraction, noted for its "iron fist in a velvet glove" characteristic. CASK 23, its premier red table wine, commands the highest wine prices in the nation.

5766 Silverado Trail
Napa, CA 94558
Tel: 707-944-2020   Fax: 707-257-7501

SOTHEBY'S INTERNATIONAL REALTY
Property Consultants
Sotheby's International Realty has set the pace for luxury real estate brokerage around the globe since 1976. Sotheby's clients enjoy an unparalleled level of service, taking advantage of its prestigious network of more than 200 affiliates from England to South Korea to Australia. Leaders in their respective markets, these associates are selected for their record of excellence in serving clients; combined with Sotheby's expertise in real estate and the firm's impeccable reputation, it is hardly surprising that the alliance has prospered.

980 Madison Avenue
New York, NY 10021
Tel: 212-606-7660
Fax: 212-606-4199

SOVEREIGN
Chauffeur Services
Preferred chauffeur service of the Museum of Fine Arts, the Houston Grand Opera and the five-diamond Omni Hotel, Sovereign Services is more like an exclusive club than a chauffeur service. Brothers Harry and Ray Karr keep 11 pristine vehicles stocked with every amenity from cellular phones to your newspaper, beverage and music of choice. Chauffeurs have a labyrinthine knowledge of the city they drive in and know quite a lot about you, too – they keep a file on your preferences. Clients include Colin Powell and Henry Kissinger.

PO Box 460105
Houston, TX 77056-0571
Tel: 713-777-0571
Fax: 713-785-3113

THE SPORTS CENTER
Fitness

Located in the enormous Chelsea Piers complex, the Sports Center offers boxing, rock climbing, swimming, dance classes, yoga and 150 other specialty services. Members can also join competitive basketball teams. The Center challenges your body with ranger school, the same training that actual army rangers endure. Private training sessions are available, as well as dietary consultation and body fat analysis.

Pier 60, West Side Highway
New York, NY 10011
Tel: 212-336-6000

THE SPORTS CLUB – LA
Fitness

When Madonna, Princess Stephanie of Monaco and Prince need to work out in Los Angeles, they often trundle down to the Sports Club (like the rest of us mere mortals). The luxury athletic facility now has a sparkling new Manhattan branch, providing the same high level of service to bi-coastal members and health-freak New Yorkers. Patrons enjoy a full range of cutting-edge weight and cardiovascular machines, plus a swimming pool, sportswear boutique, basketball court and state-of-the-art spa and hair salon. Personal trainers, as well as an on-staff nutritionist and dietitian, oversee all fitness needs, whims and aspirations.

1835 Sepulveda Boulevard
Los Angeles, CA 90025
Tel: 310-477-7799

SPRING CREEK RANCH
Hotels

Set 1000 feet above Jackson Hole, one of the most inspiring valleys in the world, Spring Creek Ranch is a luxurious ski resort and summer playground. From white-water rafting to glider rides (guests soar over the Tetons in luxury passenger aircraft) Spring Creek is pure invigoration for the senses. Schedule a Yellowstone National Park tour, with lunch at Old Faithful. In the winter, the Alpine Slide winds down Snow King Mountain through 2500 feet of woods, wild flowers and crisp, mountain air. For the best views, try hot air ballooning or an aerial tram ride. Secure a 6500 foot Executive home, your own private residence on the ranch grounds, but absolutely secluded.

1800 Spirit Dance Road
Jackson Hole, WY 83001
Tel: 800-443-6139
Fax: 307-733-8833

SPYGLASS HILL
Golf Clubs

Named in honor of Robert Louis Stevenson, whose novel *Treasure Island* was inspired by a visit to the stunning Monterey Peninsula in the late 1800s, Spyglass Hill enables members to chart their own course through tall pine trees, shifting sand dunes, slick greens and incredible ocean views. Robert Trent Jones, Sr., who designed the course in 1966, called it one of his top five. Spyglass is noted for its extremely fast greens and the par four 464-yard 16th, often described as the toughest hole on the PGA Tour.

Spyglass Hill Road
Pebble Beach, CA 95953
Tel: 831-647-7500   Fax: 831-625-8592

ST. REGIS, HOUSTON
Hotels

Houston's premier social address, the St. Regis has profited from a $6 million renovation in which the classical lines of the original Caroline Hunt property have been maintained. The Remington Grill, a local favorite, has also been preserved to enhance the St. Regis experience with its traditional Texan cuisine. Satisfied customers include Tina Turner and teen pop idols the Backstreet Boys. Spacious rooms, a splendid location and a dedicated staff, led by Englishman Duncan Graham, are all appreciated by discerning travelers.

1919 Briar Oaks Lane
Houston, TX 77027
Tel: 713-840-7600   Fax: 713-840-0616

STEINWAY & SONS
Specialty Shops

Steinway & Sons Tricentennial Piano celebrates the 300th anniversary of the invention of the piano, and embodies the Steinway tradition of handmade craftsmanship and technical innovation. Steinway's collaboration with renowned furniture designer Dakota Jackson has captured the instrument's essential beauty while creating numerous innovations, including a lid that folds back on itself with a dramatic fanned effect. Says the inimitable designer: "Steinway is synonymous with the piano. As a designer and pianist, I wouldn't consider designing a piano for any other company." For information about Tricentennial, the Steinway Art Case Collection and the Crown Jewel Collection featuring the world's most beautiful woods, call 1-800-345-5086 or visit the Steinway website at www.steinway.com.

109 West 57th Street
New York, NY 10019
Tel: 800-345-5086

SUE FISHER KING
Specialty Shops

Sue Fisher King has one of the most exclusive and unique selections of Italian sheets and bed coverlets in the United States from Anichini, Frette, Catherine Memmi and their own exclusive sources. Agnona, a famous name in Italian textiles, weaves their stunning cashmere, alpaca and silk blankets and throws. The shop imports sumptuous hand blocked velvets and Fortuny silk lamps from Venice, "chateau" pottery from France, and gutsy Palio dinnerware from Siena. Sue Fisher King have specially selected a large collection of French flatware, bath linen and table linens which can be custom ordered from a large selection of samples or chosen from an eclectic mix available immediately. Whether you are selecting home furnishings for a new dwelling, or looking to add a *soupçon* of panache to an existing decor, you will discover a plethora of exciting choices at either of their San Francisco locations.

3067 Sacramento Street
San Francisco, CA 94115
Tel: 415-922-7276   Fax: 415-922-9241

STANFORD GROUP
Wealth Management

This unorthodox investment management firm — as unlike a traditional Wall Street brokerage as it is possible to imagine — offers no proprietary products. Headquartered in Houston, the firm offers a broad range of investment alternatives to the private investor; its eclectic interests include Liot, a Caribbean airline and U.S. and Swiss trusts. The Group has its own in-house real estate development agency as well as an advertising agency. Driven primarily by relationships, the Stanford Group sponsors many charities and offers annual gifts to Houston's premier theater organization, the Alley Theater, as well as being the major sponsor of the Houston Polo Club.

5050 Westheimer
Houston, TX 77056
Tel: 713-964-8302
Fax: 713-964-8360

ST. REGIS HOTEL
Hotels

Although the St. Regis Hotel, once the tallest building in New York, has been surpassed in height, its classical splendour still towers over the heart of Manhattan. A recent renovation has not detracted from the hotel's turn-of-the-century elegance, but instead has added to its distinctive charm. Attention to detail and the comfort of the guest are priorities — each floor has a butler to cater to every need. The haute cuisine Lespinasse restaurant mirrors the lofty standards of this very special establishment.

2 East 55th Street
New York, NY 10022
Tel: 212-753-4500   Fax: 212-787-3447

STANLEY KORSHAK
Fashion

The beautiful exterior of this unique Dallas store hints at the treasures that lie within. Offering the finest apparel for men and women, as well as cosmetics, shoes, precious jewelry and a full-service bridal salon, the award-winning Stanley Korshak merits a top reputation. A wide variety of the highest quality goods, including 18 and 22-karat platinum and estate jewelry, is tastefully presented and a warm, professional service adds to the store's delightful ambience. Prospective brides should take note of the Bridal Registry Rewards Program, which grants monthly prizes to newlyweds.

500 Crescent Court, Suite 100
Dallas, TX 75201
Tel: 214-871-3600   Fax: 214-871-3617

STEIN ERIKSEN LODGE
Hotels

Clad in chic Norwegian furnishings, the Stein Eriksen lodge has 41 luxury suites, any of which are a perfect haven after a long day on the slopes. Amenities include an outdoor heated swimming pool, sauna and a heated underground parking garage. Exercise facilities and snow mobile tours are available. Ski lessons are arranged with Deer Valley slopes. Executive chef Gerard Burnett serves American cuisine with a European flair in The Glitterton Restaurant.

7700 Stein Way
Park City, UT 84060
Tel: 435-649-3700
Fax: 435-649-5828

STANFORD UNIVERSITY
Colleges

Stanford students happily allow their rivals at Berkeley to bask in self-proclaimed intellectual superiority. After all, who has Palo Alto and exquisite Mediterranean-influenced campus architecture? Who has John Elway and Tiger Woods, to say nothing of a First Daughter whose spring breaks have lately included world diplomacy? And beyond its myriad other virtues, Stanford cherishes its role as an intellectual cradle for Silicon Valley titans like James Clark and Jerry Yang — a development officer's dream.

Main Quad
Stanford, CA 94305
Tel: 650-723-2489   Fax: 650-725-6847

STARKEY INTERNATIONAL
Employment Agencies

A founder of the International Nanny Association, Mary Louise Starkey has been placing household managers, personal assistants and chefs in the nation's more affluent homes for over 16 years. Eight-week intensive training programs in a 13,000 square-foot Georgian manor ensure that Starkey graduates (there are over 400 of them working throughout the U.S.) shine in even the most demanding American households.

1350 Logan Street
Denver, CO 80203
Tel: 800-888-4904

STEMS
Florists

We love the stylish arrangements that Maggie Oyen creates at this floral boutique. Oyen's designs enhance everything from corporate events for Bear Stearns to lavish weddings in Martha's Vineyard. To the delight of her devoted clientele, Stems has now gone national. Oyen's more than capable staff will ship beautiful personalized flower arrangements coast to coast, relieving senders of the dread of wondering whether or not the exotic orchids they ordered will somehow turn into chrysanthemums en route.

98 Elizabeth Street
Redhook, NY 12571
Tel: 914-758-8080
Fax: 914-758-8082

STERLING DOMESTICS
Employment Agencies
JaNiece Rush's contingency search firm specializes in staffing the homes and properties of some of the world's most prosperous families. Named "Best of the Best" in 1997 by the Association of Celebrity Personal Assistants, the firm supplies a discerning clientele with assistants, private yacht and aircraft staff, bodyguards, butlers, nannies, chefs and maids. Sterling also offers unusual services, such as "Kid Couriers." These professional nannies travel with children to join parents for part of a vacation or to visit a parent while working on the road.
633 Third Avenue
New York, NY 10017
Tel: 212-661-5813   Fax: 212-867-9147

STEUBEN
Specialty Shops
For nearly 100 years, Steuben has been at the forefront of glass design, balancing state-of-the-art technological advancements with centuries-old traditional glassmaking techniques. Founded in 1903 by English glassmaker Frederick Carder, the firm is named after Steuben County, New York, where its design studio and sole glassworks facility are still located. Today, the company's master craftsmen create everything from graceful, fluid forms sculpted in molten crystal to complex designs cut or engraved on the cooled glass. Check out the company's brand new flagship on Madison Avenue.
667 Madison Avenue
New York, NY 10022
Tel: 212-752-1441

SURROUNDINGS
Florists
Founded in 1976, the firm's flagship store on Manhattan's Upper West Side is an integral part of the design community, serving discerning homemakers like Julie Andrews, Cindy Crawford and Steven Spielberg. President Gary Buckwald handpicks intriguing new vases from around the globe to enhance a bouquet's appearance. Surroundings also has a network of affiliates who meet their exacting standards in several cities around the country.
224 West 79th Street
New York, NY 10024
Tel: 212-675-2688 ext. 124   Fax: 212-724-9131

STEVEN HOLL ARCHITECTS
Architects and Interior Designers
In addition to winning several prestigious awards, the prolific principal of this New York firm has published some 150 articles since 1978. His designs have been exhibited at the Walker Art Center in Minneapolis and the Henry Art Gallery in Seattle. In 1989, the Museum of Modern Art presented Holl's work in a special two-man show, purchasing several drawings for their permanent collection. Holl learned his trade in Rome and founded his firm in 1976.
435 Hudson Street, 4th Floor
New York, NY 10014
Tel: 212-989-0918
Fax: 212-463-9718

STRATEGIC CONTROLS
Security Consultants
In business since 1978, Gerald O'Rourke's security philosophy is one of "total control." A former state trooper, deputy U.S. marshal and security manager of Flying Tiger Airways, O'Rourke now acts as an independent security consultant to large institutions and private clients. Although he is based in New York City, he is often called to re-evaluate and redesign problematic security situations for companies who do not employ a full-time security management team around the country.
244 Madison Avenue, Suite 147
New York, NY 10016
Tel: 888-206-8325

STONEPINE
Hotels
The only Purple Shield Relais & Chateaux property in America, Stonepine is only for those looking for serious luxury. Set in the seclusion of picturesque Carmel Valley, it was built in the late 20s and has been embellished and expanded since 1983 by owners Gordon and Noel Hentschel. Covering 330 pristine acres on gently rolling hills, Stonepine offers 16 accommodations, including two private cottages, inspired by notable designers Chanel and Cartier. Chateau Noel, the main house, is set in Italian Renaissance style with a seven-foot carved limestone fireplace, innumerable antiques, fine oil paintings, Lalique crystal and porcelain by Lladro. For those who prefer an equine environment, snag one of the four suites in the Paddock House, set on the oldest operating thoroughbred ranch west of the Mississippi.
150 East Carmel Valley Road
Carmel Valley, CA 93924
Tel: 831-659-2245   Fax: 831-659-5160

STRIBLING & ASSOCIATES
Property Consultants
Elizabeth Stribling founded her brokerage firm in 1980, setting her sights on the most exclusive addresses in Manhattan, including Park Avenue and Central Park West. With 110 experienced brokers and agents, the company's average sale price for townhouses, condominiums and cooperative apartments is $1 million and spans up to $20 million. Large enough to offer distinctive properties, yet small enough to tend to detail, the firm was honored in 1995, when Stribling won the Henry Foster Award for outstanding achievement and conduct within the residential brokerage profession.
924 Madison Avenue
New York, NY 10021
Tel: 212-570-2440

STUBBS & WOOTTON
Specialty Shops
Founded in 1993 by Percival Steinhart, Stubbs & Wootton offers a unique line of men's and women's day into evening wear velvet slippers. The shoes are made from European fabrics, including needlepoints, tapestries, linens and velvet, many featuring intricate embroideries. Crafted by an in-house team, the materials are manufactured and imported from Spain and Italy and offered at three branches: Palm Beach, New York and Southampton. The slippers are carried at select Neiman Marcus stores, as are sandals, mules and handbags for women.
323 Worth Avenue
Palm Beach, FL 33480
Tel: 561-655-4105

STUDIO SOFIELD
Architects and Interior Designers

With a resumé that boasts projects for the likes of Gucci, Donna Karan and the SoHo Grand Hotel, William Sofield is one of the most sought-after modernists in the interior design industry today. Graduate of Princeton University and former Helena Rubenstein Fellow (a prestigious curator studies scholarship granted by the Whitney) he has designed upscale retail stores, corporate headquarters and private residences in the United States and abroad. Sofield donates services and strategic support to the Irvington Institute for Medical Research, the Alzheimer's Association and AIDS Project Los Angeles – he is one of the most thoughtful talents of his generation.

380 Lafayette Street
New York, NY 10003
Tel: 212-473-1300

STYLINE FURNITURE
Specialty Shops

Jeff Wasserman has stocked Styline with rare and unusual pieces for the past seven years – the firm now has one of the most impressive collections of trendsetting contemporary furniture in the nation. Dressed up more like a gallery than a furniture store, the artistic showroom represents the best in cutting-edge contemporary style and caters to both the public and designers. At the time of writing, the inventory included a king-size bed with legs constructed from automobile shock absorbers. Check out the Wasserman's handmade rugs from Thailand, woven from pure, New Zealand wool.

116 South Federal Highway
Fort Lauderdale, FL 33301
Tel: 954-523-3375
Fax: 954-525-3375

SULLIVAN & CROMWELL
Law Firms

Many of America's more prominent moguls turn to this establishment law firm for representation, trusting its renowned responsiveness to client needs and its expert understanding of the business world. Sullivan & Cromwell has long been at the forefront of American corporate law. Coming of age with its structuring of General Electric and U.S. Steel in the 19th century, the firm has grown with the times, and now has a client list that includes Microsoft and Goldman, Sachs.

125 Broad Street
New York, NY 10004
Tel: 212-558-4000
Fax: 212-558-3588

SUMMIT AVIATION
Airplanes

If you need a Hawker to hightail it to Hong Kong, or a Boeing to blast off to Belgium, Summit will make it happen. The firm can cater for every airborne occasion, as demonstrated when President George Bush hired a jet for his 75th birthday celebration and went skydiving. Less adventurous clients prefer, however, to remain within the comfort and safety of Summit's cabins and enjoy a wide range of facilities and personalized service, which extends well beyond the flight. If you wish to holiday in style, Summit will also assist with reservations for international events as diverse as European golf tournaments and the Olympic Games.

7144 Republic Airport
East Farmingdale, NY 11735
Tel: 516-756-2545
Fax: 516-756-0809

SUMPTER PRIDDY III
Antiques

Sumpter Priddy has had an eye for antiques his entire life. As if to prove the point, there is a favorite table in his office that the venerable dealer acquired when he was only twelve years old. After honing his skills as a collector by working as the curator of exhibitions at Colonial Williamsburg, he opened his own business some twenty years ago, and now sells a variety of very select 18th and 19th century furniture, decorative pieces and fine arts. Considered one of the nation's leading experts on Southern antiques, Priddy is proud to exhibit his wares at the Winter Antiques Fair in New York.

601 South Washington Street
Alexandria, VA 22314
Tel: 703-299-0800
Fax: 703-299-9688

SUNSET COTTAGE
Architects and Interior Designers

Richard and Mollie Mulligan's work is a favorite of discerning celebrities and their company, Sunset Cottage, is among the leading country design firms on the west coast. The Mulligans' client list has included Goldie Hawn, Bette Midler and Dick Donner and they have worked on homes in upscale locales nationwide, including Aspen, Jackson Hole, Vail, Martha's Vineyard and Nantucket.

8157 Sunset Boulevard
Los Angeles, CA 90046
Tel: 323-650-8660
Fax: 323-650-8662

SUSAN CIMINELLI DAY SPA
Spas and Clinics

Salma Hayek, Cindy Crawford and Tommy Hilfiger are among the many who pamper themselves with Susan Ciminelli's luxurious massages, facials and scrubs. Dedicated to a holistic approach, all of her spa treatments and products focus on the well-being of the body, mind and spirit. Always on the cutting edge of new skin care developments, Ciminelli has created an extensive collection of skin care products and treatments, all reflecting her personal conviction – that health and beauty must come from within.

754 Fifth Avenue
New York, NY 10019
Tel: 212-872-2650
Fax: 212-872-2655

SWALLOWTAIL
Specialty Shops

Owned and operated by artist Kari Lobdell and former set designer Sheri Sheridan, this refreshingly eccentric store stocks a truly delightful inventory. From vintage phrenology tools to original WPA style photography, Swallowtail is stocked with the eclectic and the unique. Even mass-market homeware stores such as the Pottery Barn count on Swallowtail to supply imaginative pieces for their displays – curious, but an imprimatur nonetheless.

2217 Polk Street
San Francisco, CA 94109
Tel: 415-567-1555
Fax: 415-567-1503

TALBOTT

Winemakers

Interest in the seven different wines produced by this small family-run winery has been so great that the owners have recently opened the Talbott Tasting Room in the nearby town of Carmel Valley. Robert Talbott, who began his career in the clothing manufacturing business, went from producing shirts and ties to making fine wines back in 1983. He's especially proud of their Chardonnay and Pinot Noir, which can be found under the Monterey County and Diamond T labels.

PO Box 776
Gonzalez, CA 93926
Tel: 831-675-3000

TANGLEWOOD MUSIC FESTIVAL

Events

This Western Massachusetts institution is the summer home of the Boston Symphony. Under the direction of Seiji Ozawa, it features concerts in the open air at the quaintly named Koussevitzky Music Shed. A favorite weekend destination for harried city dwellers, the Festival, as well as the surrounding Berkshire Mountains, provide a relaxed, low-key bucolic stop-over.

297 West Street
Lenox, MA 01240
Tel: 617-266-1492   Fax: 617-638-9288

THEA WESTREICH
ART ADVISORY SERVICES

Art Consultants

Thea Westreich Art Advisory Services is a consultancy of specialists in Impressionism, Modern, Contemporary art and vintage photography – guiding clients with a unique combination of scholarship, market analysis, expert critical judgment and uncommon access throughout the international art world. Providing collecting opportunities not otherwise available to private collectors, the firm consistently locates and accesses those works that are high in demand and short in supply. Following a rigorous vetting procedure (benefited by a deep understanding of the market) the firm negotiates the best prices and terms for its clients. In essence, Thea Westreich Art Advisory Services serves as curator to experienced and newer collectors, helping them build collections of distinction, importance and lasting value.

114 Greene Street, 2nd Floor
New York, NY 10012
Tel: 212-941-9449   Fax: 212-966-0174

THE TASTING ROOM

Restaurants   *Rising Star*

Renée and Colin Alevras – a couple whose charm and passion look set to take them far – met in cooking school seven years ago. After falling in love and various other disasters they decided to create this tiny restaurant. The concept is to keep the menu interesting by changing the seasonal American fare every night. Odds are that you could visit the East Village eatery 10 or more times and never have the same dinner twice (although the lobster, served with sautéed pea shoots, Johnny cake and bacon is a perennial favorite). The 300-bottle wine list, composed strictly of American vintages, includes Abrew, Stagland and 40 nearly impossible to find Cabernets. Seating is limited to 25 so make reservations at least two weeks in advance. Warmly recommended.

72 East 1st Street
New York, NY 11003
Tel: 212-358-7831

Untitled (Women with baskets), by Rufino Tamayo

THROCKMORTON FINE ART
Art Dealers

Spencer Throckmorton came to New York in 1977 with a passion for art, antiquities and archeology and within three years he had set himself up as a private dealer. His interest in the photography of Latin America and the Near East, which he developed in college, spurred him to become what he is today and has been for nearly a decade: the owner of the most exclusive Latin American gallery in the United States, dealing in 19th century vintage to contemporary Latin American photography. His favorite picture is *Roses* by Tina Modotti, whose European retrospective exhibition *Tina Modotti and the Mexican Renaissance*, he is the main lendor for. The exhibit continues through early 2002. Throckmorton's international clientele comprises the Hollywood set and Wall Street businessmen, as well as European, Japanese and South American art collectors, who all enjoy visiting his gallery located in the former home of Peggy Guggenheim. Spencer Throckmorton once procured, for a private client, Tina Modotti's 1927 silver gelatin print, *Bandolier, Corn, Sickle*, which was later donated to the Atlanta Museum by Elton John.

153 East 61st Street
New York, NY 10021
Tel: 212-223-1059   Fax: 212-223-1937

Tina on the Azotea, by Edward Weston

TAYLOR B. WILLIAMS
Antiques

Established in 1963 by Mr. Williams and partner, David J. Bernard, Taylor B. Williams is a nationally recognized and acclaimed antique firm. The outfit specializes in 18th and 19th century American and English furniture, English porcelain and decorative accessories of the period. Williams and Bernard have one of the largest collections of English enamel in the world. Both lecture on the subject and appraise for museums and private collectors. They no longer have an open shop, but offer appointments for "very special occasions."

PO Box 11297
Chicago, IL 60611
Tel: 312-266-0908
Fax: 312-266-0995

~

ANDREW L. TERNER
Art Consultants

At the forefront of American contemporary art consultants, Andrew Terner deals only in "exceptional quality art," earning him a client list that includes captains of industry, entertainers and entrepreneurs. An immensely charming figure, Terner has bought and sold 20th century masters such as Picasso, Warhol and Basquiat, as well as trendsetting British "It Boy" Damian Hirst.

28 East 10th Street
New York, NY 10003
Tel: 212-505-8521
Fax: 212-979-9140

THAD HAYES DESIGN
Architects and Interior Designers

"Decorating is very personal; that's what makes it so difficult. It's so emotionally charged," says Thad Hayes, whose talent for understanding clients' needs and bringing them to fruition has won him numerous devotees, several generations of the Lauder family among them. His classic yet modern interiors have graced the cover of many magazines; *New York* recently described him as one of "New York's 10 Hottest Interior Designers" for his ability to transcend the ordinary through a thoughtful juxtaposition of styles, colors and significant details.

90 West Broadway
New York, NY 10007
Tel: 212-571-1234

~

THERIEN & COMPANY
Antiques

Therien has long been a leader in the acquisition and sale of antiques. The company specializes in 17th, 18th and 19th century European furniture. Catering to the top 1% of affluent Americans, many clients hail from Silicon Valley, next door to the company's San Francisco offices. The driving force behind the company is Robert Garcia (a true connoisseur) whose one piece of advice to clients considering a purchase is that their motivation is the love of the piece and nothing else.

716 North La Cienega Boulevard
Los Angeles, CA 90069
Tel: 310-657-4615

TIBOR DE NAGY GALLERY
Art Dealers

This exclusive Fifth Avenue gallery features beautifully curated exhibits of some of the most innovative painters and photographers of the 20th century, from American Modernists to the New York School, including Dove, Rivers, Porter and Welliver. Ask to speak to Phil Alexander, the gallery's expert on American Modernist painting, who will take you behind the scenes to see works by artists not currently on view.

724 Fifth Avenue, 12th floor
New York, NY 10019
Tel: 212-262-5050   Fax: 212-262-1841

~

THE TIDES
Hotels

Of all the glittering art deco jewels that line Ocean Drive, this Murray Dixon designed gem still stands out for sheer elegance. Renovated by Stuart Mosscrop for Island Records founder Chris Blackwell, who reopened the hotel in 1997, The Tides features 45 spacious, oceanfront rooms. Guests enjoy extraordinary pampering, with private yoga instructors, bodyguards and personal shoppers all on call. Try to book the Terra Nova Penthouse Suite, which marks the highest point on Ocean Drive. Its 1100 square feet of living space affords panoramic views in every direction — ample room for demanding guests like Mariah Carey and Jennifer Lopez.

1220 Ocean Drive
Miami Beach, FL 33139
Tel: 305-604-5070   Fax: 305-604-5180

TOM MATHIEU & COMPANY
Florists

A colorful array of extraordinary blossoms spill out the entranceway of Tom Mathieu's charming Worth Avenue shop, beckoning Palm Beach strollers to pause for a moment in his courtyard and examine the rare blooms. You won't find any mums here, no typical flowers whatsoever. Instead, Mathieu works closely with the best growers and importers in the country to assure that his customers will have the rare and special plants they covet — current favorites, for instance, include exotic orchids from Thailand and Hawaii. This busy designer has little time himself, however, to stop and smell the long-stemmed roses. He's too busy creating floral fantasies for such corporate clients as the U.S. Trust Bank and the chic Club Colette, as well as the many private clients who depend on him to make magic at everything from charity galas to society weddings. His favorite assignments, though, are the intimate dinner parties and soirees that allow him to be his most creative. Mathieu's attention to detail, which is always in play, is especially evident in such situations. It's not unusual for him to visit a client's home in order to design the most complementary floral display possible. And when an extra-special customer is due in town unexpectedly, this soft-spoken gentleman has been known to drop everything so that he can have every room in the house filled with just the right flowers in time for their arrival.

312-D Worth Avenue
Palm Beach, FL 34480
Tel: 561-655-5880   Fax: 561-655-5803

THIERRY DESPONT
Architects and Interior Designers

"One must know where the client comes from and what they desire," says Thierry Despont, architect to the super rich. As Robert Ivy, editor of *Architectural Record*, put it recently, "The houses Despont builds are not simply status symbols, signs of conspicuous consumption; they are bids for immortality, lies against time." Among the Ozymandias-like titans who have turned to the French-born architect for a stab at immortality are Bill Gates, Mickey Drexler, Calvin Klein, Terry Semel, Peter Morton and Sidney Kimmel, owner of Jones Apparel Group. The 21,000 square-foot, limestone mansion Despont built for Kimmel in Palm Beach came complete with the architect's choice of china, linens, toiletries, even the butler. While Despont often takes heat from fellow architects, the *nouveau riche* clientele he caters to couldn't be more pleased.

335 Greenwich Street
New York, NY 10013
Tel: 212-334-9444   Fax: 212-334-1847

TIFFANY & CO.
Jewelry and Watches

The New Economy? In matters of the heart, there remains only one, very old, very established economy — that of the powder blue box. Tiffany makes a mockery of shifting trends and whims by remaining the iconic temple of luxurious jewelry design. And with over one hundred stores worldwide, the experience of walking into Audrey Hepburn's palace at 57th and Fifth has been effectively disseminated, if never quite replicated. There is, for that moment, the absolute sense that one is just simply *right*. Breakfast anyone?

727 Fifth Avenue
New York, NY 10022
Tel: 212-755-8000
Fax: 212-605-0465

TIME WILL TELL
Jewelry and Watches

Steward Unger believes that watches are about more than just telling time; rather, they are personalized pieces of decorative art that express an individual's sense of taste and style. His passion for great design is evident in the eclectic inventory of unique and unusual timepieces he sells, ranging from a rare early wristwatch from the 1880s, to the much sought after "Paul Newman" Rolex from the 1960s. Time Will Tell sells and services watches from all the great makers, including Patek Philippe, Vacheron, Audemars and Cartier. And, should you have the time, the store's charming and very knowledgeable owner will likely throw in some fascinating history about your favorite piece for good measure.

962 Madison Avenue
New York, NY 10021
Tel: 212-861-2663

TONY SHAFRAZI GALLERY
Art Dealers

It is impossible to talk about the contemporary art scene without mentioning the Tony Shafrazi Gallery. One of the key players in the early eighties art market boom, Shafrazi helped make stars of Keith Haring, Jean-Michel Basquiat and Kenny Scharf, among others. The gallery has since branched out to represent 20th century masters like Andy Warhol and Francis Bacon. Ask for director Hiroko Onoda, who will gladly guide you through current exhibitions. Forthcoming shows include major new work by Italian neo-expressionist Enzo Cucchi.

119 Wooster Street
New York, NY 10012
Tel: 212-274-9300   Fax: 212-334-9499

TOCCA

Fashion *Rising Star*

Offering far more than "that perfect little dress," (although you will be able to find the best dresses of the season here) Tocca's core collection consists of coats, skirts, jackets, pants and knitwear; exotic color and distinctive embroidery abound. The Touch fragrance line is classic and simple in style, travel-friendly and used by celebrities like Amber Valletta, Natasha Richardson, Susan Sarandon and Gwyneth Paltrow. Founders Gordon Finkelstein and Edoardo Mantelli sell their line through department stores and specialty boutiques across the world. Watch for the new, complete collection of lingerie, consisting of seven different styles.

161 Mercer Street
New York, NY 10012
Tel: 212-343-3912
Fax: 212-343-3913

TOOTSIES

Fashion

Other stores may also carry high-end designers like Richard Tyler, Nicole Miller, Randolph Duke, Armani and Moschino, but none can outdo this exclusive, privately-owned chain of boutiques when it comes to customer service. Mickey Rosmarin founded Tootsies back in 1974 and he's been offering discreet one-on-one attention to a well-heeled clientele (smart executives, high-profile socialites and Texan celebrities) ever since.

4045 Westheimer
Houston, TX 77027
Tel: 713-629-9990   Fax: 713-960-0470

TOWN & COUNTRY RESOURCES

Employment Agencies

As Town & Country Nannies and Mothers In Deed, this top agency placed child care workers in some of the Bay Area's finest homes, prompting their satisfied clients to wonder why the company couldn't fulfill the rest of their employee needs. Lo and behold the new Town & Country Resources was born. Using the same extensive interviewing and screening process that made them invaluable to parents, this firm now finds clients exactly the right highly-trained personal assistant, housekeeper, cook, butler or estate manager.

425 Sherman Avenue, Suite 130
Palo Alto, CA 94306
Tel: 650-614-0276
Fax: 650-326-1556

TRABERT & HOEFFER

Jewelry and Watches

Fashioned after a European salon, this exclusive jeweler's suites for perusing in private are well known to many old Chicago families, who have been frequenting the store since 1937. Representing blue-chip brand names like Cartier, Franck Muller, Vacheron & Constantin and Bedat, Donald Levinson and his team are both competent and charming purveyors of distinctive, high end treasures like platinum and diamond jewelry, sapphire, rubies and Tahitian pearls.

111 East Oak Street
Chicago, IL 60611
Tel: 312-787-1654
Fax: 312-787-1446

TRACEY ROSS

Fashion *Best Kept Secret*

"When I realized that my knight in shining armor wasn't going to ride in and support me, I took the logical step and started my own business," says Tracey Ross about how she got into the boutique fashion business. Today, many a celebrity and movie executive consider her their own savior for the very personal service she offers. The intimate Sunset shop has more than enough eye-candy for even the hungriest fashionistas and if you're lucky you might even have the flaxen-haired Ms. Ross help you pick out your goodies.

8595 Sunset Boulevard
Los Angeles, CA 90069
Tel: 310-854-1996

TRACY FEITH

Fashion

Tracy Feith is one of the most creative designers working in America today. Not only does he hand make beautiful clothing for men and women, as well as a number of elegant items for the house, he even crafts unique long boards for his fellow surfers, by artfully enclosing the distinctive, hand-blocked silk fabrics from his Raj line in Plexiglas. Also available at both his NoLita and East Hampton boutiques: a complete selection of menswear; sophisticated, tailored high fashion suits and dresses for women and the more casual Raj line of flowing, feminine women's wear that originally put this red-hot designer on the fashion map. Look for Feith's initials, hidden in the pattern of all of his hand-crafted prints.

209 Mulberry Street
New York, NY 10012
Tel: 212-334-3097

TRAVEL AGENCY IN THE PARK

Travel Consultants

Co-owners Maureen Rafoul and Sharon Lay have been in operation in Houston since 1983 and continue to manage the firm today. Their commitment to the highest levels of technology, service, performance and customer satisfaction have resulted in numerous awards, including seats on the advisory boards of national and international air carriers. In addition to business travel management, the firm offers clients a wide range of specialty services including meeting coordination, corporate retreat planning and sporting and leisure travel.

12 21 Lamar, Suite 718
Houston, TX 77010
Tel: 713-650-8080   Fax: 713-650-7022

TRIPLE CREEK RANCH
Hotels

Amid the Bitterroot Mountain Range of the Montana Rockies, on over 330 acres of wooded hillside, Triple Creek immerses its guests in maximum privacy and unparalleled comfort. Leave your business card in the cabin and ride a snowmobile to the remote Horse Creek Hot Springs. Go for an after-dinner sleigh ride beneath the bright stars. Or stay in and enjoy the cabin's fireplaces, cozy, overstuffed pillows and cookies — delivered fresh daily.

5551 West Fork Road
Darby, MT 59829
Tel: 406-821-4600
Fax: 406-821-4666

TRIBECA GRAND HOTEL
Hotels

New York's SoHo Grand was one of *the* hotels of the last decade. Colonial chic and a lack of local competition lured Japanese pop stars, dot-com billionaires and a host of anonymous voyeurs. Today it remains one of the sleeker resting places in the city — and we'll always love the bar — but today's young hipsters demand change. Who better to provide that change than Leonard Stern, the man who built the Soho Grand? This time round the gimmicks come thick and fast — web access, local calls and *The New York Times* are all complimentary (in the broadest sense of the word). Stern claims that he has redefined "contemporary luxe." Looking at his new baby (complete with interiors by Calvin Tsao, a 98-seat screening room and a 10,000 square foot lobby) it is hard to argue with the pet food king.

2 Avenue of the Americas
New York, NY 10013
Tel: 212-519-6600
Fax: 212-519-6700

TROON GOLF & COUNTRY CLUB
Golf Clubs

Set in the hills of Scottsdale, Troon mirrors its Scottish namesake in many design elements despite a desert location, most notably with the Postage Stamp 13th hole. Designed by Tom Weiskopf and Jay Moorish and completed in 1985, "The Cliff" and "Troon Mountain" (the 14th and 15th holes) complete the signature triumvirate. With 390 members, Troon is currently full. Prospective members have to wait for a current member to resign, although the nonrefundable, $65,000 membership fee reduces that likelihood.

25000 North Windy Walk Drive
Scottsdale, AZ 85255
Tel: 480-585-4310

TRINITY YACHTS
Powerboats & Yachts

"Ten years ago, Americans were building yachts up to about a hundred feet," explains William Smith III, "but they had to go over to Holland and Germany to get bigger, high-end yachts." In the last few years Smith's company has emerged as the premier U.S. yacht builder, with a reputation for serving the needs — and whims — of a seriously demanding multi-millionaire clientele. "They can fly in with a sketch on a cocktail napkin," explains Smith, "and we can build it, no matter what!" Smith is presently constructing 126', 141', 150' and 177' yachts. Capable of 20 knots, they each have freshwater makers and sewage treatment systems. All have transatlantic range (and the bigger two have transpacific range). If you're serious about owning one of the best American-built yachts, you'll be talking to Trinity Yachts.

4325 France Road
New Orleans, LA 70126
Tel: 504-283-4050   Fax: 504-284-7318

TROQUET
Restaurants

Despite its incongruous location, this sophisticated Costa Mesa bistro serves magnificent French cuisine in an elegant setting. Chef/owner Tim Goodall (who also owns Aubergine) opened the restaurant in 1997 and has been pleasing Francophiles since with his signature dishes: *Veal en Cocotte*, served with vegetables and black truffles — and delectable lobster sweetbreads. During the summer, ask Tim's wife Liza for a seat on the garden patio.

S. Coast Plaza
3333 Bristol Street
Costa Mesa, CA 92626
Tel: 714-708-6865
Fax: 714-708-6869

TRU
Restaurants   *Rising Star*

When Rick Tramonto was 16, he took a full-time job at Wendy's Old Fashioned Hamburgers for a measly $200 a week. When Gale Gand was six, she caught the eye of a *Life* photographer while she was making a mud pie. Today they own a restaurant whose specialty — an appetizer "caviar staircase" — has grabbed the attention of critics nationwide. However, there is much more to Tru than this timely gimmick. The dining room is accented with cool black fabric and white drapes with rich blue velvet banquettes. A dynamic staircase takes guests to a private dining room, overlooking a desperately chic bar and lounge. The wait staff serves in four-person teams, and table tops are set in Onieda, Riedel, Limoges and Damask. But the real star at Tru is the outstanding contemporary French cuisine. Warmly recommended.

675 Saint Clair Street
Chicago, IL 60611
Tel: 312-202-0001

TRUEFITT & HILL
Hair and Beauty

Truefitt & Hill have the delicate dichotomy of being both 'old-school' and 'cutting-edge' in their stylist capabilities. The charming shop-salon is decorated with antique barber chairs and trademark classical music. Truefitt & Hill feature a five course haircut, hot lather shaves with straight razors, and the mandatory shoe shine. The shop's ambiance has been compared to an "old boys' club." $325 will provide you with a haircut, manicure, facial and shoeshine.

900 North Michigan Avenue
Chicago, IL 60611
Tel: 312-337-2525
Fax: 312-337-8954

TU TU' TUN LODGE
Hotels

Few resort lodges offer a more delightful mix of rustic charm and full-service luxury than Oregon's Tu Tu' Tun Lodge, named after the tribe of Indians who once inhabited this inspiring Pacific Northwest site. After a long day out boating, hiking or fishing on the Rogue River, visitors can enjoy a cocktail in the intimate lounge, a gourmet meal in the acclaimed dining room or perhaps just curl up with a good book in front of the massive stone fireplace in the main lodge, where the inn's gracious owners, Dirk and Laurie VanZante, were married back in 1977. Call at least six weeks in advance to book the Chinook suite which offers a spacious living room, private patio and a cozy cast iron fireplace.

96550 North Bank Rogue
Gold Beach, OR 97444
Tel: 541-247-6664
Fax: 541-247-0672

TULEH
Fashion

Josh Patner and Bryan Bradley teamed up several years ago to create a new line of ultra-feminine, body-conscious clothing for women; they immediately caught the eye of style-setters like Cameron Diaz, Aerin Lauder and Jennifer Lopez, who all responded to the romantic, almost retro sensibility of the line's handmade beauties. The duo's new fall and winter designs celebrate texture, with hand-printed silks, herringbone tweeds, fur trims and luxurious beading, while promising to remain every bit as feminine as former collections.

175 West 81st Street, 5C
New York, NY 10024
Tel: 212-595-3879
Fax: 212-595-1077

TURLEY WINE CELLARS
Winemakers

Dr. Larry Turley was an emergency room medical physician for 20 years before he opened this winery in 1993. Following his true passion, he set out to make Zinfandel and Petite Syrah (which he calls "big reds" because of their sheer magnitude). Today, Turley produces more varieties than any other wine maker in the region, most of which are rated in the 90s. The winery produces between five and six thousand cases per vintage. Incidentally, Turley's sister Helen is the winemaker at Marcassin.

3358 St. Helena Highway
St. Helena, CA 94574
Tel: 707-963-0940

20/20 WINES
Wine Merchants

This wine merchant stocks many of the greatest wines ever produced, frequently in multiple case quantities, including top Bordeaux from the 1800s through the present, with a wide range of older Burgundies from the best producers. Virtually every top quality California wine in the modern era is represented, including the rarest micro-producers, as well as exceptional vintage champagnes. Expert personal service has won the firm plaudits from critics and customers alike.

2020 Cotner Avenue
Los Angeles, CA 90025
Tel: 310-447-2020
Fax: 310-475-2836

21 CLUB
Restaurants

A name dropper's paradise, the 21 Club's legendary history and superb reputation have made the restaurant a regular stomping ground for assorted bigwigs: Joe DiMaggio loved the famous Chicken Hash, Aristotle Onassis would only eat the '21' Burger, and Ernest Hemingway once told a favored bartender; "Since I'm not drinking, I'll just have a tequila." If you really want to dine in the holy of holies, enter through the kitchen, down the stairs to a large boardroom table in the middle of the cellars. Lunch will set you back several hundred dollars per head, but when you're dining in the shadow of Humphrey Bogart and Lauren Bacall, amidst magnums of fine claret bottled for Joan Crawford, is price relevant?

21 West 52nd Street
New York, NY 10019
Tel: 212-582-7200
Fax: 212-586-5065

TWIN FARMS
Hotels

Once the 300-acre country estate of Sinclair Lewis and his wife, Dorothy Thompson, Twin Farms has hosted Rebecca West, a young Henry Kissinger and H.L. Mencken. Renovated in 1996, the lobby is decorated with pictures by Lichtenstein and Hockney, with utopian interiors by the late Jed Johnston. Each room has an elegant, Japanese-style bed, Frette linens and fresh flowers. Run by Shaun and Beverly Matthews, the retreat won the *Tatler* award for the Best Hideaway last year. Located on an apple orchard, evenings are best spent relaxing in the Japanese furo bathhouse, followed by intimate dinners in the wine cellar.

P.O. Box 115
Barnard, VT 05031
Tel: 802-234-9999   Fax: 802-234-9990

TWO DESIGN GROUP
Florists

Two Design Group is a talented group of designers and staff, led by Creative and Sales Director Todd Fiscus. Specializing in the creation of extraordinary events, the Dallas-based team work in corporate and social markets throughout the country and internationally. Featuring impressive floral designs, unique fixtures, linens, tabletop accoutrements and large scale decor, TDG focuses on perfection in every aspect of every event.

1113 Dragon Street
Dallas, TX 75207
Tel: 214-741-3145

U.S. OPEN TENNIS
Events

The biggest draw of American tennis, the U.S. Open features the sport's greatest names. Each Labor Day weekend since 1968, Flushing Meadows has hosted the likes of Arthur Ashe, John McEnroe, André Agassi, Pete Sampras, Monica Seles, Venus and Serena Williams – the names go on and on. Jerry Seinfeld, Paul Newman and Minnie Driver compete for fast-disappearing seats, while Bill Cosby and Rosie O'Donnell referee charity games; off-court attractions include hospitality tents sponsored by Tiffany, Evian and Lincoln cars.

National Tennis Center - Flushing Meadow Corona Park
Flushing, NY 11368
Tel: 914-696-7244   Fax: 914-696-7169

ULTRA MARINE
Powerboats & Yachts
Rising Star

A small boutique specializing in mega-yacht charter vacations, Ultra Marine provides fully tailored service. Relying on her intuitive understanding of clients' needs gleaned from years in the high-end travel industry, CEO Cindy Brown's worldwide network of boating-related contacts is unparalleled. Whether it be arranging a massage in Capri or a Bentley Azure in Cannes, exotic requests both aboard and ashore are taken in stride. And for those whose vacations or events are too big for these big boats, Ultra Marine can arrange private island getaways as well.

200 East 90th Street
New York, NY 10128
Tel: 212-423-9280   Fax: 212-289-0844

U.S. OPEN POLO
Events

Hosted at the Palm Beach Polo Stadium, Florida's premier polo grounds, the U.S. Open Polo Tournament attracts an all-star crowd as well as the world's top players. Argentinean Augustin Merlos is a frequent player, and New Yorker Peter Brant's team regularly takes the Amateur championship. In addition to the game itself, of course, the social scene under the sponsorship tents (Rolex and Louis Vuitton, among others) is another reason to make the trip to Palm Beach.

13420 South Shore Boulevard
Wellington, FL 33414
Tel: 561-793-1440   Fax: 561-790-3872

ULTIMO
Fashion

This long-time Chicago outpost for fashion-forward shoppers is undergoing major changes in the year 2000. New owner Sara Albrecht Nygren's goal is to return the store to its roots in womenswear, gradually phasing out the menswear division, while retaining the shop's cutting-edge sensibility. A face-lift is in the works as well for the dark, woody space, which will soon be significantly lighter and airier. Leading designers such as John Galliano and Randolph Duke are represented alongside newcomers like Miguel Adrover, with further American representation from Michael Kors and Marc Jacobs.

114 East Oak Street
Chicago, IL 60611
Tel: 312-787-1171

U.S. SECURITY
Security Consultants

Jack Smith and J. Peter Rush founded U.S. Security in 1991 with a combined 43 years of experience in the United States Secret Service. Dealing primarily in special events and executive residences, the team served as consultants for President Clinton's inauguration in 1993. To maintain quality service for their discerning clientele, the firm uses only former U.S. Secret Service agents as consulting associates.

10480 Little Patuxent Parkway
Columbia, MD 21044
Tel: 410-442-1756
Fax: 410-489-3669

THE UNION CLUB
Private Clubs

On any given night the Union Club's grand dining room is inhabited by the families whose names are etched into the corner stones of many public buildings in New York. The club features squash and racquet courts as well as bedrooms where guests feel miles away from bustling Manhattan. The rooms seem to be plucked from the English country homes of the last century; appropriate enough, as the overnight guests are often reciprocals from the top clubs in London. Incidentally, this is one of the few old-school clubs in which children are found "at table."

101 East 69th Street
New York, NY 10021
Tel: 212-734-5400

UNIVERSITY OF PENNSYLVANIA
Colleges

The old saw is that Penn students are forever worrying that they attend the forgotten Ivy or that — God forbid — the University is confused with Penn State. Silly stuff, especially because Penn boasts a striking combination of pedigree (founded by Benjamin Franklin, boathouses on the Schukill) and contemporary prestige: the Wharton School of Business and the Annenberg School for Communication spearhead a range of superior programs. The forgotten Ivy? Only by those who don't recognize excellence.

Walnut Street
Philadelphia, PA 19104
Tel: 215-898-5000

~

U.S.P.A. PACIFIC COAST OPEN
Events

Santa Barbara, California's Riviera, plays host to the United States Polo Association's Pacific Tournament each August. Teams from Los Angeles and Southern California head off against an international list of opponents; 10-goalers Owen Rinehart and Carlos Garcida are frequent players, while Hollywooders Tommy Lee Jones and William Devane come up to watch. Don't miss the Polo Ball, where various Southern California society strands come together.

3375 Foothill Road
Carpinteria, CA 93013
Tel: 805-684-6683

URBAN CENTER BOOKS
Specialty Shops

The Municipal Art Society founded Urban Center Books in 1980. Offering books on architecture, urban design, landscape architecture, urban, interior and graphic design, UCB is a resource for professionals and lay persons alike. The latest exhibition held was a comprehensive retrospective of Howard Meister's Art Furniture. Architect Billie Tsien recently said: "Certainly, there are other bookstores that carry architecture books but there is no place that loves them so well."

457 Madison Avenue
New York, NY 10022
Tel: 212-935-3960

URBAN RETREAT
Spas and Clinics

Majestic columns, lush greenery and shimmering pools of water await all who enter Urban Retreat, promising solutions to aches, imperfections and anxieties. Owned by former publisher Francie Willis, the spa is the largest and most comprehensive in the Lone Star state. A particular favorite for bridal parties and registries, clients can get everything from eyelash application to a Dead Sea Mud Wrap, combining volcanic mineral deposits, aloe gel, jojoba and beta carotene to completely moisturize and rejuvenate the skin. Nail services, make-up lessons, manicures, pedicures and René Furterer Capilliscope hair and scalp analysis are all offered.

2329 San Felipe
Houston, TX 77019
Tel: 713-523-2300   Fax: 713-528-3006

U.S. TRUST
Wealth Management

The venerable bank of the Astors, Whitneys and Rockefellers has recently received an injection of high-tech energy. Succumbing to the trend of consolidation that now rules financial services, U.S. Trust was bought by the Schwab Corporation, the online brokers, bringing old-school attention to wealth management together with the best electronic financial technology. Despite the high-tech trappings, however, most new clients come to the bank through word-of-mouth. The average account is $7 million, with a minimum of $2 million.

114 West 47th Street
New York, NY 10036
Tel: 212-852-1000
Fax: 212-852-1515

URSUS BOOKS & PRINTS
Specialty Shops   *Best Kept Secret*

Included in Ursus' collection of rare and quality books are originals that existed in Catherine the Great's personal library and a hand-crafted book with original Rembrandt sketches. Ursus carries exquisite French bindings of the 18th century. Located on the second floor of the Carlyle Hotel, it has all the charm of an old-time library. Ursus books and prints are shown at the International Fine Arts and Antique Dealers Show.

981 Madison Avenue
New York, NY 10021
Tel: 212-772-8787   Fax: 212-737-9306

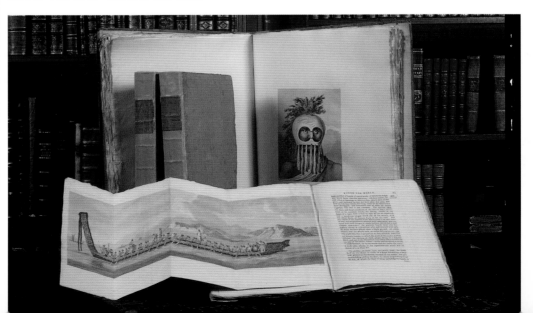

VALENTINO
Restaurants

Merging the fine food and culture of Italy with the Hollywood culture of Los Angeles is what Piero Selvaggio set out to do when he came to the U.S. as a young man. 26 years later, Valentino continues to flourish. Favorites include risotto with seafood, swordfish steak with onion and olive caponata and the veal chop, served with cream, prosciutto and Marsala wine. Pastry Chef Michelle Robie's warm chocolate cake, served with mascarpone gelato and Pronto "Aleatico" is phenomenal.

3115 Pico Boulevard
Santa Monica, CA 90405
Tel: 310-829-4313

VALERIE BEVERLY HILLS
Hair and Beauty

Valerie Sarnell's boutique, on Canon Drive in the Beverly Hills Triangle, is staffed with over 20 competent and charming beauty consultants. - which is probably just as well, because Valerie's customers include some of America's most demanding women. Her superior make-up line includes lip-glosses, concealers, foundations, blushes and application brushes. Fans include Goldie Hawn, Nicole Kidman and Tori Spelling.

460 North Cañon Drive
Beverly Hills, CA 90210
Tel: 310-274-7348
Fax: 310-274-8968

VALLEY CLUB OF MONTECITO
Golf Clubs

Even members of exclusive L.A. clubs like Bel Air and Riviera speak in hushed tones about the Valley Club, set in a peaceful valley overlooking the Pacific just a few miles from Santa Barbara. Jigsaw-puzzle bunkers and an outstanding quartet of par 3 holes distinguish the design, but its secluded setting is what sets the Valley club apart from its golfing brethren in busy southern California.

1901 East Valley Road
Santa Barbara, CA 93108
Tel: 805-969-2215

VALERIE WILSON TRAVEL
Travel Consultants

Almost two decades ago, Valerie Wilson's dream was to provide the highest level of personal service to business and leisure travelers. Today, she is regularly cited as one of the most powerful women in travel and, along with her daughters, Jennifer Wilson-Buttigieg and Kimberly Wilson Wetty, she continues to explore and develop innovative ways to serve her corporate and leisure clients. Though her firm has grown in size, with annual sales over $250 million, Wilson has refused to compromise her dedication to individualized service, and, as a result, this family-owned firm has become the first choice of such prestigious corporations as Oscar de la Renta, Forest Laboratories, Heineken USA, Liz Claiborne, Merck-Medco Managed Care and Giorgio Armani. In addition to having exclusive travel marketing and fulfillment programs with the Discovery Channel and BMW, Ms. Wilson has embarked on a new e-venture, luxury4less.com. Trips offered on this site provide a range of tantalizing travel options.

475 Park Avenue South
New York, NY 10016
Tel: 212-532-3400
Fax: 212-779-7073

VANCE JORDAN FINE ART
Art Dealers

Vance Jordan Fine Art is one of the country's leading galleries, dealing primarily with 19th and early 20th century American paintings, as well as important European — especially Italian — paintings of the same period. As part of an ongoing commitment to American art scholarship, the gallery also regularly organizes museum quality exhibitions and publications, featuring artists such as John La Farge, H.R. Newman, Richard Miller, Childe Hassam and other major American impressionist painters. Whether assisting new or veteran collectors, Jordan's aim is to educate and counsel, ensuring that the client's experience is richly rewarding — in many ways, then, Jordan is a relic of a less commercial art world, in which scholarship and passion count as much as price.

958 Madison Avenue
New York, NY 10021
Tel: 212-570-9500
Fax: 212-737-1611

VASSAR
Colleges

Perhaps the most intellectually distinguished member of the fabled Seven Sisters, Vassar was also the one that opted to welcome men as the Ivies welcomed women in the late 1960s and early 1970s. The result is a reinvented institution that has assumed a distinctive bohemian cast, without sacrificing academic excellence. Vassar students are, by and large, a brilliantly off-kilter lot, renowned for individuality and creativity.

124 Raymond Avenue
Poughkeepsie, NY 12604
Tel: 914-437-7000
Fax: 914-437-7239

VERA WANG
Fashion

Vera Wang earned a BA from Sarah Lawrence College but had no formal design training since her dad wouldn't let her go to art school — he wanted her to concentrate on more "practical subjects." The art world's loss is thousands of bride's gain. The former ice-skating champion opened her exquisite bridal boutique on Madison Avenue after a 17 year stint as an editor at *Vogue*. A decade later Wang's name is synonymous with good taste, not only among brides but throughout the fashion world.

991 Madison Avenue
New York, NY 10021
Tel: 212-628-3400

VALLEY HOUSE GALLERY
Art Dealers
Focusing on contemporary and early 20th century American painting, this family-run gallery is particularly strong on Texan art from the 1930s, 40s and 50s. Since its foundation more than 45 years ago, the gallery has gained a reputation in Dallas as an important dealer in contemporary painting, sculpture, drawing and prints. Artists represented include Lu Ann Barrow, Lloyd Brown and David Everett. An immaculate five acre sculpture garden hosts periodic exhibitions.

6616 Spring Valley Road
Dallas, TX 75240-8635
Tel: 972-239-2441   Fax: 972-239-1462

VERDURA

Jewelry and Watches

Duke Fulco Verdura was a jewelry designer for American royalty. He made a sleek gold bracelet for Greta Garbo, a pink topaz necklace for Woolworth heir Barbara Hutton and emeralds and diamonds mounted into a Maltese cross brooch for playwright Claire Booth Luce. The Duke died in 1978, leaving behind over 4000 sketches. Ward Langrigan has been creating collections from those sketches since 1884 — only producing a few of each design. His Fifth Avenue showroom is a favorite of society dames like Caroline Roehm and Sloan Lindemann.

745 Fifth Avenue, Suite 1205
New York, NY 10151
Tel: 212-758-3388
Fax: 212-753-2395

A LA VIEILLE RUSSIE

Antiques

Founded in Kiev in 1851, A La Vieille Russie specializes in European and American antique jewelry, gold snuffboxes and *objets de vertu*, as well as Russian paintings, icons and decorative arts, including silver, porcelain and enamel. Goldsmith and jeweler Carl Fabergé was a client and today, owners Mark, Peter and Paul Schaffer are recognized as international experts on his works.

781 Fifth Avenue
New York, NY 10022
Tel: 212-752-1727   Fax: 212-223-6454

VIKING YACHTS

Powerboats & Yachts

When you've got the car and the plane to get you there, you might as well have a boat just to get you away. Viking doesn't pretend to sell a tool for enhancing productivity; these machines are meant for pure pleasure. Brothers Bob and Bill Healey, who started the company in 1964, are still at the helm. One of the world leaders in semi-custom yacht production, the firm now delivers 100 boats per annum.

Route 9
New Gretna, NJ 08244
Tel: 609-296-6000
Fax: 609-296-3956

THE VIRGINIAN

Golf Clubs

Set on 538 acres of rolling hills, the Virginian golf course is the centerpiece for a 538-acre private residential community. One of the most environmentally sensitive courses ever built, a weather station monitors a variety of ambient factors and calculates the need for irrigation. A system then delivers liquid fertilizer as the course is irrigated, maintaining a constant moisture level in the soil. The Virginian is rated one of America's top 100 courses and the community is rated among the top five places to live in America.

22512 Clubhouse Ridge
Bristol, VA 24202
Tel: 800-452-8065   Fax: 540-645-7055

VISION AIRE

Airplanes

The next world-shrinker will likely be the Vision Aire Vantage jet, which upon its unveiling in 2002 promises to revolutionize executive travel. The Vantage's appeal lies in its significant reductions in capital and operating costs over existing business jets. Vision Aire's first baby will be more of an executive taxi than limousine: it will stop and start on a dime, requiring only 2,500 feet of runway. Lightweight composite construction and single-fanjet technology account for this remarkable performance (and cost savings).

595 Bell Avenue
Chesterfield, MO 63005
Tel: 636-530-1007   Fax: 636-530-0005

VOSE GALLERIES OF BOSTON

Art Dealers

America's oldest family-owned gallery is a major connoisseur's attraction on Boston's bustling Newbury Square. The first generation (the gallery was founded in Rhode Island in 1841) made its fortune selling contemporary works by George Innes and James and William Hart; the same artists' work still passes through today, in addition to 18th, 19th, and early 20th century American paintings. Fifth-generation owners Abbot and Robert Vose III (who happen to be twins) are experts on the Boston School.

238 Newbury Street
Boston, MA 02116
Tel: 617-536-6176
Fax: 617-247-8673

VICTORIA HAGAN

Architects and Interior Designers

Victoria Hagen's unpretentious style gives rooms a layered feel, rich with dimension and subtle complexities yet comfortable too. The work is distinguished by her effective use of antiques. A graduate of Parsons School of Design, the Native New Yorker has been in business since 1987 — today, she is particularly popular among young socialites.

654 Madison Avenue, Suite 2201
New York, NY 10021
Tel: 212-888-1178
Fax: 212-888-0974

VERITAS

Restaurants   *Rising Star*

Gino Diaferia and Executive Chef Scott Bryan run this small, tastefully decorated restaurant in the heart of Silicon Alley. We cannot recommend it highly enough: the service is outstanding and the food is unusually impressive for a restaurant which emphasizes the strength of its wine list — 1400 selections from every wine country in the world. Try Bryan's signature seared halibut, served with baby artichokes, asparagus and roasted pepper fricassee in a basil lobster broth. Make a point of meeting Phyl at the bar. She's one of the most charming bartenders in the country.

43 East 20th Street
New York, NY 10003
Tel: 212-353-3700

W. GRAHAM ARADER III

Antiques

W. Graham Arader III has sold rare and antique works on paper and paintings for the past 30 years. Specializing in Audubon and Redouté prints, Arader has an unimpeachable reputation within the industry. His galleries, located on Walnut Street in Philadelphia, and East 72nd Street in New York, contain pieces from the 16th to 19th centuries. Collectors will find natural history prints and paintings, color-plate books, maps and atlases, including works by Mercator and Catlin.

1308 Walnut Street
Philadelphia, PA 19107
Tel: 215-735-8811   Fax: 215-735-9864

WALTERS ART GALLERY

Museums

Considered by many to be among the greatest acts of cultural philanthropy in the nation's history, Henry Walters bequeathed his personal collection, including 22,000 works, to his native city. One of the few museums in the world to present a comprehensive history of art from the third millennium B.C. to the early 20th century, the Gallery holds a fine collection of ivories, jewelry, enamels and bronzes and a spectacular reserve of illuminated manuscripts and rare books. The Egyptian, Greek, Roman, Byzantine, Ethiopian and western medieval art collections are a historian's dream.

600 North Charles Street
Baltimore, MD 21201
Tel: 410-547-9000   Fax: 410-783-7969

WALZEL

Jewelry and Watches

Catering to an upscale, sophisticated clientele since 1950, gemologist John Walzel personally oversees a collection of unique designer jewelry, watches and gifts at his smart new showroom in Uptown Park. The collection includes design newcomers Erica Courtney and de Vroomen. Of course, there are always the glamorous standbys: Torrini, Mitchell Peck and a power roster of great watch names. Walzel's personal service and intimate ambiance meets the demands of discriminating shoppers and is the oldest independently-owned fine jeweler in Houston.

1141-02 Uptown Park Boulevard
Houston, TX 77056
Tel: 713-627-7495   Fax: 713-627-1935

THE WAUWINET

Hotels

In the mid-19th century, the Wauwinet opened as a restaurant serving shore dinners to patrons arriving by boat. Today it has expanded into a celebrated Relais & Chateaux hotel. Each of the 30 bedrooms is lavishly decorated with country antiques. In-room amenities include Egyptian cotton bathrobes, fresh flowers, hardbound books and magazines, a white wicker basket of Crabtree & Evelyn bath goods, CD players and CDs. Croquet, tennis, rowboats and an electric motorboat keep guests bus – they can also enjoy 26 miles of natural, secluded beaches. In addition, private fishing, jeep trips, golf, and massage are available. Guests have included John Cheever, Eleanor Roosevelt, Diamond Jim Brady and Prince Albert of Monaco.

P.O. Box 2580
Nantucket, MA 02584
Tel: 508-228-0145   Fax: 508-228-7135

WAYNE PRATT

Antiques

From a very early age Wayne Pratt has made collecting antiques his passion (he bought his first Windsor chair at the age of seven). With a particular interest in 18th and 19th century American furniture and accessories, Pratt has recently expanded his two stores in Woodbury, Connecticut and Nantucket. He is constantly seeking new acquisitions – he has always encouraged his clients, whether they are starting out or have become more established collectors, to buy quality.

346 Maine Street South
Woodbury, CT 06798
Tel: 203-263-5676
Fax: 203-266-4766

WEISBROD CHINESE ART

Antiques

This elegant gallery offers high quality Chinese Art to collectors and museums around the world. It was a medical doctor and art collector who founded the gallery in Toronto, and his son Michael Weisbrod moved it to Manhattan back in the 1970s. Offering fine Chinese art from the Neolithic period to the turn of the 20th century, the gallery presents an array of rare Chinese ceramics, jades, Buddhist sculpture, cloisonné, lacquer, bronzes and paintings of exceptional quality. Amongst the fine collection is a very rare, massive imperial blue and white porcelain dish from the Ming Dynasty, which once graced the Victoria and Albert Museum in London.

36 East 57th Street
New York, NY 10022
Tel: 212-319-1335
Fax: 212-319-1327

WARREN-TRICOMI
Hair and Beauty

"A salon is for the cultivation of beauty so it should be a beautiful place," says stylist Edward Tricomi. When you enter through the hand-carved wooden doors of his salon, you'll be greeted at a large silver leaf reception desk and prepared for styling and pampering in equal measure. Roses float in stone basins lined with sparkling brass in the pedicure room, while the *chic* hair-styling area features pearl-toned frescoes, stained glass and Venetian blown glass chandeliers.

16 West 57th Street
New York, NY 10014
Tel: 212-262-8899

PATRICIA WEXLER M.D.
Cosmetic Surgeons

While other cosmetic surgeons may jump to put you under the knife, Pat Wexler's specialty is non-scalpel rejuvenation of the face and body. For the past nine years, she has been injecting Botox into forehead lines, furrows, crows feet and lax necks. She also performs liposuction, recycling fat by injecting it into hollowed undereye areas, sunken cheeks and nasal labial folds to resculpt these areas.

145 East 32nd Street
New York, NY 10016
Tel: 212-684-2626   Fax: 212-684-6906

THE WHITE BARN INN
Hotels

In the thick of quaint Kennebunkport stands the White Barn Inn. Hand painted antiques, stone fireplaces, fine rugs and handmade wall coverings lend it charm and intimacy. The restaurant draws visitors from all over the country (President Bush is a fan). Facilities include an outdoor heated swimming pool, Jacuzzis and massage. The Maine coast is just a stroll away.

P.O. Box 560C, Beach Street
Kennebunkport, ME 04046
Tel: 207-967-2321   Fax: 207-967-1100

WHITINSVILLE GOLF CLUB
Golf Clubs

This nine-hole classic just south of Worcester was completed in 1925; it is one of Donald Ross' 80-plus layouts in New England. The signature par-four ninth hole, 440 yards long from the back tee, was named by *Golf Digest* as one of the top hundred holes in the country. With approximately 280 members, the club is currently full; optimists may want to sign up on the twenty-year waiting list.

179 Fletcher Street
Whitinsville, MA 01588
Tel: 508-234-6210   Fax: 508-234-2822

WELLESLEY
Colleges

Consistently ranked among the top five liberal arts colleges in the United States, Wellesley has been a leader in women's education for the past 125 years. No longer a school of white gloves and etiquette studies, the college's commitment to excellence is evident in its outstanding faculty, state-of-the-art facilities, laboratories, computer networks and magnificent 500 acre campus near Boston. *The New York Times* recently published an article entitled: "How to Succeed? Go To Wellesley."

106 Central Street
Wellesley, MA 02481
Tel: 781-283-1000

WILL ROGERS POLO CLUB
Polo Clubs

Will Rogers' love of equestrian activities extended to the horse world's most demanding sport. In 1926 Rogers bought the property that was to become his estate, landscaped the polo grounds, and then built his home. Deeded to the State of California in 1944 on the condition that the land be used for polo in perpetuity, the grounds that had played host to David Niven, Walt Disney, and Clark Gable became public. But the Will Rogers Polo Club continues its glorious tradition, as this is the only remaining polo field in Los Angeles. Horse-riding trails are also available at the edge of the grounds.

12100 Wilshire Boulevard, 15th Floor
Los Angeles, CA 90025
Tel: 310-573-5000
Fax: 310-207-3230

WILKES BASHFORD
Fashion

The Wilkes Bashford flagship houses a lavish array of hand tailored clothing and upscale fashions for men and women on seven floors. The 34 year old firm, which also sells an impressive selection of imported home furnishings, recently expanded from its original San Francisco location, opening men's and women's shops in Mendocino, St. Helena, and Mill Valley, where they feature a new line of sportswear. Bashford's legion of faithful customers can now enjoy a signature fragrance; look for the bottles that simply say Wilkes on the label.

375 Sutter Street
San Francisco, CA 94108
Tel: 415-986-4380
Fax: 415-956-3772

WENDY KRISPIN CATERER
Party Organizers and Caterers

Almost single-handedly responsible for organizing and catering parties for the Dallas social network, Wendy Krispin uses her flair for detail and commitment to perfection to throw star-studded soirées. Held in either private homes, public spaces or one of her two restaurants in the Dallas Design Center, Krispin arranges lavish fund raisers and ranch weddings. A leader in event coordination and preferred firm of the doyennes of design, her food includes Thai, French, Italian and Mexican influences although she researches and delivers any influence desired.

1025 North Stemmons Freeway
Dallas, TX 75207
Tel: 214-748-5559
Fax: 214-748-4022

WILLIAM B. MAY
Property Consultants

William B. May was founded in 1866, selling to New York's most prominent families. Today it is among the premier property consultants in New York, with seven offices and some 150 brokers. Dealing in properties across the spectrum from brownstones in Brooklyn to town houses on the Upper East Side, the firm's clients range from rock stars to diplomats. Industry peers recently gave the Henry Forster Award to Peter R. Marra (Billy May's son-in-law) for outstanding professional achievement, ethics and public service.

575 Madison Avenue
New York, NY 10022
Tel: 212-872-2200

WILLIAM CROSS
Wine Merchants

Matthew Gasco takes a broker's approach to recommending wine to his customers. Since 1998, he has offered rare vintages in his shop and adjoining wine bar. Focusing on California wines (many of cult status), the firm also offers a wide selection of French, Spanish, Italian, rare Australian and German ports. Many customers come in for a glass of Coglin or Araujo, difficult to get anywhere else. William Cross is co-owned by Windee Smith and Peter Cross, who also owns Dine restaurant.

2253 Polk Street
San Francisco, CA 04109
Tel: 415-346-1314
Fax: 415-346-1342

WHISTLING STRAITS
Golf Clubs

Whistling Straits has already earned a deserved place among America's great golf courses, a mere two years after opening for play. With a design and character reminiscent of the great seaside courses of Ireland, its location along two miles of Lake Michigan shoreline moved its noted designer, Pete Dye, to say that he has "never seen anything like it. Anyplace. Period." Another 18-hole championship course, aptly entitled the Irish Course, has just opened. Whistling Straits has already hosted the 1999 PGA Club Professional National Championship, and has been named the site of the 2004 PGA Championship. The walking only course features an international caddie corps to guide players through 18 holes of links-style golf.

1111 West Riverside Drive
Kohler, WI 53400
Tel: 800-618-5535   Fax: 920-565-6055

WILLIAM DOYLE GALLERIES
Auction Houses

Founded in 1963, this family-owned business is a leading auctioneer and appraiser of fine art and jewelry. The firm offers over 60 auctions each year, attracting a broad base of buyers and consignors. The galleries have often been the center of international media attention through the years, auctioning the estates of Hollywood legends like Gloria Swanson, Bette Davis, James Cagney, Rex Harrison and Ruth Gordon. Doyle's spectacular couture sales attract stars, models and designers.

175 East 87th Street
New York, NY 10128
Tel: 212-427-2730

WILLIAM PITT REAL ESTATE

Property Consultants

In 1949, a 23 year old called William Pitt set out to build a real estate company exclusive to Fairfield County, selling country estates, waterfront homes, horse farms and other prestigious properties. Today, the full-service brokerage that he founded sells estates for as high as $18 million, although its average sale is $1.3 million. Check out the firm's web site, which offers a room-by-room "virtual tour" of luxury properties for sale.

1266 East Main Street
Stamford, CT 06902
Tel: 203-327-5353
Fax: 203-324-7506

WILMINGTON TRUST–FSB

Wealth Management

Delaware is headquarters to many *Fortune 500* companies, due to its advantageous tax laws; it is also home to Wilmington Trust. Wealth management has a unique slant here. The Delaware Advantage, as it is known, is built into every level of financial services. Ease of use is the other byword, as each client is assigned a relationship manager who then negotiates and communicates with the various investment, trust, credit, and other planning divisions within the bank. One of the top ten U.S. Trusts, the bank has been in operation since 1903.

1100 N Market Street
Wilmington, DE 19890
Tel: 302-651-1000   Fax: 302-651-458

WILSON SONSINI GOODRICH & ROSATI

Law Firms

Palo Alto is home to many of Silicon Valley's most bustling technology ventures, and Wilson Sonsini has capitalized on its presence here to become not only Silicon Valley's largest firm, but the leading American technology law concern. WSGR's size allows it to cover all areas of technology law, including technology licensing, joint ventures and strategic alliances. WSGR's clients are on the cutting edge of change in their industries; its lawyers are equipped to assist clients with everything from IPOs to takeover and buyout proceedings.

650 Page Mill Road
Palo Alto, CA 94304
Tel: 650-493-9300

Courtesy of the Milwaukee Museum of Art: American Poppies, by Georgia O'Keeffe

WINDOWS ON THE WORLD WINE SCHOOL
Culinary Schools

Kevin Zraly's infectious enthusiasm is channeled into the noble endeavor of educating people about the wonderful world of wine. From the comfort of the 107th floor of the World Trade Center, this famous oenophile takes students on a transcendental journey through the world of wine. This intensive eight-week informal program, which runs four times a year, is a truly sensory experience.

One World Trade Center, 107th Floor
New York, NY 10048
Tel: 914-255-1456

WINDSOR COURT
Hotels

Elegant and spacious, the lobby at Windsor Court boasts a magnificent collection of art and antiques, including paintings by Reynolds and Gainsborough. The love of all things British is celebrated in everything here, from the discreet service to the statue of England's patron saint, George, in the courtroom. Every suite boasts a private balcony; they overlook the Mississippi River or the city of New Orleans. There are two penthouse suites — each some 2000 square feet — with a library, a baby grand piano and three full bathrooms. Both offer a heavenly view of the city.

300 Gravier Street
New Orleans, LA 70130
Tel: 504-523-6000
Fax: 504-596-4513

WINGED FOOT GOLF CLUB
Golf Clubs

A.W. Tillinghast designed a West course and an East course for 'The Foot' in 1921. The West course is ranked among the most challenging American courses, with 10 par fours measuring more than 400 yards, not to mention the 'The Pulpit,' the par three 10th that Tillinghast considered his finest ever. 'The Foot' is renowned for its historic clubhouse — and for a membership that takes golf very seriously indeed. Long pants are required to play on the courses and caddies are considered a must. The golfing term 'Mulligan' was coined after a member.

Fenimore Road
Mamaroneck, NY 10543
Tel: 914-698-8400

WINSTON & STRAWN
Law Firms

Winston & Strawn is among the best-connected law firms in both the political and business worlds. The present chairman was a four-term Governor of Illinois; former Senators and Attorney Generals count themselves amongst the partners. The firm also has a vigorous European practice, specializing in international arbitration from its Geneva office. Of course, it's not all national business: Winston & Strawn also handles the usual real estate and trust issues, as well as the full range of corporate law.

35 West Wacker Drive
Chicago, IL 60601
Tel: 312-558-5600
Fax: 312-558-5700

WINTERTHUR
Museums

Founded by Francis Du Pont at his country estate, this museum hosts the premier collection of decorative arts made or used in America between 1640 and 1860. The research library is an impressive resource for scholars of American art and history and the 60 acre garden is a masterpiece of American naturalism. The period rooms offer a glimpse at some of the finest examples of early American antiques, design and craftsmanship, while the galleries exhibit a variety of Americana.

Route 52 & Old Kennett Road
Winterthur, DE 19735
Tel: 302-888-4600
Fax: 302-888-4700

WOMEN'S CENTER FOR PLASTIC AND RECONSTRUCTIVE SURGERY
Cosmetic Surgeons

In an industry dominated by men, Dr. Diane Gibby's women-only practice is a breath of fresh air; she is one of only four female board-certified plastic surgeons in the Dallas area. The personalized treatment and care reflects her goal of developing a practice from a woman's perspective. Her services include full facial rejuvenation and body contouring. She also has her own line of skin care products, called Aesthessence, which will soon include a sun screen for babies.

7777 Forest Lane, Suite 820
Dallas, TX 75230
Tel: 972-566-6477

WILDENSTEIN & CO.
Art Dealers

This family of dealers has been in the fine art business since 1875, acquiring major collections of Impressionist, Renaissance and 18th century paintings and sculpture. Behind the stately doors of their 1932 townhouse are old master treasures that many museums have borrowed and most would be lucky to own. An international institution which has worked with some of the most important collectors of this century, Wildenstein remains one of the key players in the world art market.

19 East 64th Street
New York, NY 10021
Tel: 212-879-0500
Fax: 212-517-4715

THE WOODS

Florists

When Miramax and Stephen Spielberg needed flowers for their glamorous pre-Oscar parties, they turned to the husband and wife team of Wayne and Yvonne Woods. The couple, who first met each other in a florist shop, are favored by Hollywood's A-list for their lush, often extravagant arrangements. Glenn Close and Drew Barrymore are frequent visitors to this spacious Brentwood shop, while actress Kelly Preston has attended Wayne's popular classes on floral design.

11711 Gorham Avenue

Los Angeles, CA 90049

Tel: 310-826-0711   Fax: 310-826-0652

WORTHINGTON GALLERY

Art Dealers

For the past 30 years Eva-Maria Worthington has sold distinctive paintings, sculpture, drawings and graphics. Specializing in German Expressionism, she has handled pieces by Kollwitz, Kandinsky, Klee and Kirchner, as well as contemporary masters like Janssen, Triegel and Wieghardt. The gallery has also curated and circulated traveling museum exhibitions for Max Beckmann and Horst Janssen. Clients include Aerin Lauder and Oprah Winfrey. Please note that at press time Worthington was in the process of moving to a new location.

P.O. Box 11032

Chicago, IL 60611

Tel: 312-266-2424   Fax: 312-266-2461

Courtesy of the Worthington Gallery: Self Portrait with Green Turban, by Michael Triegel

YEAMANS HALL CLUB
Golf Clubs

This exclusive golfing plantation includes a 1926 Seth Raynor golf course and a small housing development planned by Olmstead Brothers. The club was founded by a group of wealthy North-Easterners, who chose Charleston because it was precisely an overnight train journey from New York – but the magnificent live oaks around the course and clubhouse, and the secluded site surrounded by river on three sides, didn't hurt either.

900 Yeamans Hall Road
Charleston, SC 29401
Tel: 843-744-5555

YORK FURRIER
Fashion

Joseph Wagner, founder of this family-run furrier, learned his trade as a boy growing up in Germany, trapping alongside his father in the Black Forest. Today, three generations of Wagners work with renowned fashion designers to create fur and leather fashions for a well-to-do clientele that includes several members of their favorite basketball team – the Chicago Bulls. York carries an inventory of more than 2000 innovative and classic designs, and is the first choice of many for fur repair, alteration and storage.

107 North York Road
Elmhurst, IL 60126
Tel: 630-832-2200   Fax: 630-832-2321

ZAO
Specialty Shops

Creative directors Assaf Ziv and Tal Lancman have created a truly unique concept in retailing. The shop, launched in the fall of 1999, makes shopping a complete cultural experience, with fashion, art, film, music and technology from all over the world. The inventory, which includes cosmetics, clothing, accessories, footwear, home furnishings, books and magazines, is largely exclusive to the store. The Gallery which adjoins the shop is equally distinctive. With an emphasis on showcasing emerging talent, it features sculpture, photography, painting and site specific installations. Curator Lisa Schroeder rotates works monthly.

175 Orchard Street
New York, NY 10002
Tel: 212-505-0500   Fax: 212-505-6406

ZUMA CANYON ORCHIDS
Florists

Barbra Streisand and Johnny Carson get their phalaenopsis here. Zuma Canyon Orchids has received notation from Princess Margaret and the firm has also been honored by London's Royal Horticultural Society. For 30 years, Zuma has been one of America's premier floral providers, arranging gift baskets, decorating private parties and shipping orchids worldwide. Specializing in denrohium, onsidian and phalaenopsis orchids, the Zuma team are committed to floral excellence.

5949 Bonsall Drive
Malibu, CA 90265
Tel: 310-457-9771

The Maccioni Family Presents

Le Cirque 2000
455 Madison Avenue
New York, NY 10022
Tel 212 303 7788
Fax 212 303 7712

Le Cirque at Bellagio
3600 Las Vegas Boulevard South
Las Vegas, NV 89109
Tel 702 693 8100
Fax 702 693 8500

Osteria Del Circo
120 West 55th Street
New York, NY 10019
Tel 212 265 3636
Fax 212 265 9283

Osteria Del Circo
3600 Las Vegas Boulevard South
Las Vegas, NV 89109
Tel 702 693 8150
Fax 702 693 8500

A Cinema Century

By Michael Dwyer

*With more twists and turns than a summer blockbuster, the history of
Hollywood is an absorbing tale. Here, Michael Dwyer surveys
the first hundred years of the dream factory.*

The story goes that Hollywood was named by Mrs. Daeida Wilcox when she and her husband, a Kansas City real estate man, retired to California in 1886 and settled on a huge ranch. Five years later they began dividing the land and by 1903 the enlarged community was incorporated as a village, retaining the name of the original ranch, Hollywood. In 1910 the burgeoning enclave was annexed to Los Angeles so that it could avail of the city's water supply and sewage system.

Meanwhile, in France, on December 28th, 1895, the brothers Louis and Auguste Lumiere presented the first program of projected films to a paying audience when they screened several short films in the basement of the Grand Café on the Boulevard des Capucines in Paris. The cinema was born.

In the infancy of American cinema, the center of production was New York City. However, in 1907, Col. William N. Selig, a pioneer showman and film producer, decided to move part of his company from Chicago to Southern California, an ideal site for film production given its real estate values, virtually guaranteed year-round sunshine and the proximity of a variety of locations; mountains, desert and the ocean. Two years later he opened California's first large motion picture studio on Mission Road in Los Angeles.

Until 1912, producers and exhibitors adhered loyally to the one-reel film, which had a running time of between five and fifteen minutes. Longer films had emanated from Continental Europe, but were looked upon as a form of foreign extravagance.

In 1911, when D.W. Griffith felt that his film, *Enoch Arden*, warranted a whole two reels, he was met with resistance from exhibitors who wanted to release it in two parts, and they only gave in when it became clear that audiences were willing to watch it in its entirety at a single sitting.

Adolph Zukor, who was then an exhibitor, scored a surprise success a year later with the four-reel theatrical drama, *La Reine Elizabeth*, which starred the great Sarah Bernhardt. But it was a European production which finally broke down the barriers of running times when, in 1913, the Italian movie, *Quo Vadis?*, which consisted of nine reels and ran for over two hours, became a huge success in the US, convincing exhibitors that audiences actually could concentrate on a film for much longer than a mere reel or two.

Page 227: Tabloid Tinseltown. Clockwise from top left — **Greta Garbo, Katharine Hepburn, Joan Crawford** *and* **Jean Harlow**. *Above: "The man you love to hate" — director and actor* **Erich von Stroheim**. *Page 229: "Sunset Revisited" — film-maker* **Cecil B. De Mille** *with Norma Desmond, a.k.a.* **Gloria Swanson**.

The advances in European film production were stalled with the outbreak of the First World War in 1914, leaving the way open for America to build and consolidate the place it has held ever since as the dominant force in world cinema. Simultaneously, more American film-makers were tearing up the rule book, with D.W. Griffith blazing the trail. Born in 1875 in Louisville, Kentucky, Griffith worked in a variety of menial jobs before taking to the stage with the Meffert Stock Company in 1897 and going on to act in one-reelers while developing his ideas as a writer. In 1908 Griffith got to direct his first film, *The Adventures of Dollie*, an action-packed nine-minute melodrama, which began his longtime collaboration with the gifted cameraman, G.W. (Billy) Bitzer.

Even in his earliest, least significant work, Griffith paid an unusual degree of attention to such aspects as casting and locations. While turning out productions at a remarkably prodigious rate, he began to develop a mastery of narrative technique allied to a unique visual style which achieved its peak in his epics, *The Birth of a Nation* (1915) and *Intolerance* (1916). Erich von Stroheim, the Austrian actor and director who later became billed as "The Man You Love to Hate," noted how Griffith had "put beauty and poetry into a cheap and tawdry sort of amusement."

Another highly ambitious film-maker from that early era was Cecil B. De Mille, an actor and theater company manager from Massachusetts who, in 1913, went into partnership with the impresario, Jesse L. Lasky and Lasky's brother-in-law, Samuel Goldfish, a glove salesman from Minsk who changed his name to Samuel Goldwyn. Together they formed the Jesse L. Lasky Feature Play Company.

Goldwyn was a great showman who went on to become the most quoted film producer in cinema history. Never one for understatement or selling himself short, he once declared: "What we want is a story that starts with an earthquake and works its way up to a climax." Of his 1946 oscar-winner, *The Best Years of Our Lives*, he said: "I don't care if it doesn't make a nickel. I just want every man, woman and child in America to see it!" And then there were all those Goldwynisms, as they became known: "Directors are always biting the hand that lays the golden egg"; "Gentlemen, kindly include me out"; "A verbal contract isn't worth the paper it's written on" and "In two words, im-possible."

In 1914 Goldwyn and Lasky co-produced Cecil B. De Mille's highly successful western, *The Squaw Man*. While seeking suitable locations for the movie, De Mille came across the idyllic small town of Hollywood, where he converted a large stable into a studio and went into production. Other producers followed suit and by 1917 Hollywood was becoming established as the film-making capital of the United States. Three years later, with the advent of the studios and the emergence of the star system, Hollywood was producing close to 800 movies a year and its name became synonymous with glamour and the art of illusion. As the movies grew in scale and cost, and became increasingly sophisticated in technique and content, the cinema acquired a new economic and social status. Cinemas no longer were converted stores, but custom-built edifices designed as splendid picture palaces in upmarket areas. Before the war the great majority of the moviegoing audience was the poor working class who flocked to didactic morality dramas and melodramas. America was depicted as the land of opportunity as the cinemas attracted large numbers of immigrants who relished an entertainment form which, in the silent movie era, placed no strain on their often limited grasp of the English language. Parallel to this was the movement of many film-makers from Europe to the US and its rapidly developing movie industry. This was a period of great technological and social revolution, as the motor car, radio, advertising and the cinema combined to change the pattern of American life. At the beginning of the 1920s the cinema was the nation's fifth largest industry; by the time that talking pictures revolutionized Hollywood, it rose to fourth. And Hollywood had adopted its definitive industrial form, with monopolistic power in the hands of the major film distributors and studios.

These powerful bodies were ruled over by moguls who, with few exceptions, had arrived in the US as poor immigrants and had learned to fight for their survival as proprietors of cheap nickelodeons at the start of the century – men such as Carl Laemmle of Universal, William Fox, Louis B. Mayer of MGM (Metro-Goldwyn-Mayer), Adolph Zukor, and the Warner brothers, Harry, Albert, Sam and Jack L. These mostly Jewish immigrants were colorful, blunt-spoken and ruthless operators who thrived on the huge risks involved in an industry where the pictures were getting bigger and more expensive. Making movies continues to be a high-risk venture in which, no matter how cynical or sophisticated their marketing campaigns, producers and studios ultimately rely on the whims of the paying public, who time and again have resisted some of the most apparently attractive and commercial packing, and rejected stars when they appeared to be at the peak of their powers.

As William Goldman, the Oscar-winning screenwriter of *Butch Cassidy and the Sundance Kid* and *All the President's Men*, famously observed in his canny 1983 book, *Adventures in the Screen Trade*, in terms of making hits or misses, "nobody knows anything" in

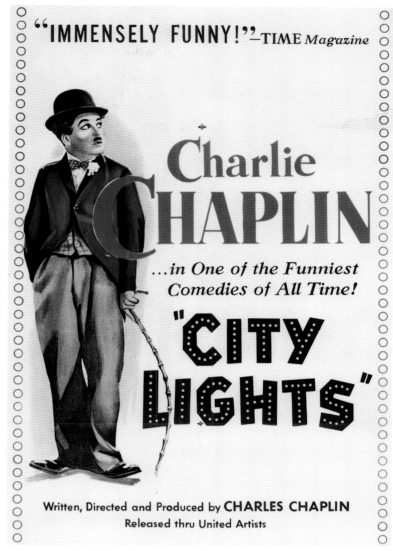

"IMMENSELY FUNNY!"—TIME *Magazine*

Charlie CHAPLIN

...in One of the Funniest Comedies of All Time!

"CITY LIGHTS"

Written, Directed and Produced by **CHARLES CHAPLIN**
Released thru United Artists

the film business. What scared the moguls more than the commercial risks and the sex scandals that began to emanate from Hollywood was the rising power of the movie star.

Founded in 1924, MGM would boast in later years of having "More Stars Than There Are in Heaven." Their stellar roster included Jean Harlow, Spencer Tracy, Katharine Hepburn, Joan Crawford, Clark Gable, Myrna Loy, William Powell, Judy Garland, Mickey Rooney and arguably the most enigmatic star of them all, Greta Garbo, whose unique features were adored by the camera.

However, even in the late 1910s Mary Pickford and Charles Chaplin had become screen idols of such stature that they could command huge salaries and deal with the moguls on their own terms. In 1919 Pickford and Chaplin joined forces with D.W. Griffith and Douglas Fairbanks to form their own company, United Artists Corporation, through which they would produce and distribute their own films.

The consensus in Hollywood was that, despite their collective star power, United Artists, which owned neither studios nor cinemas, could never compete with such powerful forces as Paramount or MGM. Nevertheless, it did survive and this daring and visionary enterprise served as the blueprint for the many stars and directors who went on to produce their own pictures at the expense of the studios.

In recent years, Steven Spielberg, for example, joined forces with the music industry mogul, David Geffen, and the former Disney executive, Jeffrey Katzenberg, to form DreamWorks SKG, which made Spielberg's own *Saving Private Ryan*, the Oscar-winning *American Beauty,* and the big box-office hit, *Gladiator*. The hugely successful *Mission Impossible II* was produced by its star, Tom Cruise, and his former agent, Paula Wagner. And most of today's major stars and directors have "housekeeping deals" with the major studios, who pick up the bills for their offices and staff.

Today Hollywood remains as potent a magnetic lure for international talent as it was in the ground-breaking period of the Twenties and Thirties when many of the most celebrated studio productions were made by the Irishman, Rex Ingram (who launched Rudolph Valentino's career with *The Four Horsemen of the Apocalypse* in 1921); the Irish-American director John Ford; the Sicilian immigrant, Frank Capra, who made American classics like *It Happened One Night, Mr Smith Goes to Washington* and *It's a Wonderful Life*; and the London-born master of the thriller genre, Alfred Hitchcock. Hitchcock was brought to America to direct *Rebecca* by David O. Selznick, who was the prototype of the creative, independent Hollywood film producer who could succeed in his own right without being in thrall to the studios. The achievement that is the immortal classic, *Gone With the Wind* (1939) is

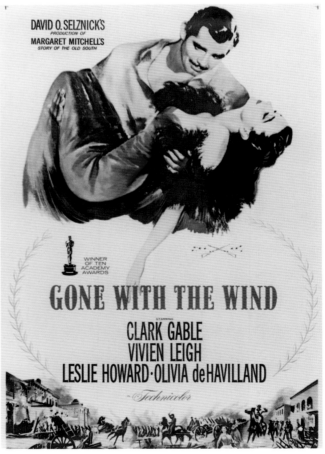

Page 230: Taking a break from Ginger, **Fred Astaire** woos **Rita Hayworth**.
Page 231: Top —
An early publicity poster for City Lights released by United Artists.
Bottom: Left to Right —
D. W. Griffith, **Mary Pickford**, **Charlie Chaplin**, **Douglas Fairbanks** and two onlookers sign the papers that formed United Artists.
Above and Left: David O. Selznick's Oscar winners for best picture, Rebecca and Gone With the Wind.
Page 233: Pin-up **Veronica Lake** salutes the troops.
Page 235: MGM's **Louis B. Mayer** with "More Stars Than There Are in Heaven."

credited not so much to its director, Victor Fleming (who replaced George Cukor on the project), but to Selznick, who was responsible for bringing all its key creative elements together and for forging ahead with such a complex production on an epic scale.

The year after he received the best picture Oscar as producer of *Gone With the Wind,* Selznick was back on the podium to collect the best picture Oscar for Hitchcock's *Rebecca.* Selznick was a humorless, intense man and a notoriously hard taskmaster, prompting the Oscar-nominated writer-director Nunally Johnson to demur when asked to work for Selznick: "I understand that an assignment with you consists of three months' work — and six months' recuperation." The producer's famous memos were so numerous that they were collected in book form as *Memo From David O. Selznick* and so long that Hitchcock commented dryly in 1965: "When I came to America twenty-five years ago to direct *Rebecca,* David Selznick sent me a memo. I've just finished reading it. I think I may turn it into a motion picture. I plan to call it *The Longest Story Ever Told.*"

Selznick's production of *Gone With the Wind* was the first color film to win the Academy Award for best picture, and on the same night the Technicolor company was presented with an honorary Oscar for "its contributions in successfully bringing three-color feature productions to the screen." The advent of color was one of the technological advances which the Hollywood studios regularly employed to retain the audiences they cultivated so assiduously. The novelty of sound was a crucial factor in helping the studios weather the aftermath of the Wall Street crash, and in tandem with facilitating the arrival of a new genre in the musical, contributed substantially to maintaining cinema audiences during the difficult years of the Depression. Weekly admissions at American cinemas jumped from 57 million in 1927 to almost double that figure in 1930.

During the bleak war years of the 1940s the studios responded by churning out hundreds of assembly-line escapist entertainments for the masses — comedies, musicals, westerns, melodramas and a string of popular pictures starring the favored pin-up girls of the GIs: Claudette Colbert, Betty Grable, Rita Hayworth, Veronica Lake, Hedy Lamarr, Dorothy Lamour and Lana Turner. The war years became a boom period for Hollywood with films having longer runs, allowing the studios to make fewer films for bigger audiences. Production costs increased, but profit margins rose even faster as a result.

After the war, however, inflation forced production costs ever upwards, and there was rancor within the film industry as names were named and blacklisted as the House Un-American Activities Committee held hearings into the alleged infiltration of the industry by Communists. Worst of all, the movies had a terrifying new enemy in commercial television. No longer would audiences need to leave the comforts of their home for audio-visual entertainment, albeit in black-and-white until the 1960s. The studios fought back – sometimes pointlessly, with gimmicks such as Smell-O-Vision, Aroma-Rama and 3-D – and more successfully by enhancing the spectacle of the cinema going experience through the dramatic new widescreen system, CinemaScope.

Hollywood decided that if the system could not be beaten it was better to join it. Television became a valuable source of revenues raised from selling old movies for screenings on the small screen, and Columbia Pictures, Walt Disney, Warner Brothers, 20th Century-Fox, MGM and Universal all became involved in making television fare. The next formidable enemy came from within – video and its advent marked a major slump in cinema attendance, causing many exhibitors to quit the business and close down their outlets. Other cinemas were arbitrarily split into smaller auditoria. They would later be replaced by custom-built multiplex cinemas, complete with vast screens, digital sound systems, perfect eye-lines and seating comparable to business class on an airline.

Above all, the industry was saved by an ambitious new generation of young film-makers like Steven Spielberg and George Lucas, who had been experimenting with amateur movie-making in their teens and who seized upon new technological developments in special effects to deliver a new, visceral, action-driven style of blockbuster in Spielberg's *Jaws* (1975) and Lucas's *Star Wars* (1977). Opening on usually wide release patterns, they became the first films to break the $100 million mark in film rentals.

Millions more were earned from the shrewd exploitation of the market by offering tie-in merchandising, so much so that some blockbusters appeared to have given more thought to potential marketing opportunities than to any creative thinking in the scripts they brought to the screen. And the profits of the studios were boosted further by the increasing domination of foreign markets by Hollywood productions with the star power and the budgets to decimate smaller, indigenous productions around the world.

When a new wave of independent production companies came to the forefront at the Oscars – and sometimes even at the box-office – in the Eighties and Nineties, the studios responded by buying them up. Each studio now has its own specialist division, the most high-profile being Disney's acquisition of Miramax Films. That enterprising company regularly outstrips the studios themselves in terms of nominations and awards at the Oscars, with its eclectic range of productions and acquisitions from *Pulp Fiction* to *The English Patient* to *Life is Beautiful* to *Shakespeare in Love*, and they have delivered many profitable successes from some of the least commercially likely material.

With the exception of Harvey Weinstein – the clever and imposing figure who runs Miramax with his brother Bob – the men and women who run the Hollywood studios nowadays are a breed apart from the colorful pioneers of yesteryear. While they are well-regarded for their business acumen, they are operating in a business where the tables have well and truly turned, where in that early spirit fostered by the United Artists team of Mary Pickford, Charles Chaplin, Douglas Fairbanks and D.W. Griffith, it is the studios who are now in thrall to their major stars and directors. Ⓐ

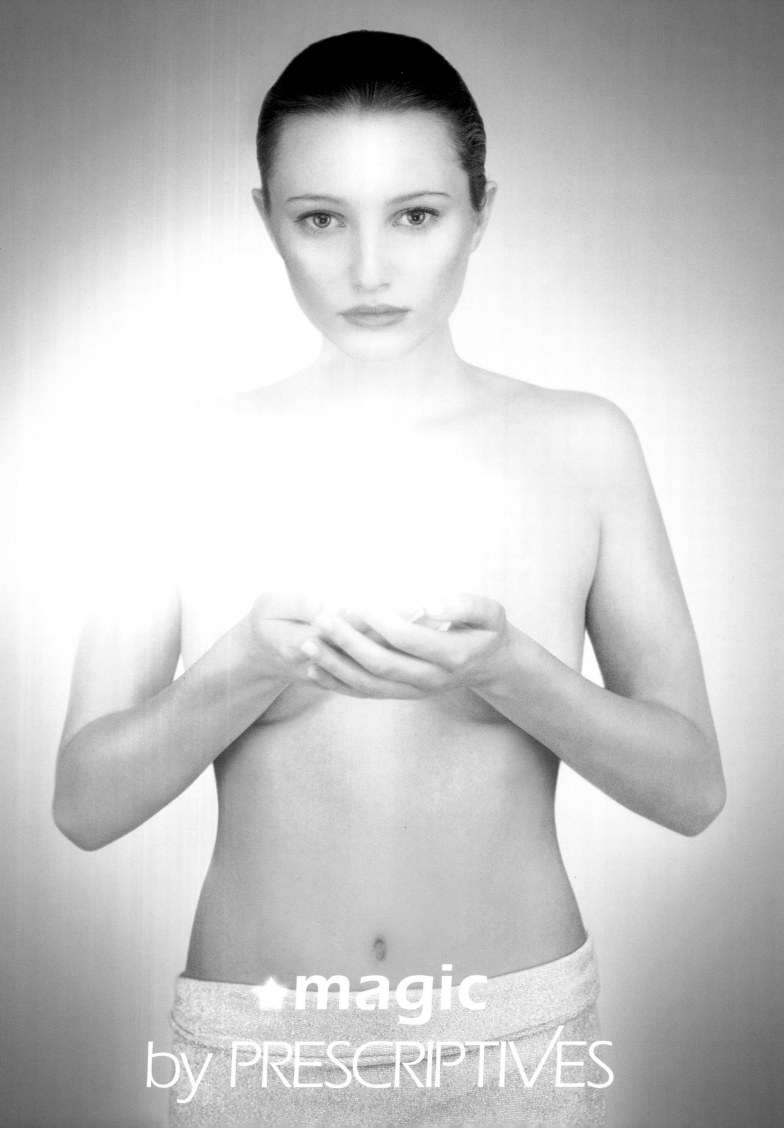

★magic
by PRESCRIPTIVES

LEADING LADIES

By Christopher Lawrence

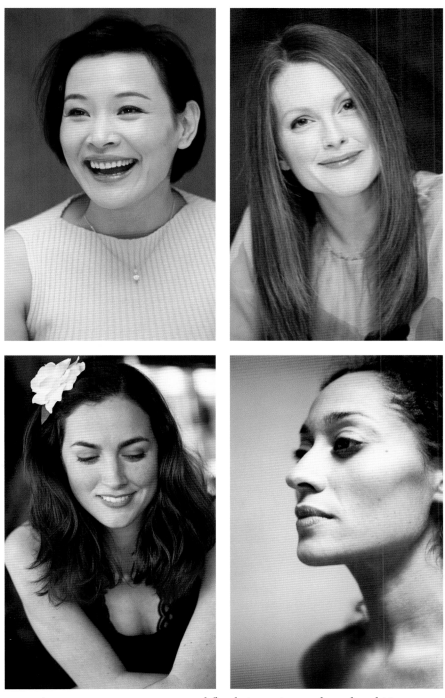

American women are renowned for their passion, style and ambition.
Today, they are gracefully redefining the rules for success
in the arts, education, finance, politics and philanthrophy.
Here, Christopher Lawrence profiles 70 of America's Leading Ladies.

AMANPOUR

Christiane Amanpour is English by birth and Iranian both by lineage and upbringing. But in the hearts and minds of "Mr. and Mrs. America and all the ships at sea," she is an American citizen – first by her training, career and impact; and second by her recent and much-celebrated marriage.

After spending much of her childhood in Tehran, she completed her secondary education in England, before heading to the United States for university. Amanpour shared a house with John F. Kennedy, Jr. and other friends while in Providence before graduating summa cum laude from the University of Rhode Island. The association continued for the rest of Kennedy's brief life. In the wake of his death, Amanpour's commentary on her friend was light years removed from the ramblings of the media circus—there was affection and loyalty, but above all, dignity.

Poise and toughness carried her from a job as an assistant on CNN's international desk in Atlanta to her celebrated coverage of the fall of Communism in Europe. The networks, she would later say, wanted someone "blond and from the Midwest," but Amanpour's presence as a supremely balanced and cosmopolitan observer shot her to an unquestioned leadership role in international news. Based out of Paris or London, she has covered Afghanistan, the Balkans, the Persian Gulf, Africa and beyond. Peabody Awards, du Pont awards, a Polk award and an Emmy are but a few of the honors that now permit her airtime not only with CNN, but on CBS as a correspondent with *60 Minutes II*—an unprecedented arrangement in a business of brand-name faces.

And after almost 20 years of shooting and shelling and jumbled time zones, Amanpour is a wife and a mother. Her 1998 marriage to State Department spokesman James Rubin garnered headlines around the world. The transcontinental journalist returned to Washington for the birth of their son earlier this year.

ARMSTRONG

Once upon a time, women weren't allowed to wear pantsuits in the West Wing of the White House. In 1973, Anne L. Armstrong could serve in a Cabinet-level post, as Counselor to the President of the United States, and not be free to choose her own wardrobe in the morning. "I wasn't a confrontational, marching type," she says when asked about her leadership role as a woman. "We just worked steadily and quietly to move things along and we did move things along, I believe." Listening to Armstrong talk about those years and especially about Watergate is to be astonished at her place in a man's man's man's world: "...I went to Al Haig, who was then Chief-of-Staff and said 'I've got to ask the President eye-to-eye, face to face, if any of these [Watergate allegations] are true.' Nixon was then recovering from pneumonia and he was at Bethesda Naval Hospital. Haig and I went out there and I was alone with President Nixon who was in his sickbed. I asked him for the truth and he looked me in the eye and told me that none of these terrible things I was hearing were true."

Armstrong served as Ambassador to Great Britain in the late 1970s and maintained a key policy role in the Reagan and Bush administrations. Today, she chairs the Executive Committee of the Center for Strategic and International Studies, a Washington think-tank, and sits on the boards of American Express and Halliburton. Married for 50 years to Tobin Armstrong, the couple have five children and live at the Armstrong Ranch, Armstrong, Texas. It's one of the great dynasties of the Southwest, but she gracefully downplays the size of the family seat, reluctantly allowing that it has "it's own zip code and a population of thirty-five." Noblesse oblige and gentle modesty guide her right back to public service: "My career doesn't make much of a story because it was pretty easy for me," she says. "Some women can't afford the luxury of politics and must work full-time. But for women who can choose, it offers a unique chance to make a big difference."

BENING
Was anybody ever truly interested in Warren Beatty as President of the United States? Imagine Shirley MacLaine anywhere near the Oval Office and that seems reason enough to push the notion "President Beatty" to the farthest reaches of the mind. The best thing Beatty had going for him in any assessment of his candidacy was his wife. And Bening had already done an impressive job in the role. 1995's *The American President* was a starry-eyed look at presidential courtship in which the actress bouyed a sanctimonious Michael Doulgas by sheer force of her screen appeal. Why not, the reasoning went, let Bening have a shot at 1600 Pennsylvania Avenue?

Warren, it seems, is not the only one besotted by his wife. Bening was born in Kansas, but reared and educated in San Diego. She was working with the San Diego Repertory Theatre by her teens and after graduating from San Francisco State University was accepted by the American Conservatory Theatre. Broadway led film. In 1990's *The Grifters*, Bening proved at least a match for Anjelica Huston and snagged an Oscar nomination along the way. After that arrival, Bening was swept up into the orbit of one of Hollywood's greatest icons. After marriage and four children, her status has shifted from that of talented actress — in *American Beauty* and a lot more besides — to something quite different. The strange laws of celebrity dictate that she is less thespian than royalty. Whether she chooses to act or not, Annettte Bening is a grand lady of celluloid and a Movie Queen bathed forever in golden light. The White House would have been a step down.

BERKE

Looking back, Deborah Berke's career has been a signpost for the evolution of taste. It's almost touching, seven years and God-knows-how-many tech billions later, to think that in 1993, Charles Gandee of *Vogue* saw the architect's understated minimalism as the harbinger of a decade "repentant" for the overt excesses of the 1980s. Berke's star was just beginning to shine widely but a popular critique went that her blue-chip clientele (William Wegman, Calvin Klein, Caroline Kennedy) was at odds with the principles of spare functionality for which she was being celebrated. Along the way, of course, a slicker minimalism exploded into the mainstream to become the luxury item of an exceptionally luxurious moment. Formal rigor was somehow co-opted into a mirror image of the Donald Trump aesthetic.

"I think that, in opting for minimalism, people are often showing off discipline—you could buy that Queen Anne commode, but you have the willpower to say no," she says lightly. Berke savors ironies, like the fact that her work maintains its integrity by celebrating …integration. Where so much expensive design looks monolithic and sheer, she likes to see the internal relationships of structure: "I'm interested in how things go together... how, for instance, corrugated steel will fit against plywood. I'm interested in the seams of a building." And she's well-known for venerating humble materials: "why not clad a building in aluminum that looks like aluminum, rather than cutting it to look like wood clapboard?"

Berke holds a Yale professorship and although her booming practice has of late made that commitment more of a stretch, it's easy to discern the teacher in her. She's a generous conversationalist and she'll arc from "office hours" to "scholar" to "funky mom" without missing a beat. Berke is lately married to a surgeon, living on the Upper East Side and enjoying herself by taking her small daughter for walks in the park. And while she'll gently fret about the trappings of adulthood, she needn't. Just mention Bob Dylan and she can instantly transport back to the Rhode Island School of Design, circa 1974. And that's a fine thing, because in architect years, Deborah Berke is still a baby. Just wait for the next act.

BETTS

The photograph on the editor's letter has changed. Katherine Betts's first issue of *Harper's Bazaar* featured a conventional portrait of the new-for-the-new-millennium editor. A month later, Betts's metamorphosis began in earnest: the magazine had been dramatically overhauled and she was conferring with cover girl Gwyneth Paltrow. A month after that, she was smiling whilst leaning into the telephone – as if she were listening to the awkward details of a girlfriend's blind date. Meanwhile, the sign-off for the accompanying letters had departed from her bylines and masthead identification. It was now simply "Kate Betts" who was addressing the reader at the opening of the magazine's monthly proceedings.

Cleaner, more crisp, youthful and engaged: the fresh image and tight syllables of the shortened name are a perfect metaphor for the larger changes she has wrought at the grand old house of *Bazaar*. The cool and distanced look of the magazine has been overhauled with sweeping changes to the logo and typefaces. A style designed, she told Charlie Rose, to be "bolder and more confident—with more of a journalistic sense of urgency."

Betts could very easily have been describing herself; she's a thoroughly modern woman with smarts and pedigree to burn. After Fieldston and Choate came Princeton, where she was a player at the *Daily Princetonian*. Her work in Paris for *The International Herald Tribune* led to a 1988-91 tenure as bureau chief for *Women's Wear Daily* and *W*. From Paris, then back to New York and *Vogue*, where she came to be a very highly regarded and very visible protégée to Anna Wintour. At the age of 35, nine months pregnant with her first son, Betts jumped ship to take *Bazaar* in the summer of 1999. "A journalistic sense of urgency," indeed.

Today, she remains an ardent Francophile while never compromising her own quintessentially fresh, American style. Her vision for the magazine is to reflect fashion's role as a "thermometer" for the culture at large. Kate Betts is an observer and a writer, not merely a fan of the rag trade. She has said that she wants to reach people "who are interested in how fashion relates to music, culture and art, not just people who are interested in hemlines."

She's upbeat and determined, with warmth and beauty to spare – an American sweetheart for the new millennium. Halle Berry's first brush with fame came in the 1980s when she walked away from modeling to test for the television deity Aaron Spelling's *Charlie's Angels '88*. Much to the detriment of Western Culture, the revival never made it to the airwaves. More than a decade later, we've caught up with the TV impresario's vision: Berry has been steadily building an impressive resumé around her grace, humor and formidable acting abilities. Oh, and the look: Sunshine and optimism, the girl next door.

BERRY

The public persona belies the struggles of growing up in Cleveland as the daughter of a troubled union between an African-American father and an Irish mother. When the family moved to the suburbs, Berry was routinely taunted for her biracial background. She responded by becoming an honor student, editing the school newspaper and winning the presidency of her senior class.

After breaking through in *Boomerang* and an acclaimed performance in Spike Lee's *Jungle Fever*, Berry held her own opposite Jessica Lange in 1993's *Losing Isaiah* and Warren Beatty in 1998's *Bulworth*. The heightened visibility and prestige enabled her—after years of pitching the project to wary studios—to produce and star in a film biography of pioneering black actress Dorothy Dandridge. *Introducing Dorothy Dandridge* features Berry as the brilliant and doomed woman who had inspired her to take up acting. The unstinting look at Dandridge's ordeal as a black woman in a white industry was praised lavishly and won Berry a Golden Globe in 1999. But for an actress who has been honored by the Harvard Foundation for Intercultural and Race Relations, the project was an acknowledgment of a debt and a reminder of work yet to be done: "There is still racism in this country," she has said. "That I know all too well."

BLACK

Cathie Black, President of Hearst Magazines, calls 20 minutes early: "I've just had some time in my schedule open up unexpectedly, would you be able to do the interview now?" The words come quickly, but there is no pressure and no sense that she has been inconvenienced by the appointment. There is "slow and courteous" and then there is "quick and brusque." Black has refined the game to the point where she makes one feel perfectly well cared for at a lightning pace. Chalk it up to what she cheerfully calls "a solid midwestern upbringing" in Chicago. That and an intelligence akin to a laser beam.

66 million people read her magazines annually: *Harper's Bazaar, Esquire, Town & Country, House Beautiful* and so on. Think of the editors and the advertisers and the Internet and the shareholders. And the moonlighting on the boards of IBM and Coca-Cola as well as acting as an advocate for women in business. Then, there is the family: Black's husband of 18 years is an attorney in Manhattan and the couple have two children. Weekends in northwest Connecticut are, she says, "a nice contrast to our life in New York." It's upbeat and matter-of-fact, not beleaguered.

Cut to the business and she takes verbal flight. It's riveting to listen to her talk about the inception of *USA Today* (she was part of the founding team), or about Hearst's success in new media. It's riveting and somehow uplifting, because all of that analytical good sense and all of those smarts are coupled with real passion. Black laughs that she "flew in from San Francisco at one-thirty this morning," but that doesn't matter now that we are talking about media brands being built and the changing face of the popular culture that she is harnessing. It doesn't matter because her faculties are engaged in the pursuit of excellence. And when the call is finished, this writer wants to work for Hearst, revamping and extending *Citizen Kane*'s domain. Call it "leadership style." Or just "a solid midwestern upbringing."

BOARDMAN

"As humans, we need narrative mythology or the oral tradition or the fairy tale. The ones that have lasted for so long satisfy a craving for us to have beginnings, middles and endings. And renewal." Sam Boardman will talk about Palm Beach and the Bath & Tennis Club and she'll talk about her days at St. Paul's. Just parts of the picture, parts of the story. Give her a hole, though, a question with an opening for philosophical speculation, and she'll teach you a few things about thinking on your feet. And she'll pull it off with such humor and feathered grace that you'll never know that you've expended actual brainpower.

Boardman is the one who used to wear thigh boots into dinner at St. Paul's. No L.L. Bean footwear for the New Hampshire woods, no sweatshirts and no synchilla. People often spend the balance of their lives celebrating the intellectual and social splendor of St. Paul's, but she just wanted to move on to the next thing. And so after the fifth form, with degree requirements already in order; she took the next step and made her way to the Department of History at Harvard via a year of independent study, work and travel. Somewhere during the history major, things took a new turn. "I took some chemistry," she says breezily, "and it just worked out." Biology was next and "as it went on, I just got the feeling that I could do it." Boardman had elected to become a physician. "Everyone thought I was a little crazy to try it, but I liked the idea of working in a hospital and I wanted to be able to contribute academically and intellectually to one."

So Sam Boardman spent the latter half of the 1990s at Cornell Medical College in Manhattan and managed to be both an outstanding student and a blue-chip boldfaced name. Along with her roommate and sister Serena, she's become an icon of the new society life: she's an Astor and she knows her way through clothes, clubs and benefits. She's dating James Truman, a key lieutenant in S.I. Newhouse's Condé Nast empire. By taking her residency in psychiatry, she has found a way to integrate the keen ear and tongue of the party circuit with a formidable erudition that is never overbearing. "Psychiatry," she says, "is more about the intellect. I love stories and I love to hear people tell their stories. For me, there's more humanity in it as well. It really was, I think, a natural place for me to end up."

BLAIR "There's nothing I'd rather talk about than the Harvard AIDS Institute," says Mrs. William McCormick Blair. She's "Deeda" to her friends and in the boldface of society pages worldwide. She's also the Co-Chairman of the Institute. "It was the first lab to hypothesize that HIV was a retrovirus causing immune suppression," she notes proudly. It is the kind of information that leads one to suspect that Blair's mind is often diverted from the exquisite homes, gardens and parties for which she's so well and widely known.

Deeda and Bill Blair were married in Copenhagen while he was serving a tour of ambassadorial duty under the couple's close friend Jack Kennedy. Later in that decade, while on post to the Philippines, Deeda found herself slipping away from the Manila summers to New York's Memorial Sloan-Kettering. Not a standard holiday, but a unique chance to immerse herself in a then-growing passion for cancer research. It was the early phase of a self-directed graduate program in biology that has now lasted for more than 30 years.

"Marguerite Littman and I call ourselves 'the serene hustlers,'" chuckles Blair. She's a famed hostess, but beyond a certain number, entertaining is no longer entertaining; it is a means to the end of promoting and funding the causes. That shrewd approach coincides with Blair's professional life and her consultancies to major pharmaceutical and biotechnology firms across the United States.

In what little downtime there is to snatch, Deeda Blair enjoys traveling. "But I don't want to go to an island and lie on the beach. I'd much rather go to Paris and walk for six or seven hours a day while visiting the museums and shops and exhibits. It is my home of the heart."

BOYLE

She is angles and bones, a walking scalpel—but never fragile. The blue eyes alone could be her meal ticket because while she can effortlessly set them to a lethal glare, they never quite divest themselves of a certain unmistakable heartbreak. She'll scorch the earth with that look and seem only to be collecting on an outstanding emotional debt. Lara Flynn Boyle is a complicated knockout.

She is now a million miles from the North Side of Chicago, where she was raised by a single mother struggling to make ends meet. It was, she once observed blackly, "a bad movie of the week." At the age of 18, she landed in Hollywood by way of the Chicago Academy for the Arts and was working with David Lynch on *Twin Peaks*. The series didn't last, but much of its considerable buzz attached itself to Boyle. And out of cult starlet status, she began to build a varied and memorable film resumé. Boyle has turned up in odd but memorable places, usually stealing the show. A turn as Mike Myers' delusional girlfriend in *Wayne's World* was brilliant physical comedy, while Todd Solondz's midnight-black comedy *Happiness* let her play self-absorption as sexual cruelty.

These days, she hangs the proverbial hat on David E. Kelley's *The Practice* and has helped the show to its newly breathtaking Nielsons. Episodic television gives her a steady gig and a place to build a steadier relationship with the viewing public. And it is oddly reassuring to know that none other than Jack Nicholson has been keeping extended company with the actress. Think of it as a public service on Boyle's part. Who better to teach a soulful old dog a few brilliant new tricks?

BOXER

Barbara Boxer, Democrat of California, is nothing if not a fighter. Not the fighter of cheap campaign rhetoric, but across the combative professions of politics and journalism—across her life in the arena.

Consider the moment in early 1999, when she fell ill during the Clinton impeachment hearings: Boxer felt faint and had to be carried from the Senate chamber in a wheelchair. After examination by a Capitol nurse, she was back on the floor in 30 minutes to assume her duties as a juror in the proceedings against the President. Two nights later, she was dining with the Commander-in-Chief at a party in honor of her husband's 60th birthday. The Senator is not a woman to be thwarted, even by illness.

Just ask Matt Fong, would-be Senator from California. In 1998, months before Boxer's illness at the Capitol and with all that Monica business in full flower, Fong was poised to take a race that had been treated as a lay-up by the GOP. Boxer's record on the environment, abortion and health care (compiled during a decade in the House of Representatives and six years in the Senate) had made her, by most accounts, the most liberal member of the Congress. Boxer was running at a five percent deficit in polls conducted three weeks from Election Day, but surged to beat the challenger by a ten percent margin that stunned even her closest aides.

"I think I'm underestimated," she has said. "My opponents don't understand how I connect with voters." A note to aspiring senatorial candidates: Boxer connects with California voters by sheer force of will and a refusal to practice the poll-driven politics of the day: "On any given issue in California, one-third of the people will hate you, one-third will love you and one-third will say 'Barbara Boxer, is she my councilwoman?'" she once said with her characteristic bluntness.

"You'll drive yourself crazy if you try to please everyone, so all I can do is go out and make my case."

"An elegant informality is what I love," says Pat Breen. "Small dinner parties with 12 to 24 people. Warmth # BREEN and intimacy, with good food and good conversation." It's hard not to be swept up by the idea of a small supper with Mrs. Daniel Breen of Houston, East Hampton and Lyford Cay. If that gilt-edged itinerary of residences and a legendary sense of style seems intimidating, be advised that the woman radiates such a disarming personal warmth as to completely undercut suspicions of pretense. Mrs. Breen has raised no fewer than six sons and it's an experience that seems to pervade everything she does. She's a Norman Rockwell mother. Except she's in couture. At La Cote Basque.

"I was born in New York City and raised in Dublin. That's probably where my fashion sense started. We would actually buy the material for our clothes in Paris with my mother and then take it to an Irish dressmaker and have dresses made up like the ones we had seen in *Vogue*." But, she says, "fashion is not something that I've ever thought that much about. I've always been interested in clothes, but never to the point of a fetish because, obviously, with raising six sons..." she says, her voice trailing off into an audible smile.

With her youngest now in college, she has allocated more time than ever to her philanthropic work: "I'm on the boards of the [Houston] Ballet and the University of Texas Health Science Center. And I'm a member of the Textile and Costume Institute. My chief commitment, though, is to the Houston Grand Opera, where I am the Executive Vice President and on the Executive Committee of the Board of Trustees." The appreciation of music, like clothes, began back in Dublin and was nurtured by trips to the Paris Grand Opera. But here again, there is no pretense; just warmth and an infectious sense of fun: "I like all kinds of popular music as well, except maybe hard rock. I mean, the works of Billy Joel – why not?" Why not indeed, Mrs. B.?

Stockard Channing was born to play # CHANNING
the most eccentric and entertaining
guest at one of the best dinners – the type who knows good Parisian bistros, Motown records and eastern mysticism. Stockard Channing, regal beauty and funky WASP. "I'm off-center," she has said. "I don't live an average, normal life. I am not insane or anything, I don't mean that. But I have been told this too."

Channing's aristocratic bearing is neither accident nor contrivance. She was born Susan Stockard to a shipping magnate father and educated in Manhattan before boarding at the Madeira School for Girls in northern Virginia. With stables and over 300 acres of riding trails, the school has always enjoyed a reputation for turning out the most exquisitely refined young ladies. Years later, Channing told *Movieline*: "I can't type, I can't write a letter. I'm absolutely ignorant in many ways that everybody takes for granted," but her subsequent cum laude graduation from Radcliffe belies the claims. Just another bit of genteel self-deprecation, so as not to threaten the Lawrenceville boys at dances.

She married businessman Walter Channing and while the union didn't last, the stage name did. She has done superb work in every medium, but it is on the stage where she has shined brightest – including a Tony-winning performance in 1985's *A Day in the Death of Joe Egg*. Tony and Oscar nominations for her work in the respective stage and screen versions of *Six Degrees of Separation* launched her into the 1990s and she has been a steady force ever since, with recent film roles in *The First Wives Club*, *Practical Magic* and *Where The Heart Is* as well as on television's smash *The West Wing*.

With showbiz in order, Channing retreats – not to Palm Springs or Malibu – but to her house on the coast of Maine and to that well-bred understatement: "I like to sit on the deck playing with my dog and pretending like I'm an eight-year-old in summer camp," she laughs. "That's probably one of the reasons I'm not a major movie star—I don't like to get dressed up that much."

COPPOLA

When Sofia Coppola brought *The Virgin Suicides* to the French Riviera, she could remember visiting the Cannes Film Festival with her father to launch *Apocalypse Now* more than 20 years earlier: the boats, the paparazzi, her seventh birthday party. What a peculiar slab of personal history to graft onto the experience of making one's feature directorial debut before the world's toughest audience! Needless to say, Coppola handled the affair with considerable aplomb. "A knockout directorial debut," cried *The Hollywood Reporter* in its write-up.

The Virgin Suicides made its way to theaters in spring 2000 and marked a consolidation of the triumph begun at Cannes. Francis Ford Coppola's daughter confronted the shadow of the family business head-on and won big. She had written a script on spec and secured the director's chair before coaxing superior performances from James Woods, Kathleen Turner and Kirsten Dunst. All of this while steeling herself against the inevitable comparisons and charges of nepotism: "I knew if I started to worry about the end result," she has said, "and what people would think, it would have been too terrifying and I wouldn't have done it."

Raised between the family's 1600 acre estate and working vineyards in Napa Valley and their compound in Belize, Sofia Coppola was trained as a painter at Cal Arts. The Coppolas are not only not Hollywood, they are haute bohemia and it is an artist's eye and sensibility that has run through her photography (for *Paris Vogue*, *Details*, and *Interview* among others), fashion design projects and most certainly through The Virgin's stunning compositions.

Coppola married the celebrated young director Spike Jonze in what was perhaps the young celebrity wedding of 1999. Nicolas Cage (Sofia's cousin) his wife Patricia Arquette, her brother David Arquette and his wife Courtney Cox were among the young talents to celebrate the nuptials at the Napa estate. The family business is in safe hands.

CARTER

"I'm not very comfortable with the term 'interior decorator,'" says Cynthia Carter. "I want to make rooms that make people feel good to be in. I don't like the idea of interior decoration because there's something false about that, as if you're making a place into something it's not; like turning a small Third Avenue apartment into Versailles."

Carter's thoughts are pointed, but roll on a spirit of gentle good humor. They also come with a new and heightened sense of purpose. For years, this mother of four children has put together the houses and parties which enable her husband, *Vanity Fair*'s Graydon Carter, to practice the social diplomacy of the modern editor. The Carter's unaffected style and generosity encourages both intimacy and the funky creativity of guests from across the spectrum of literary, political, business and entertainment fields – consolidating the magazine's position as the white-hot center of New York publishing. Now, Cynthia has decided to take the show on the road by launching a small, highly personalized architecture/design firm with longtime friend and collaborator Basil Walter.

Diplomacy and style run deep in Carter's bones. Her foreign-service education began in Beirut, crisscrossed Africa and culminated at the University of Virginia: "Everything in Africa had such an alive, beautiful look to me. The colors and the light and the sky and the ocean and the women's costumes, everything. My grandfather was a painter and so the ideas of color and dimension were impressed on me that way as well." Color and dimension? There's a little more to it than that. But Carter winningly refuses to blow her own trumpet. Today, she looks set to emerge as one of the more exotic – if restrained – interior designers in America.

CHEN "I love the whole Bay Area; it's both far enough and close enough to Hollywood that I don't feel the urge to run away," says Joan Chen from Napa Valley. "LA is so dominated by the film industry... San Francisco is a beautiful place to be unemployed. It's possible to sit down and focus and actually create a new career. Had I not been here, I wouldn't have been able to make the move into directing."

Chen has spent eight years in San Francisco, gotten married and given birth to a little girl. The tale of flight from the Hollywood Babylon has become a recurring theme in the last decade, but it has an added resonance in Chen's case. At 38, she has created a new career for herself by directing the acclaimed *Xiu Xiu: The Sent Down Girl,* which she filmed in the most remote corners of her native China. The film is set amid the Cultural Revolution of the 1970s and has, she giggles, "put me on the political shitlist." Chen has largely opted out of the formulaic parts available to her. "I'm glad that I've opened new doors for myself," she says. "We're obliged to give birth to ourselves now and again, I suppose." The struggle of the transformation is audible in her laugh; Joan Chen is a tough and ironic optimist.

It's an independence and an intelligence that she has been showing off since her arrival from Shanghai in 1981. A soulful wanderer, she has worked with and been influenced by a stellar cast of directors: Bertolucci, Lynch, Stone and, perhaps most importantly, Anthony Minghella: "I really see him as a mentor. He has the mind and the heart and the poetic, operatic filmmaking that I aspire to." Finally, there is the odyssey from China to America and back again: On my bad days, I'm an outsider in both places. On my good days, I feel I quite belong to either."

DANNER

Blythe Danner is one of the most well-loved and respected figures of American theater and cinema. Lately, she is both in the midst of her own career resurgence and shouldering a new identity as America's most graceful and grounded Hollywood mom—the inspiration for her daughter Gwyneth Paltrow's exploding career.

This daughter of a Philadelphia banker began acting at Bard College during the 1960s. In 1970 she won a Tony Award for *Butterflies Are Free*. Since then, she has rarely been without work on television, stage or screen, garnering additional Tony nominations for *A Streetcar Named Desire* and Harold Pinter's *Betrayal*, and critical acclaim for roles in films like *The Great Santini* and *The Prince of Tides*. Danner and her husband, television producer Bruce Paltrow, elected to raise their children in New York, in order to insulate them from the film business. It didn't work.

A critical link between the two women has been forged during Danner's more than 20 summers at the Williamstown Theatre Festival in northwestern Massachusetts. She is legend in the impossibly bucolic college town, not just for her commitment to the festival, but for her accessibility and warmth. Williamstown's local delicatessen serves a sandwich named in her honor. In 1999, her daughter was in residence, appearing in *As You Like It*. "I've spent my life here," said Gwyneth, and besides, "my mother is basically the mayor of Williamstown and is so well loved, that by proxy we are too."

Ample testimony to the grace and intelligence of Blythe Danner, actress and mother. For her own part, Mom has no worries about her daughter and fame: "She doesn't get carried away with this hoopla," she told *Life*. "I think she gets that from me. Of course, I'm very small potatoes compared to my daughter."

FAIRCHILD

Whitney Fairchild is warmth and good humor—a woman ready for a laugh and very much at ease in her own skin. Widely respected across the slippery worlds of fashion and charity and very much in the business of connection with others. And yet, when the conversation moves to fashion or the decorative arts, there is a corresponding shift in tone. There is no mistaking the depth of her passions: "I have to admit that we're avid antique hunters," she says, referring to her husband James Fairchild. "We love to explore and the thrill of hunting down some great pieces no matter whether in Europe, Florida, or Barbados. I think it's just something that gets in your blood."

One of "those" Whitneys, she was reared in London and Sagaponack, before packing off for boarding school and college. It was a life of art and horses, coupled with an ever-growing awareness of the elements that comprised the beauty around her. That burgeoning sensibility led her from the "classic, very conservative" atmosphere at Trinity College to the downtown life at Parsons and the New School as well as an apprenticeship for designer Adrienne Vittadini.

If the stint at Parsons sharpened her eye for the world in which she had grown up, life as a design director at Polo Ralph Lauren has closed the circuit. Working on the Black Label, Fairchild draws on her travels and a ravenous eye to refresh and reinterpret the classics. "I'm constantly being inspired by the people around me, by the movies, by Europe. There are so many things that influence me and I'm lucky to bring it all back to the process for Mr. Lauren." The net effect is an almost seamless exchange between sensory input and creative output, a state of affairs that makes life at Polo an absolute pleasure. "It's a family atmosphere that I really love," she says of the work environment. Husband James (son of *W* and *Women's Wear Daily* founder John Fairchild) also works in design for Polo, so "the family feeling" extends well beyond the office Christmas party: "Mr. Lauren designed my wedding dress and the whole wedding party wore Ralph Lauren. It was beautiful."

DUBIN

At a quarter past nine on a Saturday evening, Tiffany Dubin is refining a marketing plan for the Auction Channel. Meanwhile, she is also editing *Vintage Style*, a thoughtful how-to guide for getting the most wear out of a handful of classic elements. Dubin enlisted the help of friends like Sam Boardman in showing off the clothes, but shouldered the authorial duties with Ann Berman.

Appearances in Suzy bear witness to her travels with the smart set, junior division. But whenever destiny has seemed to usher her into gilt-edged coasting, the daughter of the late garment czar Herbert Rounick has always bucked the system. College is a case in point: "I decided that Georgetown was not teaching me any skills that would give me any independence in life," she says chuckling. "So I went to Washington School for Secretaries and waitressed at a restaurant called The Pleasant Peasant for six months. I must say, I'm a really good typist."

The independent streak didn't desert her once she landed at Sotheby's. The august house designated her head of its fashion department but when vision for the business was lacking, Dubin stepped on bureaucratic toes to begin staging fashion sales as high-concept "happenings." Four years later, Sotheby's has a successful fashion business and Dubin's entrepreneurial spirit is keeping her home on Saturday nights. "Every time I've ever taken a risk, there has been pain involved," she says, "but I've always been better off for having done it." The long hours have not dampened the mood. "All I have ever feared," she says, "was a life of lunch."

ERTEGUN

"Mick Jagger has very good taste," says Mica Ertegun. "Beautiful taste and beautiful gardens." She's sitting in the offices of MAC II, the legendary design firm that she and the late Chessy Rayner founded in 1970. 30 years on, it's hard to think of a more imperial perch from which to make pronouncements about matters of taste and style, but Mrs. Ertegun isn't having any of it. Press her on the sense of décor and style that has made her a singular fixture in the worlds of society, business, diplomacy and yes, rock'n'roll, and she will demur: "It's really so personal, taste is so incredibly personal."

Mica Banu Grecianu Ertegun was born to a landowning Romanian family and had, by the early 1960s, made her way to a New York prowled by Atlantic Records founder Ahmet Ertegun, who had begun to transform himself from a successful and innovative record man into something else altogether: a social titan at the crossroads of cultures both high and low. The two met at a Greenwich Village dinner party and one of the great wandering eyes of its day was transfixed. Their myth was cemented in large part by the exquisite work that Mrs. Ertegun did in decorating their Upper East Side townhouse, a retreat at Southampton's Shinnecock Bay and later, a villa at Bodrum in Turkey. Even as an outgrowth of such a signature style, MAC II ("my husband always said it sounded like a trucking company") does not exist simply to foist "Mica chic" on its clients.

"It's a much more interesting job to collaborate with an involved client," she says. "When you live in a house, you have to have your own ideas and personality." Mrs. Ertegun doesn't so much talk as purr and if the effect is as calming as her interiors, it masks the intensity of her social and professional lives.

FLEMING

Time was when being one of the shining lights of opera involved some extended extracurricular responsibilities: Visits to the Stork Club and Maxim's, sailing the Aegean onboard the Christina. Scandalous and enigmatic love affairs, all to be documented by the likes of Walter Winchell. The job requirements have changed. As we chat, the soprano Renée Fleming is not with some latter-day Onassis aboard a yacht or a Gulfstream. She's at home in Connecticut gathering herself and her voice in the wake of an opening night at the Met. Many reviews are not yet in but Fleming has, barely *twelve* hours earlier, won wide acclaim for her Marschallin in Strauss's *Der Rosenkavalier*.

The praise hasn't come easy. To begin with, there is the issue of language. Fleming's German was acquired during Fulbright studies: "I studied in Germany because it was the easiest grant to get... It's worked out beautifully though; a part like the Marschallin would be very difficult for someone who doesn't speak the language." The problem cuts to the special peril and possibility of an American singing career. "We're taking on a very old European tradition. When an Italian singer gets up and sings Italian music for an entire career, that is something that is entirely natural to her. Not to discount what they do, but we have to go that extra mile and do the language work as well." But, she points out, "the one great advantage is that we're never pigeonholed. No one ever says 'she's an American, she can only sing American music.' That's why I have such a broad variety of repertoire—because I can. And I love that."

Even as she has vaulted through the opera stratosphere, Fleming has maintained eclectic tastes. Her Blanche DuBois in André Previn's *A Streetcar Named Desire* was a smash in national broadcast from San Francisco and listeners reserve a special place for her readings of Duke Ellington. The influences lend a distinctive touch to her opera work that sets it apart from counterparts abroad and they make a recent gig in Washington that much more special: "It's the pinnacle," she says of her appearance at the millennium celebrations. "For an American artist to appear at the White House or to even be at the White House as a guest...you feel like you've reached the pinnacle of everything."

FOSTER

From *Taxi Driver* to *The Accused* to *Silence of the Lambs*, millions of Americans feel a strange and deep stake in a life that has unfolded before them. Jodie Foster elicits protectiveness—her twelve-year old prostitute and her rookie FBI agent are imperiled daughters to their audiences and it is Foster's intelligence and humanity that gives them their sympathetic qualities. And her history: if we have tended to worry about the dark places into which the actress ventured at tender ages, John Hinkley was there to embody and amplify all the worries.

With all of the emotional travails endured by our girl Jodie, there is also a sense of relief. She is, as Larry King recently pointed out, "proof that some child stars grow up to be terrific." A magna cum laude graduate of Yale, Foster is the only woman to have won two Academy Awards before the age of 30 and is rated the biggest female box-office draw in the business, after Julia Roberts and Meg Ryan. Her successful production company, Egg Pictures, has now given her a platform from which to produce, direct and act in films and she has become mother to a young son, Charlie. Less and less, it seems, do we need to worry about her. Foster is perhaps, more than any other, the movie star that one can feel good about listening to, caring about, admiring, venerating. And there are at least two good reasons for this:

Jodie doesn't believe the adulation: "I admit that some people put me on a pedestal," she has said. "I guess what people look up to are the decisions I made. But they weren't made for the sake of impressing; they were made to bring me pleasure with a capital 'P.' Things for my benefit, wholly selfish decisions." Have you ever heard an actor be modest about following his or her passions? And then, "To me, it's all about your body of work. Maybe I'm foolish. But I do believe that you win out in the end if it's about the work," she told *W* recently. "Maybe you don't get as rich as other people. The globalization of this business has trivialized everything. I don't make movies to rip people off and open Planet Hollywood and make more money for myself."

GRISCOM

Ask a movie producer for his idea of the perfect lead in a "New York woman" romantic comedy and he'll probably suggest a classic beauty cut with devilish wit. Pedigreed, but with a vibrant career and family life. A traditionalist with a strong sense of curiosity and adventure. Nina Griscom is such a creature. The daughter of Ambassador and Mrs. Felix Rohatyn, Griscom has been a fixture in the local media for many years. But as a writer for *Food & Wine* and a contributing editor to *Allure*, she's both a respected arbiter of taste and, at the same time, mightily bored with the idea of leading a 'society' existence: "The larger part of my life is not those things, but my work and my family and my friends. I have a daughter, Lilly, who is seven, and the writing takes quite a bit of time because I have a monthly column and I do freelance writing. I'm also writing a book on entertaining and I've become a partner-investor in an internet venture."

Travel off the beaten path ("the sights, smells and visual stimulation of exotic places") provokes and inspires both her work and her own heartily cosmopolitan sensibilities.

And then there is Southampton. Griscom offers a pointed rebuke to the chorus of doom-sayers who claim the Hamptons have been overrun: "more people and a wider cross-section of people is what makes it stimulating and fun. Time doesn't stand still for anybody, so either get with the program or stay at home and throw away the key." Small, informal dinners are her métier, ("I like to actually talk to people, rather than just collect them.") with only one rule: "Stay away from having just married people—that's death. There must be sexual tension," she laughs. It's a young Lauren Bacall laugh carried on a cloud of cigarette smoke: "I earned this voice, baby," she says. And with that, it becomes difficult to imagine any shortage of sexual tension at all.

HARRIS What Beyer, Blinder Belle has done for New York's Grand Central Station, Emmylou Harris does for that most American of institutions: country music. She'll strip the house down to the bones and then lovingly reconstruct it to accommodate a new, more varied and richer life. Harris doesn't confuse forms and essences; after more than 30 years in the business her recent work (most notably the album *Wrecking Ball*) has challenged Nashville's notions of what the music can accommodate while pointing the way back to the haunted stoicism of Appalachia. Imagine Shaker designs in brushed metal – but still unmistakably Shaker.

Architectural metaphors abound. Harris began the 1990s by recording with a bluegrass band at Nashville's then-neglected Ryman Auditorium. The former home to the Grand Ole Opry wasn't just a theater, it was "almost like a Carnegie Hall of the South," she says. Harris' decision to use the hall sparked extensive restoration, which has in turn prompted a revival of Nashville's historically vibrant downtown. Harris is famous for both lithe beauty and sly wit, but like the Lady she is, she'll delicately steer the conversation away from herself. Still, there's a note of pride when she declares, "it's now a place where people really want to come and play. The Ryman has been brought into the realm of world music and artists of all stripes make their way there."

The creative stewardship of Americana is not confined to buildings or songs; it includes people as well. A grande dame of the Nashville aristocracy, she's writing her own material more than ever before and in the midst of working on a new record in New Orleans. "I'm amazed, not only that I'm still going, but that I'm more excited about music than I was when I was 25 or 30."

HALE *Vanity Fair* has called her "one of the most influential women in America" and "the cult icon of San Francisco." *The New York Times* has covered her annual December circuit of Manhattan's most elite destinations and citizens. (So much revelry in so many of the best salons that it's known as —what else?— "Hale Week.") And *W* just calls her "the Queen Bee." Denise Hale, the Belgrade-born, Hollywood-bred (husband #2: Vincente Minnelli) widow of department store millionaire Prentis Cobb Hale, is a force to be reckoned with. As she told the *Times*, "everybody knows I'm the biggest pain-in-the-you-know-what. I am the first one to say that."

Hale has no apologies to make for a lavish lifestyle (Russian Hill, world travel and the 10,000-acre H-E ranch in Sonoma County) nor for an unyielding code of conduct to which everyone is held accountable. Hale's remarkable cross-generational following endures because she makes everyone feel that they know exactly where they stand: "I don't have feuds with anybody," she says. "When somebody disappoints me, I turn the page. They do not exist."

That same diamond clarity frames her life away from the soirée. "I like many people or I like solitude," declares the lioness. "I go to the ranch and spend weeks in my garden, on my hands and knees. Six or seven hours a day. For me, silence is very important." More important still is her work with San Francisco charities like the Symphony Orchestra, where she has long underwritten a biennial concert series. But it is the Delancey Street Foundation that lays claim to what are perhaps her deepest affections. The residential drug treatment center is a national treasure famous for turning even the hardest cases. Hale calls founder Dr. Mimi Silbert "one of the most incredible people in the world. She takes the people nobody else wants." And after the glamour and opulence of early December and Hale week, after Le Cirque and the Knickerbocker Club, Denise Hale has Christmas dinner at the center with "people who had the guts to turn their lives around. I can't even imagine the courage."

Just as the buzz was building among the editors and their fashionistas that Carolina Herrera, Jr. was Manhattan's new "it girl" – the most well-heeled, well-bred and lavishly dressed of all the young things – she up and quit New York for something else # HERRERA
altogether. Along with best friend Victoria Clay, the third daughter of designer Carolina and legendary man-about-town Reinaldo Herrera has been dividing her time between Los Angeles and Madrid, where the two are immersed in a five-year documentary film project. It is *Maletilla*, named in Spanish for the "little suitcases" carried by children as they seek the life of the bullfighter. "We're trying to get inside the culture of bullfighting, but more than that, we're trying to get into the lives of these kids," she says in a Venezuelan accent, retained through Brown and an earlier life as a pre-med student. "From the innocence of wanting to do something to then doing it and either succeeding or not, these children still go through it. The process is the same, no matter the result."

That sense of possibility and risk pervades the filmmaking itself. Herrera and Clay travel and work as a duo. It's a female buddy movie and talking about it opens up the warmth and humor that makes her beauty so freewheeling and generous: "We had a car that we bought for $200 and it literally exploded" she says, laughing. "There was fire and smoke and smells. We couldn't pull off the road, but when we did, it was like Starsky and Hutch — we jumped out of the car and then waited to put the hood up." The self-described "gypsy" found herself standing roadside in Spain, a very long way from Madison Avenue, mourning a wreck: "That car lasted six months and took us everywhere. A love affair come to an end."

HORNE
Try to comprehend that when Lena Horne began dancing the chorus line at the Cotton Club, the White House was occupied by F.D.R.. In his first term. The Lady was also just beginning to find her feet; at 16 years old and fresh out of Brooklyn, Ms. Horne was at the epicenter of the Harlem renaissance. And with Duke Ellington and Billie Holiday providing both inspiration and potent examples of success, the gig marked the dawn of a career that has now stretched north of 66 years.

Lest one be blinded by the beauty, know that there are also guts to spare. Horne's earliest work helped her family survive the Depression and testifies to the sheer toughness that has enabled her to navigate the shoals both of show business and American race relations. Her performance in the 1943 classic *Stormy Weather* was a signature piece and offered a sad leitmotif in her relations with a film community that would draw on her when needed, but quickly discard her when threatened with controversy. Marriage to white musician Lennie Hayton only complicated matters, a point on which Horne has never equivocated: "we were caught in three kinds of prejudice—against Negroes, against Jews and against mixed marriages."

"My life has been about surviving," she famously remarked. "Along the way, I also became an artist." That defining moment came in 1981, when she opened *The Lady and Her Music* and proceeded to knock audiences flat with the longest running one-woman show in Broadway history. Horne was 65, but in complete control for the first time: "I said what was real and what really happened," she told an interviewer, "so there was no artifice…that's when I began to think I'd made it, sort of." Yale agreed with the box office and in 1998 conferred a Doctorate of Humane Letters to recognize both the art and a survival that never fails to be as stylish as it is inspiring.

HUNT
Laura Hunt was born in New York City, but reared in the Lone Star State. At 20, she married into one of the most storied dynasties in Texan history, but she left the family fold; first for Washington and later, for Manhattan. Her children ate at Mortimers when visiting from Hotchkiss and Brooks, but she continues to think of Dallas as home, "no matter how long I've been away." The city has shaped a life as notable for business, politics and philanthropy as it is for elegant good cheer. Laura Hunt is the smart, successful, modern woman—high Texas edition.

Hunt's "pioneer spirit" means noblesse oblige and it was integral to her upbringing: In Texas, she says, "you're raised in a way that emphasizes service by those who are fortunate. Particularly as a woman, you receive an early education in putting together events and raising money." Even while pursuing ventures in real estate, art and the film business, Hunt's philanthropic attentions have benefited the Sweetheart's and Cattle Baron's Balls, New York's Henry Street Settlement and the Republican Party. Hunt describes herself as a "centrist" and her enduring loyalty to the GOP does not make her unwilling to criticize the party's rightmost planks. She's a shrewd political thinker with a quick and illustrative wit—a baby boom Republican unafraid to be a "renegade."

"Style," she says, "has got nothing to do with money. It's a presence and an attitude. It's a woman with confidence in herself and confidence in her ability to do or to wear or to be whatever she pleases without following trends. A stylish woman knows what's good for her. When she walks into a room, there is a sense that someone has arrived."

KEOHANE
In more than three decades of teaching and administration at some of the nation's premier institutions of higher learning, Nannerl O. Keohane has consistently drawn on her distinguished scholarship to exercise leadership of the highest and most thoughtful order. Her 1997 remarks before President Clinton's Commission on Race are signal: "I believe," she told the assembled dignitaries, "that a just and democratic society must appreciate the many values of diversity, both for reasons of political principle and of enlightened self-interest…In return, we will all experience new ways of living and learning, working and worshipping, that provide precious new dimensions in our understanding of what human life, in its multifaceted variety, is all about."

Keohane serves as President of Duke University and as an alumna and former president of Wellesley College. She is the first woman to head both a preeminent liberal arts college and a major university. The appointment to Duke perhaps ushered her to a new stratum of professional and public recognition, but the eloquence and star power have been in place since she made Phi Beta Kappa at Wellesley and rode a Marshall Scholarship to First Class Honours at Oxford. As president of Wellesley, she engineered the shattering of records for gifts to a liberal arts college. Now, with Duke in the midst of a $1.5 billion fund drive, she continues to find time to serve on the boards of IBM, the National Humanities Center, the American Philosophical Society and the Council on Foreign Relations, among others.

It is the kind of resumé that makes just about any option available, but the work and life remain firmly anchored in the delicate scholarship honed in her Ph.D. work at Yale. Keohane derives her central authority from thoughtfulness and decency, not from raw administrative power. She continues to hold a professorship of political science at Duke (as does her husband, Robert Keohane, who was recently lured to Durham from a Harvard chair) and manages to hold both regular office hours and lunches with students.

The solution for the ills of civil society, she recently asserted, "lies not in a retreat from work, love and learning, but in a more informed understanding of ourselves and the ethical parameters that make life with others possible and enrich our own…colleges and universities, both public and private, are uniquely well-placed to lead such renewal and reaffirmation."

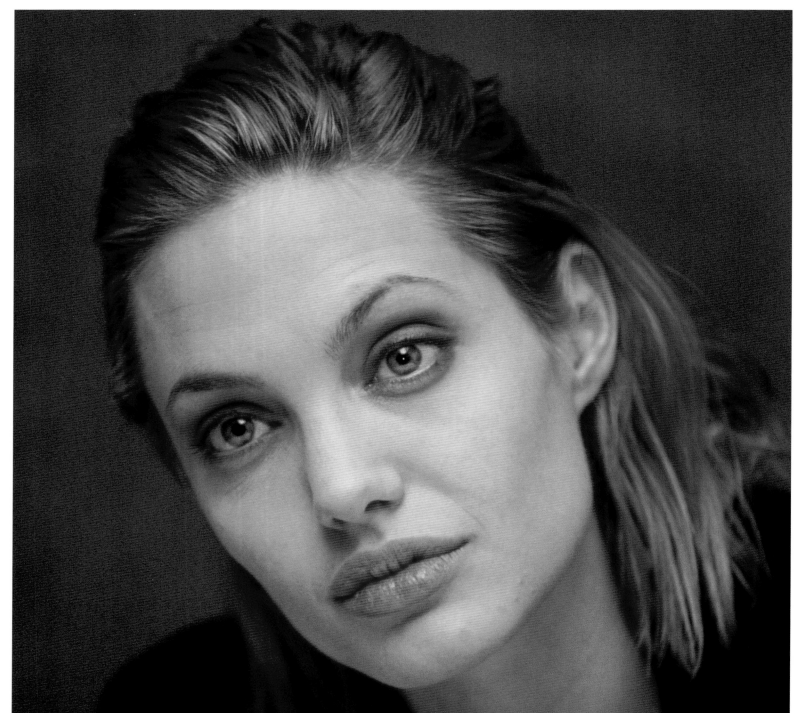

JOLIE In an age when actresses show off feng shui approved bungalows and workout routines for *InStyle* magazine, Angelina Jolie appears to have fallen from the world of rock and roll. Old, reckless, sexy rock and roll. Jim Morrison and pre-Bianca Mick Jagger rock and roll. Her birth to Jon Voight and the model Marcheline Bertrand came a good six years after *Midnight Cowboy* and five after *Deliverance*, but the actress has dragged that gritty black magic into self-help millennial Hollywood. It is paying off in spades.

Her breakout came in the title role of 1998's *Gia*, in which she won a Golden Globe (at 25, she has won three) for her performance as a heroin addicted model. As she publicized the film, Jolie admitted that she had enjoyed liaisons with women. Along with her tattoos, vivid descriptions of her knife collections and her willingness to emotionally bleed during interviews, Jolie left no doubts as to the enormity of her emotional stake in a role like Gia. The risks in venturing so close to absolute darkness were plain; Jolie's career and her psyche had become a high-wire act in which the payoff would be unforgettable performances.

In 1999, Jolie again made good on her dangerous stance and candor by delivering a knockout performance as a sociopath in *Girl, Interrupted*. The film's all-girl psychiatric hospital setting suggested "female Jack Nicholson" comparisons, but the role had, in truth, pushed Jolie into territory all her own; with a Best Supporting Actress Oscar in hand, she had moved into artistic respect without compromise. The acting has caught up with the animal sexuality. Angelina Jolie's high-wire act promises to captivate us for years to come.

LAUDER ZINTERHOFER
This is her moment. Aerin Lauder Zinterhofer, granddaughter to cosmetics genius Estée Lauder, is back in the office a few months after giving birth to her first child with husband Eric. There has been a massive new promotion to "Executive Director of Creative Marketing, Estee Lauder USA & Canada" and she's talking about the Spring 2000 look: "I definitely think there's this whole ladylike classic look that's going on…we saw it for Spring and we'll hopefully continue to see it for Fall. It's a great look. I love what Calvin did for Spring and even that whole Palm Beach style that's so strong this season." What Lauder fails to mention is that she was largely responsible for bringing about the swing to socialite chic. Along with a small cadre of Upper East Side gals, she's become the muse for the designers now marketing "Society Elegance, Millennium Edition." In a post-PC world, it's hip to be doing the charity circuit before going home to a King Charles Spaniel, a baby and a husband in private equity.

"I love antiques and silver and old English glass. That's my taste. I also like very contemporary art, so I like to mix things," she declares in the clipped, gotta-run-now cadence of the marketing executive. "But my taste is constantly changing. When I was first out of college, I loved chintz, but now I'm more into colored textured fabrics. Thank God I got that out of my system."

If it all sounds just a little too fabulous, bear in mind that Lauder is also grounded in ways not immediately apparent. She's working hard and life as a mother has changed the social equation: "I used to entertain at home a lot, but that was before we made the dining room into a nursery," she laughs. Eric, with whom she's been involved since their days at the University of Pennsylvania, is her "best friend in the whole world."

LIN There's a certain project in her past and it still locates her. When Maya Lin was a 21 year old undergraduate at Yale, one of her design submissions was selected to become a major American monument in Washington D.C.. And after all the subcommittee meetings (famous for aesthetic and philosophical sensitivity), when the Vietnam Veterans' Memorial had become a national treasure, it was time for her to have a career and a life.

The success and accomplishment of all that has come since is such that Maya Lin doesn't really want to discuss the Memorial. She's been doing distinguished sculpture and architecture, both public and private, she has married the art collector and dealer Daniel Wolff and she has borne two children. She'll even admit, sheepishly, to having abandoned the Bowery for the Upper East Side ("I don't carry a cell phone though, I can't do it.") It's a refreshing counternarrative to the tale of the celebrated artist later run amok. She's reserved, yet incisive and is more than willing to let go with a good laugh at her own expense. There's an exquisite sensitivity to her; she's highly attuned to exteriority. What follows is a concern for the environment—built or natural, that has underpinned her work in all media.

LAWRENCE-LIGHTFOOT

Sara Lawrence-Lightfoot has returned to her Cambridge office after a celebratory lunch with research assistants. "I've been partying," she chuckles before gracefully pivoting into reflections on her life and her work as a sociologist. "From a very young age, I was a journal keeper. There was something in me that was trying to capture the strange in the familiar—the exotic in the ordinary. If we are discerning enough, we will see how most of ordinary life is really exotic and interesting and fascinating." The abiding interest has been an exploration of children, families, schools and the intersections between them. Lawrence–Lightfoot has called her field "human archaeology" and the term, with its connotations of layering and depth, evokes the woman herself: generosity and decency, a style that extends from the deepest kind of substance. After her earlier merriment, her thoughts come in gentle, rhythmic cadences. There is both warmth and a gathered sense of purpose in her speech – an exquisite authority.

It's well-earned. Almost three decades of teaching and writing the sociology of education have brought Lawrence–Lightfoot accolades from all corners of the Academy and beyond: only the second African-American woman to receive Harvard tenure, she has collected honorary degrees and fellowships, testified before Congress on secondary education, and authored six award-winning books. She sits on the boards of the National Academy of Education, *The Boston Globe* and, as a 1983 "genius grant" recipient, the MacArthur Foundation. With this fullest of plates, Lawrence–Lightfoot practices her scholarship as "portraiture—a blending of literary narrative and empirical description." And with research, writing, speaking and lecturing, there are still other, more important fronts: "Mothering has put me in touch with the deepest of all passions, which is advocacy and love for one's children. Love life and extended family life, very significant friendships and all those things combine to create this very, very full and very rich and…" she laughs, "complicated existence. I wouldn't have it any other way."

"My father was **MARTON** with *The Associated Press* and my mother was with *United Press International*. While we were in Budapest, they were imprisoned as CIA agents, simply for doing their jobs." Kati Marton is back to her Eastern European childhood during the Cold War and the outrage is rising in her voice. After almost two years of incarceration, both were freed in 1956 and the family made its way to political asylum in the United States.

Marton is best known as an author and journalist of print, radio and television. As she speaks, however, she is most single-mindedly an activist on behalf of free speech and human rights. "No matter how well things are going I never get over that feeling that I'm very, very fortunate. I never get over the feeling that I have to keep getting better."

Kati Marton has been "getting better" for three decades of life in the media and diplomatic communities. Along the way, there have been four books and, not least, motherhood to two children from a 15 year marriage to Peter Jennings. Now, after five years of marriage to Richard Holbrooke, the Permanent Representative to the United Nations, Marton juggles her commitments with the duties of an ambassadorial spouse.

"We're trying to draw the 'U.N. village' further out into New York life," she says, "and to bring many Washington figures to the United Nations." The couple travel together and work closely on shared passions for peace and human rights issues. "We love more than anything to be together and we're never bored in each other's company. It's an endless conversation."

Life with the United Nations brings a distinctive focus to Marton's forthcoming history of presidential marriages, but it does not interfere with a hallowed annual ritual: "My son Christopher and I have been going to the Telluride Bluegrass Festival for the last five years. I missed Richard's ambassadorial appointment at the White House for it and I just got my tickets today!"

McDONALD

Her life really is a musical—for the most part. Still shy of 30, Audra McDonald is the kind of success that graces the musical theatre perhaps once a generation. Critics struggling for comparisons have been reaching back to the Barbra Streisand of the early 1960s in order to communicate both her promise and her already staggering accomplishment. Stephen Holden of *The New York Times* recently wrote that she has "a major voice" before noting her "beauty, intelligence, taste and formidable acting ability."

Her three Tony awards, for the 1993 *Carousel*, 1996's *Master Class* and 1998's *Ragtime*, constitute an unprecedented streak: no-one had ever managed to win three Tonys in their first three outings. McDonald has stepped into the breach during a turbulent moment in the life of the American musical theatre and salved the wounds of a critical community disheartened by both lackluster revivals and spectacle-laden new offerings. At the heart of her enterprise—along with the voice, of course—is her thrilling hybrid of the contemporary and the traditional. McDonald champions young composers while paying fresh homage to the classics.

"My work really defines who I am," the singer, who, as a hyperactive child took theatre in lieu of Ritalin, has said. "I'm just now learning that I need to learn to relax." She will be learning with the bass player and fellow Juilliard alumnus Peter Donovan, to whom she was engaged in August of 1999. The show goes on...

MOORE

For the last five years, actor Julianne Moore has been flirting with out-and-out movie stardom. In 1995, *Vanity Fair* had her tagged as an up-and-comer on its first annual "Hollywood" issue, a reflection of her work in Robert Altman's *Short Cuts*. By late 1999, *Time* was saying just about the same thing: never mind the Spielberg movie and the Oscar nomination already under her belt (she has since added another); this would be the year that Moore captured the wider public imagination. For her own part, Moore continues to produce work that endears her to directors and fellow actors, even if it hasn't yet given her the ability to open movies on her own.

The "problem," of course, is the subtlety and intelligence with which she slips into a character. As Neil Jordan, who directed her Oscar-nominated performance in *The End of the Affair* put it, "She can be transformingly beautiful, and yet in other instances, you wouldn't even notice her." The flaming red hair matters not; Moore becomes, in Jordan's words, "a different person." It's the highest accolade for an actor, but murder on the audience identification that makes for bankability..

Moore is the daughter of a military judge and a psychiatric social worker and had lived in no fewer than 23 cities by the time she graduated from high school. She credits both her "peripatetic" existence and her parents' professions for giving her a keen eye for character. As her star has ascended, however, her life has taken on a new and very happy stability: Moore has for years made her home in Manhattan and now shares it with the two men in her life: the filmmaker Bart Freundlich and their young son, Caleb. The movie star vs. great actor dilemma takes a back seat to yet another of Julianne Moore's metamorphoses. Her son has, she recently remarked, "completely transformed me personally. Having a child is the demarcation between childhood and adulthood. Because you are finally and always an adult...it gives you access to emotional things you've never had access to before."

PARLANGE

In 1884, John Singer Sargent's *Madame X*, a portrait of the American expatriate Mrs. Pierre Gatreau, caused a sensation when shown at the Paris Salon. The painting was elegance itself, woven with more than a whiff of irreverence and sex. Its New Orleans aristocrat looks perfectly composed as she gazes into a highly eroticized distance.

It's more than the bloodline shared with Mrs Gatreau that led *Vanity Fair* to photograph the thirtysomething Angele Parlange as homage to Sargent and his scandalous masterwork. It's her sense of both perfect décor and perfect decorum and the wit to startle with a fresh take on traditional motifs. She's a New Orleans-based home furnishings designer and consultant, a decorator and a lecturer. She's connected "from Paris to Oklahoma City and beyond" and, in a little over a decade in the design business, she has made the national taste establishment take notice of bayou elegance.

History and tradition play more than an anecdotal part in this life and career: The Parlange family seat at False River near New Roads, Louisiana, has been home to the clan since the mid-eighteenth century and was the birthplace of Mrs Gatreau. The Bousillage (a mixture of mud, ashes, Spanish Moss and crushed oyster shells) foundation of the house is indicative of just how deeply Parlange's roots are set and the plantation continues to produce sugarcane, soybeans and Brahman cattle. Meanwhile, family archives offer the ancient books and prints that inspire designs which have now leapt from dresses to pillows to chairs to china and beyond.

So the lifestyle wing of the family dynasty grows: grace may be Parlange's business, but there's no mistaking the drive that has brought her to this point. Armed with her MBA and "an artistic bent," she left the petroleum business in the late 1980s and has never looked back: "One thing leads to another," she says, "but those oilmen sure taught me how to negotiate."

PFEIFFER

Michelle Pfeiffer was once crowned Miss Orange County. Today, the incandescent smile, golden hair and delicate bones conspire to make her the most luminous of screen presences. There is no imaginative leap required to see the boys fawning over her. It is just that they have been joined by audiences worldwide.

Pfeiffer has been at the epicenter of the film business for nearly two decades and, as with all great movie stars, it is difficult to pinpoint any particular role or film that actually elevated her to the ranks of the elite. Even with three Oscar nominations, Pfeiffer's status isn't tied to this or that success or failure. Nor has she ever been fodder for the tabloid press: the feline lands on her feet and gently prowls the lofty terrain of the Movie Star.

Pfeiffer managed to appear in 15 films during the 1990s while marrying the television superwriter/producer David E. Kelley and starting a family with two children. She has periodically wondered aloud about retiring, but recently said "I don't think I'll ever retire, because I love working...I'm not really happy or fulfilled unless I feel I'm contributing to something."

She is barely 19, yet we **PORTMAN** have known her for six years. "Watched her grown up," in the hoary old phrase. When, in 1994, Natalie Portman made her screen debut in Luc Besson's *The Professional*, she set Hollywood ablaze. It was the presence, the poise and the ability to navigate difficult material that knocked observers out.

When she stole 1996's *Beautiful Girls* right out from under Timothy Hutton and Uma Thurman, the "new Winona Ryder" concept began to take root. "I'm young, but I have an old soul," she said in character. By the following summer, she had George Lucas planning *Star Wars: The Phantom Menace* shoots around her high school schedule.

Portman winningly refuses to keep the end of the child star bargain that says she must already have a cocaine habit, a bad young boyfriend "in the industry," or bulimia. While audiences worldwide were camping out to see her in *The Phantom Menace*, the committed vegetarian was finishing the advanced placement tests that helped land her a spot at Harvard.

"She's going to be running a studio and acting and producing and doing whatever she wants," the director Ted Demme said in the wake of *Beautiful Girls*. "I don't see any limits for her—and you can't say that about many people." The young woman who has been a muse to Isaac Mizrahi isn't at all sure that she wants to remain forever in the acting business. "There are so many things that interest me," she has said. "I love math, literature, languages."

But while on holiday from Ivy walls, she has once again been with George Lucas, preparing for the next installment of *Star Wars*. And, after roles opposite Susan Sarandon and Ashley Judd, there is a new comparison. Natalie Portman, they are saying, is the next Audrey Hepburn.

REED Eliza Reed Bolen is in Miami's Delano Hotel. She's looking at the beach and recovering from the nuptials of some friends from Brown that ran well into the wee hours. It was, she says, "a big Latin wedding. Lots of fun." The proceedings have left her a little wiped out, but she remains in fine humor with quick and energetic answers at the ready. The Delano is a few hours down the Florida coast from Hobe Sound, the beautiful and super-exclusive WASP enclave created and presided over by her late grandmother. It's also in an entirely different social universe, something that suits Reed just fine, thank you. "I've just never really spent that much time there, actually. My mother, especially, felt that as children we should travel and be exposed to different people and places. That's a curiosity I've tried to maintain. Hobe Sound is fine, but I never wanted to live entirely within that culture."

Reed's own wedding, to the young banker Alexander Bolen, was perhaps the social pinnacle of metropolitan 1998. The pair were married on the Connecticut estate of the bride's mother and stepfather, Annette and Oscar de la Renta. Robert Isabell handled the flowers in best country style and *W*'s Aileen Mehle told the tale in best *Suzy* fashion. And amid a guest list that included Kissingers and Herreras and von Furstenbergs and Boardmans, the show was notable for the way it went down as a true family event, carried off with the most gracious informality possible.

Reed works at Oscar de la Renta, where she is both a guardian for the quality of the overall brand and a sterling example of just how well the clothes are adapted to the sensibility of a young professional woman: "I love wearing the clothes and showing off just how youthful and feminine they really are. And I love working closely with Oscar. It just makes the whole thing even more meaningful to me."

ROCKEFELLER

Sharon Rockefeller is the daughter of a distinguished former member of the United States Senate and the wife of a current member. She sits on the boards of PepsiCo and Sotheby's, the National Gallery, the National Cathedral and the Public Broadcasting System. She works full-time as the President and Chief Executive Officer of WETA, the Washington member station of the PBS and the point of origin for much of its programming, including the News Hour with Jim Lehrer. And then there is The Name itself, which has enjoyed not a little recognition for the last hundred-odd years of American life. All very interesting, but there is one striking detail about this curriculum vitae, with all its service and accomplishment, honorary degrees and good works: the home address and telephone number.

After all, Sharon Percy Rockefeller is accessible. Not ostentatiously, "see-I'm-just-folks" politically smart accessible, but actually fun to talk to. About the radio station that she listens to on her way to work and the wedding she's planning for her daughter in Sydney. About her varied commitments and, most especially, about public television, the idea she has been championing for most of her adult life. In the early 1970s, she was living in West Virginia and "we had three children under the age of five and they were watching Sesame Street and I was watching Masterpiece Theatre, but it hadn't occurred to me that they were on the same station," she says. "Public broadcasting was really quite new then and it was often started in rural states like West Virginia to help with the school system. Then the Watergate hearings came on and I realized that this also was the same station and I just…" Fell in love? "I fell in love. And I've been in love ever since."

ROSS

Way out near the end of the fabled South Fork, something is afoot. East Hampton, a place where real estate deals are usually the biggest news and who's in or out at the Maidstone causes a frenzy, has become the backdrop for a bold new type of institution. The Ross School, founded by Courtney Sale Ross and her husband, the late Steven Ross, has been growing by leaps and bounds since the couple began home schooling their daughter, Nancy (pictured at left) and another student in 1991. It is now home to a culturally and socioeconomically diverse population of over 200 students and has become the centerpiece of an expanding Ross Institute designed to transform the practice of education worldwide. Mrs. Ross remains at the philosophical, financial and management heart of this extraordinary project.

Courtney Sale had already had a successful career as a gallery owner, museum curator and documentary filmmaker when she married Warner Communications chairman Steve Ross, a man whom she called "my Prince Charming." Steven Spielberg, a longtime friend of the school, has echoed the sentiment, calling them "the best couple I've ever known" and enlisted Mrs. Ross (famed for her exquisite taste) to decorate his East Hampton home.

When Steve Ross became critically ill shortly after engineering the groundbreaking merger of Warners and Time Inc., the couple began to educate their daughter both at home and on extensive field trips abroad, so that she might spend more time with her father. From the start, they drew on the wisdom and research of leading educators to develop a curriculum organized around an upward "spiral" conception of global cultural history. The spiral continues as the philosophical centerpiece of a school that places unique emphasis on learning across cultures and disciplines while fostering appreciation of children's "multiple intelligences." Students benefit from beautiful buildings and art, the latest media and communications technology, and worldwide travel.

Not exactly standard stuff for sixth-graders. The Ross School's sophistication and humanism are reminders of a marriage that allied intellectual and aesthetic sensitivity with a vision for a world brought closer by the power of communication. Out on the East End, Courtney Ross has paid living tribute to her husband.

ROEHM

As we talk, Carolyne Roehm is in her studio at the base of northwest Connecticut's Berkshire Hills. "I'm able to do the reverse of the fashion industry thing," she says. "I'm in Manhattan usually for two days a week and up here for the remaining five." If that happy equation calls to mind a life of leisure, don't be deceived. Roehm is building an empire out of her passion for the home, entertaining and most especially, for gardening. Her 1997 *A Passion for Flowers* is now in its seventh printing and is regarded as the zenith of the form. Her weekly two days in New York have also included visits to *Good Morning America*, where she has served as a contributor, while a nationwide range of speaking engagements rounds out the agenda.

Caroline Roehm was born and reared in Missouri, but took the fashion world by storm almost from the moment she arrived in New York. There was the celebrated decade as Oscar de la Renta's right hand, then the marriage to financier Henry Kravis and another decade as the head of her own fashion house. She was a smash and wound up as President of the Council of Fashion Designers of America, but after almost 20 years in the industry, was feeling burned out. When the marriage to Kravis ended in 1993, it was time to reevaluate. Roehm reinvented herself brilliantly and, of course, in high style.

"I decided to disappear," she says. "I went to Oxford and lived in a dormitory while taking summer classes. Then, I went to Paris, took cooking classes and worked in a flower shop. It was a relief to separate from the whole world in which I'd been living." When she returned, she set up shop at Weatherstone, the 18th century Connecticut house where her work continues to this day. "I need rolling hills," says the woman who walked away from one life to find herself in the country. "And I need flowers. They bring me a joy that I hope I can share in my work."

ROSS Tracee Ellis Ross doesn't talk; she verbally surges out to meet the listener. Having made contact, she'll spiral around to offer up funny and soulful takes on, well, just about any subject under the sun. And she's actually getting Hollywood's attention by doing what comes most naturally. "I'm a chatter. I'm not linear, I'm a feeler. I feel my way through life. I call my condition "artistic schizophrenia," says the 27-year-old actress, comedienne and yes, daughter of Lady Diana of The Supremes. Between acting with Meg Ryan (*Hanging Up*) and a steady life on MTV (*The Lyricist Lounge*), Ross is staking out terrain as a funny babe with tons of style and a goofy, cross-cultural, new-age wisdom all her own.

That persona and the accompanying "schizophrenia" was nurtured by a childhood and adolescence that swept from Los Angeles to New York to Europe and back again with stops at Dalton, Le Rosey and Brown. It's a breadth of experience that finds its best expression in the sketch comedy of her television work: "I have a lot of people living in me and that's really an extension of my life and of an eclectic background…sketches are what I should be doing. It accesses every part of my being."

No small thing, that being. As Ross somersaults through voices and characters, she notes the Italian influence on life and style at Le Rosey: "I loved the way they wore everything—even their track suits. It was so extravagant!" Track suits notwithstanding, Tracee traffics in an extravagance of the emotional kind, carried on the back of raw energy and a generosity of spirit. It's hard not to get swept away and probably best if one does. She wants to connect: "It's a gift just to be able to make people feel… to see someone laughing and know that it's because of you. It's the most beautiful thing I know."

SARANDON

"Have you been believing all the press that says Hollywood is liberal?" she demands. Susan Sarandon is at home taking care of her kids. But 15 minutes after beginning a conversation by begging exhaustion, she is busy lambasting the entertainment industry. "It's not that there aren't people doing groundbreaking things both in terms of entertainment and politically, but really, Hollywood is almost entirely market-driven."

Sarandon is every bit as witty and knowing as the public persona she has developed over her 30-year career. She has acted in more than 50 movies, and won an Academy Award for her portrayal of Sister Helen Prejean in *Dead Man Walking*. The film was directed by Tim Robbins, with whom she lives in downtown Manhattan, along with their two sons and Sarandon's daughter from a previous relationship. She's a movie star just like they used to make 'em, but her streetwise stance on business and politics is rooted in the routines of a daily life in the markets and coffee shops of New York. It's a grounding that separates her insights on power and injustice from the "little red ribbon" posturings of so many film stars.

Sarandon has been working with the Center for Constitutional Rights, a watchdog for civil liberties and human rights abuses, for two decades. "I love those people. I trust them to educate me, I trust them to be on the right side and I trust them to use me properly... I'm very happy to go and lick envelopes, but that's not where they can use me best," she says. Instead, she has used her high visibility to spotlight victims who don't have a voice—most famously at the 1993 Academy Awards. "The infamous 26 seconds," she laughs as she recalls her plea on behalf of political émigrés with AIDS then living in refugee squalor while the U.S. government denied them entry and medical care. Sarandon was banned from the Oscars for going off-book (the ban has since been lifted), but within 24 hours of her remarks, the White House was moving on the issue.

"It goes against my Catholic upbringing to in any way go against the program," she laughs as she remembers the cold stares of her peers at the awards show. "Has it hurt my career? That's the question that everybody asks me, but these issues are bigger than a career. I mean, if you're running from a burning building, do you worry if your slip is showing?"

If one were to write a series of books chronicling the life of a great American dynasty – from bowler hats and dry goods to the dawn of the information age – Marina Rust would probably figure as a hopeful character in the last pages. A child of the confusion and tumult of the 1960s and 70s, she would have established herself as the living reconciliation of society traditionalism and contemporary flexibility. The poise and grace of the past would frame a fresh wit and engagement with popular culture.

It turns out that none of the above would require any great leap of imagination: Rust is indeed descended from the great merchant Marshall Field and her upbringing – split between an Oregon commune, Washington DC and the Westminster School at Simsbury, Connecticut – straddled the cultural divide of the 1970s. After finishing studies at Duke, she remained in Durham to work on the novel that became 1993's acclaimed *Gatherings*. She has subsequently continued her fiction work—with as many as three novels simultaneously under

way—but her day-to-day life has centered on her journalistic contributions to *Vogue*. Rust's funny, street-smart approach to fashion and beauty is a window into the life of a woman who never lets her own swan-like bearing interfere with a wry good time.

RUST

There are more serious developments: she recently made the investment banker Ian Connor a very lucky man in a wedding ceremony off the coast of Maine. In conversation, Rust brings her self-deprecating wit to bear in discussing their courtship and the wedding. The humor gives the whole series of events the feel of an English screwball comedy, as it makes plain just how thrilled she is by the marriage. The couple are happily ensconced in Manhattan and mix an active life of charity work (she's particularly involved with the East Side House) with small dinners at home. Rust loves to cook, but panics at the thought of orchestrating large meals. It's a happy new phase in a life marked by grace and a fine note on which to end a novel.

SALTZMAN

Watch her strolling through the lobby at Condé Nast and it's difficult to believe that you're not staring straight into celluloid. Elizabeth Saltzman, fashion director at *Vanity Fair*, is plainly a movie come to life. She's the glamour queen with the absurd sense of humor, a Prada-clad leading lady carrying an L.L. Bean canvas beach bag. Elizabeth can hold court in Nobu on Monday and then turn up Tuesday for the Rangers with hot dogs and beer. It all adds up to make her one of the most recognized and adored figures in that smartest of New York sets – the Manhattan fashion elite.

Saltzman's father, the late Renny Saltzman, was a celebrated and much-loved interior decorator while her mom, Ellin, was an influential buyer at Saks. Together, the pair were a force in American style well before the emergence of the modern fashion industry. The Saltzmans commissioned a young Richard Meier to build their house in the Hamptons in the late 1960s. The house is still in the family and it is now considered a treasure of American modernism.

"I was always permitted to go somewhere and to be included somehow," she says of nights out with Calvin and Halston and Bianca, "but then I had to maintain that by being myself and by being a contributor. I don't know that I ever put on any airs. My parents gave me this belief that you really can do whatever you want as long as you're honest and straightforward and you go for it." Saltzman went to work in Italy for Giorgio Armani at 18, before making her way back to New York and the Condé Nast fold, first with *Vogue* and then with Graydon Carter's *Vanity Fair*. Nowadays she supervises the look of the magazine's shoots while acting as chief ambassador to the world of "Seventh."

The look, she says, is "Pretty classic, but not staid. It's not silly, it's classy with a laugh." And what about the attitude? "My basic motto is: Trust everybody until they prove you wrong. Give people the benefit of the doubt. That goes for everyone except for boyfriends."

SPEAR

"I started out life as a pre-med at Brown," says architect, mother and marathon runner Laurinda Hope Spear. "But when I realized I didn't want to be a physician, I decided that architecture really combined art and science and that it was a great profession. I mean, why not?" she asks. "Why not be an architect?" Why not indeed? Along with her husband and partner, Bernardo Fort-Brescia, she's an empire builder. Their firm, Arquitectonica, is based in Miami and New York with offices around the world. "I like that in architecture, you really see people at their best: when they're going to build, they are at their most optimistic and most energetic and most happy, whereas as a physician you often see them at their worst."

After a little more than two decades in the business and at an age when most architects are realizing their first high profile successes, Spear's vibrant modernism has received just about every accolade under the sun, beginning with the Rome Prize in 1978. Spear and Fort-Brescia are also dynasty builders. The couple have six children and the line of succession begins with their eldest, now at Barnard. How, in God's name, does she do it? "The answer is, I really don't do it. I just do the best I can on a daily basis. It's like juggling: you have one kid and one job and then you add another and another and you get the hang of it," she laughs, rattling the pedestal of architectural superwoman. At that moment, she's just a witty mom from South Florida who really enjoys running marathons.

STACK

"Well, we had the same agent," says Rosemarie Stack, who is still giddy talking about an afternoon in 1954. "A man named Bill Schiffrin. In those days, the business was different. It was almost like a family and young actors could go by an agent's office and just talk shop. Bill secretly called Bob up and told him he had to come down to the office to meet me. They kept making excuses to keep me there, but when I met him, it was very immediate. We were finishing each other's sentences."

Mrs. Stack's life in Hollywood, and her famous marriage to Robert Stack, conjures up images of ceiling fans, Studebakers and signs for Burma-Shave – all bathed in that warm California glow that seems to be patented for use in flashback scenes. Rosemarie Bowe packed bags in her native Tacoma, Washington, but she laughs, "when I got a look at sunny California," there was no going back. She had done some modeling, made the cover of *Life* and began a career in films. Then, there was Schiffrin's office. Robert Stack was a fifth-generation Californian, an Angeleno aristocrat and an established leading man. By the time *The Untouchables* came along, the two had married and begun a family at the Bel-Air property Mr. Stack had purchased from silent film star Colleen Moore.

It was around that time that she took up painting, just she says, "something I did for expression." Mrs. Stack has worked in acrylic, but prefers oils and her work has now been shown in Los Angeles, Palm Springs, New York and Paris. The recurring theme? Caviar tins—a tribute to a beautifully packaged favorite food. She has a gentle sense of humor about what has become a distinguished career at the easel. Caviar tins "have become my m.o. or something," she laughs, not sounding at all like Elliot Ness.

The stories go on: "Once when [close friend] Ronnie was president of the Screen Actors Guild, the communists who were in the union were making trouble for him and after a meeting he went to dinner at Trader's with Bob and [Charlton] Heston. And Bob was teasing him and said that he should run for President. Of course he never dreamed…" Robert Stack wound up serving a six-year tenure on President Reagan's National Council for the Arts.

SORVINO

There is the height (5'10") and there are the legs, which, like they say, go on forever. And there's the beauty, which is formidable indeed. But when Mira Sorvino harnesses these elements in the way that young actresses typically do, something comes out a tad…twisted. The unfettered starlet ego that carries young women into the media circus just isn't there. As a *GQ* interviewer once observed, she is "mercilessly intelligent, profoundly unrelaxed."

Paul Sorvino was struggling toward what would be his own distinguished career as a character actor when she was born. "My dad didn't want me to be a professional actor," she observed. "He felt that acting was too full of pain and rejection." As his daughter was clutching the 1995 Oscar for best supporting actress (in *Mighty Aphrodite*), Paul Sorvino captured the vicissitudes of thespian life by exclaiming, "She was a cocktail waitress a year before winning the Academy Award."

And so it was that the young Mira initially shied away from her father's craft and attended Harvard. She spent eight months in Beijing during 1988 and established ties to students in the pro-democracy movement while becoming fluent in Mandarin. Plans for a post-graduation return to China collapsed with the Tiananmen Square uprisings in the spring of her senior year. The violence "shut a door," she reflected. "If this terrible thing hadn't been done, my life might have happened in China."

Sorvino spent the 1990s assembling a distinguished body of work in movies both art house (*Barcelona, Beautiful Girls, Aphrodite*) and cineplex (*Romy and Michelle's High School Reunion, At First Sight* and *The Replacement Killers*). Her performance as a neglected young wife in Spike Lee's *Summer of Sam* single-handedly lifted the film above its own sprawl. Nuanced and emotionally raw, her performance rode on intelligence and beauty. Just another Mandarin speaking Harvard grad at work.

SWANSON

"We produce about 30,000 cases of wine annually and while that gives us excellent distribution opportunities…" Alexis Swanson starts to grin. She's about to switch gears out of "young businesswoman" and down into "good 'ol gal." "It's small enough for us that I'm out sweepin' the doorstep and shakin' a leg and hawkin' the wines. I'm not exempt from any menial duty." Swanson, you see, is a master communicator and a keen student of the human condition. Not merely a matter of words, her conversation is a quicksilver performance that draws from all corners of a young life and is dominated by snappy good cheer. She has settled in San Francisco and Napa Valley, she has married Mr. Marshall Farrer of Louisville's Brown distilling family and, most important, she has assumed a key role in the winery founded by her father. Alexis Swanson is a social philosopher of the grape and Swanson Vineyards is thriving.

Born in New Orleans, Swanson grew up as daughter of a frozen foods business long cashed out for ventures in publishing, cable and real estate development. She spent her first eight years as an only child in Naples, Florida—a setting which made for unusual playmates: "Whether in the South proper or in a community like Naples, it's a matriarchal society. All my friends and neighbors were elderly widows whose husbands were either murdered or died of alcoholism at 50." Boarding school and college were spent in New England, but the Faulkneresque oral histories and the sense of powerful women eventually carried her to a columnist's job in New Orleans, where then-fiancé Farrer was completing business school. Once again, the most compelling characters were female and the sense of society and history was all encompassing. By the time the couple had left for San Francisco, Swanson had further prepared herself for the business of a vineyard.

"What really inspires me about what we're doing is that we've been able to create something so traditional and so distinctive. Maybe because I've always been surrounded by women, I thrive on men. I've developed a confidence and a strength of self that helps in a male-dominated business," she says cheerfully. And then the shift for emphasis: "you have to know your stuff and you have to hustle hard."

TAYMOR

At the farthest reaches of the entertainment world, there is a mystical state of grace and transcendence. It is a place beyond the dreamscape of most who would, as they say, "get into the business"—the earnest film and theatre students, the impoverished writers and the waitressing actresses. It is a point where the worlds of art and commerce intersect, where a person can be both a gold-standard critical darling and a massive box-office draw. That person will be accorded the highest praise from the most concerned guardians of the arts and will have "the suits" groveling for more of the golden eggs.

Julie Taymor is currently residing in this creative nirvana, and *The Lion King* delivered her there. Taymor spent many years designing and directing theatre productions before Disney enlisted her to adapt an animated world-wide box office smash to the stage. She, in turn, weighed in with a visual spectacle driven by her legendary penchant for costume and puppet design. The woman trades heavily in texture and scale, transforming actors into kinetic cave figures that are both mythic and immediate. Taymor's African savanna opened up and rolled out over audiences, sweeping them into what had been a prosaic coming-of-age story. And she had only been to Africa via *National Geographic* and *Wild Kingdom*. The dazzling representation was, she said, "totally authentic" because it was "authentically from my imagination." *The Lion King*'s Africa had begun in the sunlight and space of its director's childhood summers on Martha's Vineyard.

The Lion King made her the first woman ever to receive a Tony award for Best Director of a Musical, a prize that she can add to, among other honors, a MacArthur Foundation "genius grant" and a Guggenheim Fellowship. But those come from an earlier era, in which she was an admired figure in theatre. Now, she has directed Sir Anthony Hopkins and Jessica Lange in a successful screen adaptation of Shakespeare's *Titus Andronicus*. Julie Taymor is a one-woman production juggernaut with critical and commercial juice to spare.

THRASH Ms. Becca Cason Thrash has been delighting, amazing, baffling and bewildering Houston society for almost 20 years. "It's just what comes naturally," she says in her rapid-fire way. Thrash has the striking ability to thread an "old soul" wisdom and perspective through the conspiratorial tones of the sleepover party: "I didn't excel in school, but I was captain of the debate team. I've just always had that ability to analyze and verbalize. I'm a talker. Came out of the chute that way."

Believe it. Thrash is nothing if not persuasive and her ability to throw the verbal arm around just about anybody has carried her far and wide. Born in South Texas, she ignored college altogether to make her way to 1970s London. After heady times in the rock'n'roll orbit, she wound up taking a gig launching *Vogue* en Español from Mexico City. After that, it was on to Houston to form a public relations firm. "I've always had an interest in design and style; an innate curiosity and love for that whole aspect of life," she says. Those loves and an eye sharpened during her earlier incarnations helped her firm to land top clients while fostering a new, more fluid kind of society life in the city.

Business success helped her to find a new, elevated and occasionally controversial social niche for herself. "I'm a Type-A, high-energy person," she says. "I'm always out trying to get things done." Detractors who have labeled her an *arriviste* have missed the point. Thrash isn't manipulative; she's a forward thinking woman for whom career and society lives are thoroughly intertwined. She hasn't circumvented old rules. She has worked to explode them. Her story is about renewal and reinvention of oneself: about wide-open possibility. Becca Cason Thrash has moved Houston society in that most meritocratic of directions by using smarts and elbow grease to be exactly who she wants to be.

TURNER

It is not about the legs. You may think it's the legs, but it's not. Once, long ago, people thought of the voice and the dancing and the Ikettes and those things she could do with a microphone. Tina Turner taught Mick Jagger how to move on stage. In those days, it was the Revue and the sequined fringes and "Proud Mary" or "River Deep, Mountain High" belted out with the whole cast absolutely vibrating. Except for Ike. Back then, Ike would stalk around the stage and he was menace head to toe and nothing else.

Ike's menace is what you see now, because in 1981, the story changed entirely. Tina — and Tina alone — went in a few short months from being a club act with incredible cachet and fans like Mick Jagger, Keith Richards and David Bowie to making a record (*Private Dancer*, 11 million copies) and finally, to standing at a mobbed autograph signing in Manhattan. She had just learned that "What's Love Got To Do With It?" had hit number one in the trades and she was laughing and screaming and at an absolutely new place in her career.

And after that, it was never really about the legs again, even though nobody can get over them and they are, after 61 years and almost four decades in the business, still insured for millions. It's because Ike beat Tina and he messed around on her and she finally just walked away. She left from nowhere and nothing to become one of the biggest concert draws in the world. And as she was storming through the 1980s and 1990s with hit records and standing-room tours she was actually transcending show business and stardom altogether to become The Story: Humor, Nerve, Sex, Soulfulness. And Survival. Oprah comes to Tina for interviews because Tina is Hope and Possibility. Tina is Change and she is Courage: "The real power behind whatever success I have now was something I found within myself— something that's within all of us, I think. A little piece of God just waiting to be discovered."

TURLINGTON

She was never merely a super-model. One could never fit her into the Patti Hansen, Naomi Campbell, Kate Moss rubric of trashed hotel rooms and nightclub decadence; nor was she a Christie Brinkley or Cindy Crawford—no mass-market blandness. Christy Turlington's complexity reads as powerfully as the cheekbones, the lips or the eyes: yes, sexy but serene, contemplative, wholesome as well.

"She's an all-time classic," the photographer Terry O'Neill once observed. "You can place her in any decade and she'll still be beautiful." When the Costume Institute at New York's Metropolitan Museum of Art commissioned the artist Pucci to mold a face for its mannequin displays, Turlington's was chosen—beauty itself, transcending fashion.

The Miami-reared daughter of an American father spent childhood summers riding in the countryside of her mother's native El Salvador. That happy period was cut short by the civil wars of the 1980s. Turlington has consistently drawn attention to the country's sufferings. And her father's death from lung cancer prompted her to become a spokesperson for the American Lung Association.

Turlington's causes have been undertaken against a shifting professional and personal background. Her endorsement work has been lucrative (*Forbes* estimates an annual income of $7 million), but she has abandoned the catwalk and spent much of the 1990's studying for a Bachelor's degree at New York University. Recently, she has become a key investor in Sundari skin care and a line of yoga-wear. Fitness and beauty, of course, but multifaceted—substance to go with high style.

vanden HEUVEL

"If you don't have a big budget," she says, laughing, "you need a point of view. And I think we have a point of view that will always be attractive and that may grow in terms of a following with some of the excesses that we're seeing." Katrina vanden Heuvel is talking about her venerable magazine, *The Nation*, and the excesses of market capitalism at the turn-of-the-millennium.

The New Yorker once theorized that had "Katrina vanden Heuvel" sprung entirely from Judith Krantz's fevered imagination, the character would have been somehow-even less believable than the author's standard heroine. And with the Hollywood studio inheritance (grandfather Jules Stein founded MCA), the youth and beauty (both undiminished at 40), the smarts, the marriage, a daughter and a successful and principled magazine, she is something like a composite of Charlie Rose guest qualities: The Woman Who Has It All.

If you are tempted to resent the abundance of good fortune, know also that vanden Heuvel picks up her own phone and manages interview requests promptly. And she works hard. Very hard. As I'm imagining a house in the Berkshires and long dinners with Paul Newman and Robert Redford (two of her partners in the magazine), she starts laughing. "They're going to commit me if I don't take a vacation. I've spent all of my spare time in the last ten years going to Moscow." Vanden Heuvel's daughter has been to Russia no fewer than 25 times in her eight year life while her mother has been bringing feminism to Russian women: "*The Nation* for the wrong reasons used to be accused of being a 'pinko' publication, so I love to make the joke that I'm editing it from Moscow." More dark wit. And more vodka, please: "What is an optimist? An informed pessimist. There will always be a place for *The Nation* because we fight for causes lost and found. We're going to keep fighting, in good spirits with some good humor I hope, and with a passion."

WALKER

She is a truth-teller and an itinerant spirit. Alice Walker has spent her life as a literary activist of body and soul and her work is driven by a kind of passion that sets her very much apart in a "go along to get along" world. Yet when *The Color Purple* exploded out of the literary prestige that had been Walker's province since the early 1970s and into the popular consciousness, Hollywood inevitably came knocking. Compromises had to be made. Walker's treatment of the book wasn't used, but she remained involved enough in the production to be deeply disappointed with the finished product. "The first time I saw it," she has said, "it looked funny, it sounded funny and I thought everybody was a cartoon."

Perhaps she needn't worry. The book itself does not lack for exposure: As of the mid-1990s, The Color Purple had been translated into 22 languages and sold over four million copies worldwide. If the novel's popular success tends to overshadow the rest of her prolific and acclaimed career, it has also made her a very comfortable woman. Walker lives alone (she has renounced the idea of marriage "and besides, I like to be courted") on a 40 acre property north of San Francisco and relaxes by tending to her lush gardens. She is the model of new-age style: "I'm as happy now as I was sad during my childhood."

There's no doubt that she has earned her happiness. After finishing Sarah Lawrence in 1965, Walker married and returned to her native Georgia to work on the civil rights movement – when Dr. King was assassinated, she miscarried a child. Walker published essays, poetry and a first novel before taking a teaching post at Wellesley. While in residence there, she established one of the nation's first women's studies programs. The teaching and publishing that dominated her life in the 1970s culminated in both a Pulitzer Prize and an American Book Award for *The Color Purple* when it appeared in 1982.

And if the difficulties of the film have pushed her away from public life, her productivity has not been affected. Walker has written 16 books, including her most recent novel, 1998's *By The Light of My Father's Smile*, and continues to be outspoken on issues of race and oppression.

WELD Jacqueline Weld is back to her days at Sarah Lawrence College and the ways in which her studies there continue to inform her life: "I was hugely attracted to [Joseph] Campbell's study of mythology. He was interested in the ways in which people create stories in order to have the experience of living. You have to create your own culture through myth." She's covering her early years with the wide-open, freewheeling style that has laced her life and a varied career as a lawyer, businesswoman, environmentalist and, especially, as an author. There's lots of good humor and a willingness to reflect: "I was a typical Sarah Lawrence girl...they tend to be bohemians in their souls – which I am, though I have the trappings of a more traditional life."

Trappings or no, Weld's journey has taken her far and wide—across cultures, continents and careers. She is the great-granddaughter of the martyred Uruguayan President Juan Idiarte Borda and as a child, her family would regularly shuttle between Manhattan and both Venezuela and Uruguay, leaving her somewhat caught between social worlds. She doesn't regret the experience, but the straddling of Latin and Anglo cultures provided challenges as well as opportunities and exposure.

Weld worked in both Colorado and Manhattan as a lawyer on behalf of the Latin poor while embarking on a marriage within the storied Weld investment banking family. The marriage ultimately failed (she is now married to Rodman Drake) but her work on behalf of the Hispanic-American community is ongoing. She has also written the definitive biography of the art patron and dealer Peggy Guggenheim.

With her first novel, 1998's *Rara Avis*, Weld turned inward: "When you write fiction, you don't really find out what the book is about until after the fact. *Rara Avis* drew on the experiences and consciousness of my earliest childhood and it turned out to be a way to make sense out of an unusual immigrant experience." The book won raves for the surreal imagery and the dark humor of its portrayal of a wealthy South American family. Professor Campbell was right. Having made her myth, Jacqueline Weld is having the time of her life.

WEAVER

It is quite an effect, that look. When fixed in just a certain way, Sigourney Weaver's face radiates an intensity unlike anything else on the market. It's almost forcefully interrogative, but never lacking for soulfulness. The variations abound and when she's playing it, Weaver comes across as a lady – perhaps with some deep bruises – quite unwilling to settle for less than the dignity of a complete answer. Modulate the look for battle with aliens, for the study of Gorillas, for quizzical looks at Bill Murray, for a mid-life crisis in Connecticut—it is the vital core of her screen persona and a point of departure for her famous range.

Weaver's father was one of the pioneers of the golden age of television. Pat Weaver created both the *Today* and *Tonight* shows and ran NBC during the 1950s. His daughter grew to her present height of 5'11" by the time she was eleven. She followed an Upper East Side education with Stanford and Yale Drama School. To this day she is fond of telling stories of Yale professors who declared that she was bereft of talent and manages to do so without sounding the least bit smug.

Weaver made her feature film debut with 30 seconds in *Annie Hall*, but broke it big commercially and critically in *The Year of Living Dangerously* and *Alien*. When she made the sequel *Aliens* in 1986, her portrayal of Lieutenant Ellen Ripley as goddess of vengeance made her an icon for the decade. That look again—armed to the teeth for the Reagan years. Weaver hasn't returned to that pop culture summit, but has decamped for more interesting and significant ground. Her recent work, like *The Ice Storm* and *A Map of the World*, is actually her best. And with a new production company funded by Fox, Weaver, now 50, has skipped the career gap that traditionally befalls actresses between the ages of "assistant D.A. and Miss Daisy."

WELLS

Allure editor Linda Wells is reflecting on her early years in journalism and on an important mentor: "At the [New York] *Times* I worked with Carrie Donovan, who was the most hilarious, inspiring person and a huge influence on me. She brought new mainstream respectability to the world of fashion by mixing the sobriety of newspaper journalism with the frivolity of the subject matter."

Donovan's sensibility found its way into the uppermost reaches of Condé Nast and in 1990, Wells was summoned to a meeting with owner S.I. Newhouse and editorial mandarin Alexander Liberman. "Out of the blue," she laughs, the two offered her the challenge of building a new beast: the smart and culturally savvy beauty magazine. "It was completely incomprehensible. I played it cool, told them I'd think about it and then went rushing off to a payphone to call my parents, screaming. It was better than my greatest fantasy."

Ten years later, *Allure* is an established part of the Condé Nast firmament and Wells' breathless retelling declares an undiminished love for the job. There is nothing guarded about her, none of the world weariness usually evinced by smart folks in media jobs. It's an appetite for popular culture and a curiosity about its role in women's lives.

"I try to see every movie I can. When you're a magazine editor you pay attention to everything, you have to. Before I had children, I'd go to two movies a week or I'd feel a sense of withdrawal." The children are two sons with the banker Charles Thompson and when the cultural radar begins to short-circuit, they escape the claustrophobia of Manhattan for a house in New Jersey horse country or a rental in Southampton.

"*Allure* is really about looking better," says Linda Wells. "The underlying belief, the way we give the subject meaning to us, is that when you look better it affects your behavior in many significant ways. If you care about the way you look, you usually feel good and that makes you more effective in whatever else you're doing."

YOUNG

"Communication is the essence of human life," says Pegi Young, quoting Daniel Webster. Communication had become a critical issue for her son Ben, born in 1978 and diagnosed shortly thereafter with Cerebral Palsy. The condition had rendered the child quadriplegic and unable to speak – an almost complete entrapment within his own burgeoning interior life. Her son was imprisoned and opportunities for his education were virtually nonexistent.

Along with Jim Forderer, she began discussing ways in which they might close the gap between what non-speaking children were experiencing and what they were able to express. Marilyn Buzolich, who had been working with technology to assist speech-impaired children, joined the pair in designing an ambitious program that would enable these children not only to communicate via computers, but also eventually to make the transition into general educational settings.

The Bridge School was launched in 1986 by a benefit concert featuring Ben's father and Pegi's husband, the guitarist and songwriter Neil Young. Friends like Crosby, Stills & Nash, Robin Williams and Bruce Springsteen turned up to inaugurate what has become one of pop music's biggest annual events—drawing David Bowie, Simon & Garfunkel, James Taylor & Elton John, among many others to support and promote the school. Along the way, the musicians and entertainers have been able to spend time with Bridge students: "It never fails," says Pegi Young. "People come to me and say it's been a life-altering experience for them."

Meanwhile, Bridge alumnus Ben Young is using a new integrated communication system to run graphics programs, PhotoShop and his video programs. After obtaining a certification from the state of California, he has 150 chickens producing organic eggs on the family's ranch near the Pacific. "The computer helps him keep his business records," says his mother. "But the coyotes can be a problem."

WILLIAMS

Ten months after being crowned the first black Miss America in 1983, Vanessa Williams was blindsided by nude photographs taken in her late teens. The story was a national sensation and she was forced to resign in disgrace. What's remarkable about Williams' subsequent comeback is that it never operated on the fuel of shamelessness that is so prevalent in American popular culture. At the time, she said, "I made a terrible error in judgment and I know I'll have to pay for it as long as I live…somehow I am going to make people believe me." By dint of talent and deep strength, Williams simply worked her way back into the public's good graces – first with a breakout recording career (including 11 Grammy nominations) and more recently, on Broadway and in film. By 1995, she was even Disney-approved and scored a smash with the *Pocahontas* soundtrack. Williams has starred in hit films opposite Arnold Schwarzenegger and sung the national anthem at the Super Bowl—as all-American a redemption as one could possibly imagine.

"It was a setback, not a defeat," she said of the Miss America crisis. "It wasn't like my vocal chords were cut." A close family has been the foundation for her odyssey back and Williams now lives unpretentiously in the suburbs of Manhattan, about ten minutes from her parents and the house in which she was reared. She was divorced in 1996, but the structure grounds her three children from that marriage with plenty of time at their grandparents' home. And the family is an expanding group: Williams married Los Angeles Lakers star Rick Fox in 1999 and the couple welcomed a baby last Spring, as mom was planning both television and stage projects.

WOODS

Emily Woods is the all-American woman of our dreams. She's on a beach, with friends. An old college roommate is there and so is the guy from home who started the literary review (those two were an item at one time.) Another pal has returned to the stomping grounds from a "grand tour" that never seems to end. It's late in the day and they are about to have showers outdoors before breaking out a bottle of white wine. *Baywatch* it's not, nor even Southampton. It's the Vineyard or Cape Cod—Yankee, with texture and lots less glamour than good taste.

In 1982, Woods was barely out of college when she joined the firm started by her grandfather and introduced a new concept in marketing and design. She would design a line and a brand from scratch, based on the clothes she liked to wear in Colorado or Nantucket or New Mexico. "Understated design was the essence of my vision," she now says. "I never thought of J. Crew as a catalogue business and I think that's why we changed the industry." By 1999, annual sales from retail, the web site and the original book (now in 24 editions) had exceeded $700 million.

Maybe the most important thing Woods ever did was give the catalogue its signature look of fresh-scrubbed congeniality. The "cast of characters," as she puts it, is usually composed of friends and employees who somehow had the look that placed them in scenes like the one described above. The J. Crew catalogue is a world unto itself, a Kennedy-compound thing, ca. 1955, and it's frankly autobiographical: "All of the look of J. Crew comes from me. I don't wear makeup, I don't wear jewelry and I was always athletic."

These days, much of Woods's athleticism happens on her rooftop in lower Manhattan where she boxes or does yoga. And while she's still the all-American woman of our dreams, the knowledge that she's "plotting strategy and designing retail stores" makes it harder to pop her into fantasies of an endless summer. Emily Woods is still young and beautiful and the Rolling Stones are still playing in the house. And the book on the table is Jack Welch's biography.

WYATT "My roots are Texan," she says. "My persona is Texan." Far and wide, across the mighty Lone Star State, to the French Riviera and beyond, there is scarcely a soul who would disagree. In Texas, where social pride-of-place is perhaps more closely scrutinized and more fiercely contested than anywhere else, Lynn Wyatt reigns supreme.

"I was a head cheerleader in high school," she says simply. Then, from the corner of her mouth, "and my husband [oil magnate and rancher Oscar] says I haven't stopped yelling since." Wyatt speaks in alternating cadences: she's ambling and thoughtful in a way that generates a little mystery and draws the listener in. Then, suddenly, she'll leap out with a funny or insightful verbal burst. When the Lady falls away for that brief moment and the head cheerleader appears, it is warm Texas sunlight on the listener's face.

And it is precisely those contrasts which have made Wyatt both emblematic of Houston and a superb ambassador for the City. "A lot of people have moved to Houston in the last 20 or 30 years and I've seen it go from a town to a city. Houston is very cosmopolitan. I think people who come here are surprised at the breadth of the cultural arts and the first-class museum and the first-class opera." Wyatt is a long-standing force on the boards of both institutions and many others, but doesn't connect herself directly with the sophistication boom in the city. Instead, she'll talk about "the frontier spirit" of Texas and her love for the family's Tasajillo Ranch. Worldly, but earthy and unpretentious.

It's a combination that travels well: The Wyatts have for years summered on the French Riviera, first at Cap Ferrat and more recently, at Villefranche. When, in the late 1970s, Princess Grace asked Mrs. Wyatt to organize a benefit for the Red Cross in Monte Carlo, she turned a one-night affair into a weekend bash. Friday night, Wyatt imported the most exotic elements imaginable: Lone Star Beer, a Country & Western band and a "chef with a real Texas barbecue with beans and all the accoutrements." Europe's elite were smitten and insisted that the band return the following evening to perform alongside a symphony orchestra at the formal dance. "Texas," says Lynn Wyatt, "has always had a bigger-than-life reputation." And the best head cheerleader around.

WILLIAMS

A few years ago, neither the men's nor women's tours were generating stories to match the days of Connors and McEnroe, Evert and Navratilova. Sure, there were great athletes all over the place. But professional sports does not rely merely on great athletes. Pro sports is about charisma and star power, rivalries and feuds; pro sports is about the great story.

And so, the deities hanging over women's tennis not only blessed Venus (left) and Serena (right) Williams with beauty, fearsome power and yes, great talent. The gods made them just about the most compelling and unlikely story imaginable. Then, just for fun, those same deities sent the sisters Williams hurtling at one another, just as the Pete and André saga was burning out. And they set the stage in New York! Consider: First, the Horatio Alger element. The sisters, born fifteen months apart, learn tennis with their father Richard on the public courts in Compton, California. This is akin to training in Kosovo, but the two thrive under the tutelage of Richard and their mother Oracene while continuing to excel academically. When the girls are in their early teens, they are packed up and sent to a Florida boarding tennis academy.

Next, the breakout: Older sister Venus turns pro in 1994. She is immediately tagged as a rising superstar and eventually boasts a serve of 127 m.p.h. In 1997, she is joined on the tour by Serena, whose rise becomes perhaps even more meteoric. The sisters meet in the quarterfinals of the 1998 Australian Open, with Venus emerging victorious.

By September of 1999, the sisters are each white-hot going into the U.S. Open. Father Richard, apparently a graduate of the P.T. Barnum school of public relations, has a field day with the New York media circus as he predicts that the two will face off for the championship. "I know it sounds crazy," he tells reporters, "But I think that Venus and Serena will control women's tennis." The dream ends when Venus falls to Martina Hingis, who falls to…Serena for the Williams family's first Grand Slam victory. She is the first female player of African-American origin to take a Grand Slam since Althea Gibson's Open victory in 1958 and she does so at Arthur Ashe Stadium. In a twist beyond even a drunken hack screenwriter, the sisters provide a coda to the Open by winning the doubles championship.

Will Richard Williams drive them both crazy while finally alienating a rabid media? Will Reebok top its $12 million endorsement deal with Venus, now that she is a Wimbledon champ? And are the Williamses, despite their own protests to the contrary, the Tiger Woods of tennis?

Tune in to these beautiful young women to find out the answers to these and other questions. The WTA will thank the gods. Ⓐ

Summit's completely storable Sun Deck Collection by the ASID award-winning designer John Munford

Antibes • Atlanta • Chicago • Dallas • Dubai • Fort Lauderdale • Houston • Los Angeles
New York • Paris • Philadelphia • Phoenix • San Francisco • Seattle • Toronto • Vancouver

SUMMIT

VINTAGE PARKER

By John Anderson

Even the greatest French winemakers pay homage to an American wine critic.
His name is Robert Parker, and he is the Colossus of the wine world.
Here, John Anderson explains why.

The first thing you notice about Robert Parker is that he's big. Really big. This tower of oenophilic power claims to stand just six foot-one, but he seems at least a couple of inches taller, tall enough, that is, to carry 250-plus pounds comfortably. Whether it's at a black-tie dinner at the Fifth Avenue home of former Kennedy-era Treasury Secretary C. Douglas Dillon (whose extended family owns both Chateau Haut-Brion and Chateau La Mission Haut-Brion) or at a more informal tasting of 1989 clarets, Parker dominates the room. Both literally and metaphorically, Parker is a colossus of the wine world.

To put it brutally, Robert M. Parker, Jr. can make or break a wine - or a winemaker. His 50-100 point markings heap praise or condemnation on wines that range from the simple but tasty (if obscure) to the grandest of names fetching the highest of prices. Parker has tasted them all, literally tens of thousands of wines a year, sniffed, swirled about, rolled over the tongue and spat out. And however quickly an offending wine is disposed of, Parker's ratings endure in the pages of his bimonthly newsletter, *The Wine Advocate*, and in his numerous books, *Bordeaux, Burgundy, The Rhone Valley*, as well as the best selling *Parker's Wine Buyer's Guide*, now in its fifth American edition.

Parker's power is such that his enemies claim that winemakers not only kowtow to him, they even try to make their wines with Parker's tastes in mind: big, powerful, richly extracted wines that sometimes fall short of elegance. A more generous way of putting it is that Parker seems to like extroverted wines that, well, seem to reflect the man himself. His legion of fans, including many of France's top winemakers and America's best importers, credit him with de-industrializing the production of fine wine. Parker's own assessment of his work is typically forthright: "I like to think of myself as the Ralph Nader of the wine world: honest, unbought, and unbuyable." Whether one agrees or not with this self-assessment, few deny the man's power.

Previous page and above: Bob Parker in his cellar at home in Monkton, Maryland.
Opposite: The caves at Château Mouton Rothschild

The young Bob Parker could hardly have guessed that one day he'd be hobnobbing with the likes of the Duc and Duchesse de Mouchy, Princesse de Luxembourg, drinking pre-1900 Bordeaux. Parker grew-up in Monkton, Maryland, a small town some 30 miles north of Baltimore. It was there, at the age of 12, that he met Pat Etzel, the woman who would one day become his wife. Three years later, Bob and Pat began dating. The young Parker's most memorable early experience with wine? Getting stone drunk at Pat's 18th birthday party on Cold Duck sparkling wine.

It was thanks to his future wife that Bob later got a somewhat different introduction to wine. In December 1967, he went to France to visit Pat, who was taking her junior year abroad studying French at the University of Strasbourg. The two agreed to meet-up at a bistro in Paris. There, Parker tasted his first glass of dry white wine. It was, he says, a revelation. Throughout this initial *Tour de France*, Parker continued to drink wine, amazed by the subtleties he found in the refined juice of the grape. When he got home, Parker promptly founded a college wine-tasting club. And, later, as a law school student at the University of Maryland, his interest intensified. It was then that he began, tentatively at first, buying wine by the case, beginning with the 1966 and 1970 red Bordeaux (two fine vintages). By now it was clear: Bob Parker, who had been in love with Pat since he was 15, had found a second, equally-enduring passion: it was called wine.

Real estate transactions and banking law bored the newly minted attorney. So, with $2,000 borrowed from his parents, Parker started *The Wine Advocate*, then known as *The Baltimore/Washington Wine Advocate*, as a sideline. The 16-page newsletter debuted in 1978 with some 6,500 copies mailed out and given away for free. So how did this obscure banking lawyer then go on to become the world's most celebrated wine guru?

The short answer is the 1982 Bordeaux vintage, although in retrospect, one senses that it was all a matter of incredible timing. It's worth recalling where the wine world was at the time: the market, and particularly the Bordeaux market, had tanked in the mid-1970s. The 1970 vintage was fine but expensive, the 1971 vintage was good (though not nearly as good as 1970) but much more expensive. The 1972 vintage was perfectly wretched, yet even more expensive. Then the inevitable happened: the boiler burst, thanks to the recession brought on by the oil crisis, leaving merchants stuck with huge quantities of those then-ultra-expensive 1972s. The next two vintages were far from thrilling, causing Parker's opening salvo in issue number one of *The Wine Advocate* to be a no holds barred condemnation of the pretty but rather watery 1973s.

The market only began to recover with the 1975 vintage, which was followed by the good (but not great) 1976s, 1978s, and 1979s. When the equally good (but also not great) 1980s came on the market, they were

Bob Parker's Desert Island Reds

1. Paul Jaboulet 1961 Hermitage la Chapelle.

2. Marcel Guigal 1978 Cote Rotie La Mouline.

3. Henri Bonneau 1990 Chateauneuf du Pape
   "Réserve des Céléstins".

4. André Brunel 1990 Chateauneuf du Pape
   "Cuvée Centenaire".

5. 1945 Chateau Mouton-Rothschild.

6. 1947 Chateau Cheval Blanc.

7. 1947 Chateau Lafleur.

8. 1947 Pétrus.

9. 1997 Harlan Estate
   Cabernet Sauvignon.

10. 1997 Bryant Family Vineyard
    Cabernet Sauvignon.

gobbled up. By then the Reagan dollar had begun to make its presence felt. The wines, in short, were cheap, which was why so many American merchants took a big stand on 1981 and many lived to regret it.

The 1982 harvest was big, a near record, in fact. Coming in the midst of an incredible heat wave, the grapes, in some cases, literally steamed in the picker's harvesting baskets. By Christmas of 1982, top European wine critics, like the Frenchman Michel Bettane and the English master of wine David Peppercorn, were already talking up the vintage as the best since 1961. But American wine critics Robert Finigan (whose newsletter was the dominant voice in the field) and Terry Robards (a columnist for *The Wine Spectator*) took strong counter-positions. The 1982s, they warned, lacked acidity and, thus, staying power. They were soon joined by New York wine promoter, William Sokolin, who took out a full-page advertisement in *The New York Times*, adjuring consumers to stay clear of the '82s.

Bob Parker, though, was saying something else. In March 1983, accompanied by wife Pat, a high school French teacher, Parker went to Bordeaux to see for himself. While Pat translated, Bob sniffed and tasted. His verdict: "I can unequivocally state that 1982 is a monumental vintage." It would, Parker predicted, "go down in the annals of Bordeaux wine history with such legendary vintages as 1929, 1945, 1959 and 1961."

The wines were certainly cheap. Sold *en primeur* (while still in casks awaiting bottling), third growths such as Chateau La Lagune were selling for as little as $72 a case. Super-seconds like Chateau Léoville-Las Cases went for $135. And the grandest names of all? How about $360 for a case of 1982 Chateau Mouton-Rothschild? The formula was this: Big vintage, lots of wine, virtually all of it fine (some great), and a perfectly incredible 10 francs to the dollar exchange rate. Of course, Parker was right.

Everything, in fact, about the timing of the vintage was right, including the state of the American market. The recovery was on, the bubble hadn't burst; a ton of upper-middle class yuppies had entered the workforce, and there was plenty of money to spend on wine. Buy, buy, buy, cried Bob Parker; and those who did early in the game didn't regret it. Today, the 1982 Las Cases sells for upwards of a $1000 a case; the Mouton is far pricier still. The 1982 vintage made Bob Parker; or perhaps, one should say, he made it. But there is no question that the fate of the vintage and the man are now intertwined.

Still riding high two decades later, the 52-year old Bob Parker is also a very wealthy man. With a paid circulation of 40,000, *The Wine Advocate* alone brings in over a million dollars in revenues. But it's his books (Parker is working on a new one, this time on the wines of California) and, now, the prospect of sharing his expertise on the internet, that are the well-springs of his fortune. Monkton, Maryland, is still where Parker calls home and it's where his office and cellars are located. Bob, Pat and their daughter Maia live in the same house where Pat grew up. Parker has three wine cellars and countless bottles - he won't disclose just how many, but

Above: Labels from some of Parker's favorites.
Right: Wines from the Côtes du Rhône vineyard of Marcel Guigal, whose fame is due in major part to Parker.
Page 296: Château d'Ampuis

Los Angeles Times wine critic Dan Shaw put the number at over 20,000. It's a family affair too: his mother does secretarial work in the offices of *The Wine Advocate*.

Parker's day begins early. It's not uncommon to find him tasting wines at seven a.m. Nor is it uncommon for him to taste as many as 100 or more wines at a sitting. Tasting, mind you, not drinking - Parker never drinks when he tastes. He saves his favorite pleasure for meals, usually evening meals. His consumption is down from two bottles a day to just a tad more than one. He seldom spends more than eight to ten seconds sniffing any wine, as he makes up his mind fast. Only the greatest wines get a second or third sniffing. Detractors (and there are a few) claim it's impossible to make serious judgments about wine, especially young wine, in such short order, and cite "palate fatigue" as one of the chief dangers of Parker's methods. Others claim he doesn't taste often enough in winemakers' cellars. Among those critics is the English master of wine, Clive Coates, author of *The Vine*, an influential monthly newsletter, who claims to spend many weeks each year tasting *in situ*, particularly in Burgundy.

Parker remains unimpressed suggesting Coates does not have the same cut and thrust background that he does, and that as a former wine merchant, Coates still has close ties to the trade. This is a problem Parker believes many English writers have in general, citing two other leading English wine writers, David Peppercorn and wife, Serena Sutcliffe, M.W., the head of Sotheby's wine department. By contrast, Parker proudly points to the fact that he never, ever accepts free travel or free wine from producers. Those who imagine Parker as something of an old grouch, should think again. After all these years, he is still wild about wine and it's this enthusiasm that has propelled him forward. When it's right, Parker doesn't just like a wine, he loves it. He has never become jaded, "largely because I feel that with each new vintage, I am a student returning to school." What excites him is the same thing that's always excited him: great wine. Owners come and go, some are polite, some are charming, but "the only thing that makes a visit to a vineyard special is the quality of the wine."

Although Parker freely admits that his heart is still in Bordeaux, his horizons have expanded exponentially. Some of the growers who ring Parker's bell today include the Domaine Zind-Humbrecht in Alsace; Domaine Leroy in Vosne-Romanée, Marcel Guigal in Cote Rotie, Michel Chapoutier in Tain L'Hermitage, and Maison Louis Jadot in Beaune. At such places, says Parker, you can bet that the wines will be "extra special."

So, too was the day in 1999 when President Jacques Chirac personally awarded him the Legion of Honor, which was "the greatest professional achievement of my life. It was beyond anything I could have ever dreamed." Chirac spoke on national television about what Parker's writing had meant for the country and its winemakers and about the impact he'd had on the quality of French wines. "The emotions and memories of this event will remain with me the rest of my life," Parker says, adding that it still seems "surreal" to him.

The international wine world has recently changed almost beyond recognition. As late as twenty years ago, Bordeaux had yet to emerge from its slump. Prices were low, and there was no incentive for change, either in the vineyards or in the cellars. At least one, if not two, of the First Growths were coasting by, making wines that in no way reflected their position in the hierarchy. In Burgundy, the story was similar, if not worse. Artificial fertilizer was being salted pell-mell not merely into low-lying regions but also into premier and grand cru land. The resulting thin red burgundies were then regularly "beefed-up" by the "magicians" of the trade, using Rhone and Algerian plonk.

But where was the outrage? 25 years ago, there were only a few books being written about wine. The most famous wine writer was Alexis Lichine, and he, of course, was a vineyard owner and wine merchant as well. Lichine's vintage charts from those days show the latest vintage, whatever it was, was always good. But time and truth will out: today we know that there were a lot of truly awful vintages in the sixties in Bordeaux (1963, 1965, 1968 and 1969). But you would never have known that from the charts. Today you would. And Bob Parker is largely credited with that sea-change, bringing his exacting standards to the tasting room and refusing to compromise on quality.

While some people do not approve of his catchy 50-100 ratings system, suggesting it trivializes the tasting process, others criticize his enthusiastic, sometimes overwrought prose, or argue that his palate is fit more for big Rhone reds than for elegant burgundies. Few, however question his objectivity.

The biases that were once so prevalent in the wine press are notably absent in the prose of Parker, who, whatever faults he may have, is brutally honest. The salutary effect of the Parkerization of the wine world cannot be understated. Parker calls the vintages and the wines as he sees them; but he's also had a profoundly important effect on the way fine wines are themselves made. As he points out, technically "correct" wines are frequently denuded of flavor. Excess filtering, for example, "cleans up" the wine but leaves it stripped and thin. Similarly, the use of artificial fertilizer stimulates crop growth - and results in wines that inherently lack concentration. Throughout his career, Parker has taken on all comers and he shows no signs of winding down his crusade any time soon. He is a character of truly epic proportion and not everyone loves him for it. With passion and pride as his guide, Parker has made an indelible mark in the world of fine wine. Ⓐ

Interiors by Alberto Pinto

ALBERTO PINTO   HÔTEL DE LA VICTOIRE   11 RUE D'ABOUKIR   75002 PARIS   TEL: +33 1 40 13 00 00   FAX: +33 1 40 13 75 80

INDEX I

LISTING BY ALPHABET

ALPHABETICAL INDEX

PLEASE NOTE:
Entries which begin with a definite article (*The, le, La, etc.*) appear under the first letter of the proper name. For example, The Levison & Cullen Gallery is listed under L. Hotels and resturants normally appear under the first letter of the proper name, except in a few cases where the name cannot stand alone.

PREVIOUS PAGE: *Courtesy of the Museum of Fine Arts Houston: Portrait of Lady Blount, by George Romney*

INDEX I

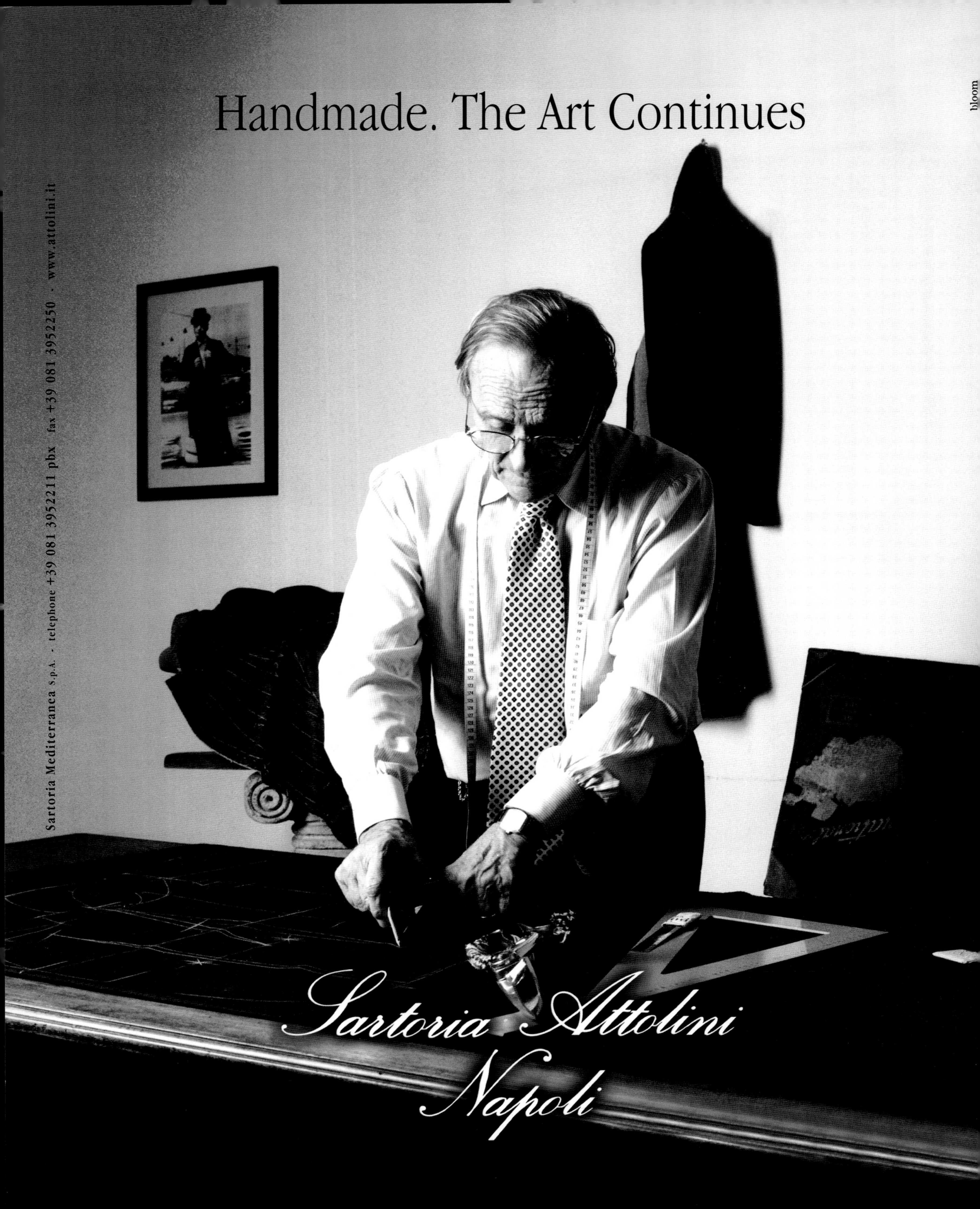
Handmade. The Art Continues
Sartoria Attolini
Napoli
Sartoria Mediterranea S.p.A. - telephone +39 081 3952211 pbx fax +39 081 3952250 - www.attolini.it
bloom

INDEX II

LISTING BY STATE

INDEX BY STATE

INDEX II

INDEX II

INDEX II

Garden Designers
Architects & Interiors
Fine Art Dealers
Antiques

Polo/Golf Clubs
Sporting Estates
Museums

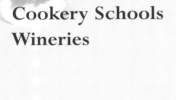

Restaurants
Cookery Schools
Wineries

VISIT THE ULTIMATE GUIDES
TO LUXURY LIVING
www.elite1000.com

Wealth Management
Gentlemen's Clubs
Private Banks

Grand Hotels
Spas & Clinics
Travel Consultants
Yachting

Couturiers
Specialist Shops
Objets d'Art
Auction Houses

Now you can visit **The Elite 1000** at **www.elite1000.com** - the ultimate resource for luxury online.

Readers from anywhere around the world can access information and advice on the finest purveyors of luxury goods and services.

An invaluable reference point when visiting Europe or America.

INDEX III

LISTING BY
PRODUCT CATEGORY

INDEX BY CATEGORY

INDEX III

INDEX III

INDEX III

INDEX III

INDEX III

INDEX III

EDITORIAL CONTRIBUTORS & RESEARCHERS

Michelle Collotta, Emile Dinneen, Killian Fox, Fiona Keane, Ralph Martin, Guerda Nozile, Stephen O'Neill, Marcella Paraskevas, Dorothy Rompalske, Wendy Schatzman, Shiba Scott, Lior Sofer

FEATURE WRITERS

John Anderson is Deputy Editor of *The American Lawyer* magazine.

Michael Dwyer is a film correspondent for *The Irish Times*.

Christopher Lawrence is one of the finest young writers in America today.

Curt Sampson is a leading authority on golf around the world. He is the author of *The Masters: Golf, Money, and Power in Augusta, Georgia*.

ACKNOWLEDGEMENTS

Many people selflessly devoted time and energy to this project. The editors particularly wish to express their gratitude to the following individuals, who provided unstinting support and wise counsel: Luciano Bellorio, Mariana Cordero, Geralyn Delaney, Greg Furman, Shelby Hodge, Myra Langsam, Norah Lawlor, Alicia Livingston, Marie Loftus, Patrick McMullan, Daniela Novati, Sheri Rohne, Alice Slimmer, Liz Smith, Clive Watson, Alicia White, Mary Beth Wilson, Ellen Yost, Toby Young.

PHOTOGRAPHIC CREDITS:

Russ Adams: Page 213; Kosta Alexander/ Rex USA: Page 36; Richard Barnes: Page 114; Ruda Blair: Page 120; Andrew Bordwin: Pages 64, 92; Clive Brunskill/ All Sport: Page 288; Tori Butt: Page 173; David Cannon/ All Sport: Pages 45,66; Donna & Ken Chester: Page 213; Walter Chin: Page 270; Barron Claiborne: Page 262; Matthias Clamer: Page 268; James Cooper: Pages 240, 254, 260, 261, 280, 286; A.C. Cooper: Page 103; Jon Cuban/ All Sport: Pages 40-41; Bob Daemmrich: Pages 30-31; Jonathan Daniel/ All Sport: Page 37; Bill Davila: Page 274; Patrick Demarchelier: Page 52; Jason Dewey: Pages 70, 84, 89; Susan Dirk: Page 198; Andrew Eccles: Page 238; David Eulitt: Page 32; Feliciano: Page 85; David Fields: Page 72; Peter Figen: Page 36; Philip Friedman: Page 217; Nadine Froger: Page 199; Armando Gallo: Pages 33, 47, 239, 243, 249, 253, 258, 263, 264, 265, 269; Mitch Gerber: Page 279; David H. Gibson: Page 216; Gayle Gleason: Page 130; Robb Gordon: Page 116; Steve Granitz: Pages 50-51; Caroline Greyshock: Page 255; Jeff Gross/ All Sport: Page 42; Dave Hogan/ Rex USA: Page 283; Philippe- Louis Houze: Page 124; Harry How/ All Sport: Page 43; Alex Irvia: Page 66; B. Jarvinen/ All Sport: Page 34; Joan Jedell: Page 158; Tom Jenkins: Page 97; Emily Jenkins: Page 151; Forest Johnson: Page 155; Craig Jones/ All Sport: Page 39; G. Steve Jordan: Page 71; Marty Katz: Pages 291, 297; Mort Kaye: Page 160; Alex Kirkbride: Page 76; Aisling Klink: Page 287; Winnie Klotz: Page 163; Bernhard Kuhmstedt: Page 285; Kim Kumpart: Page 196; Karl Lagerfeld: Page 244; Dan Lecca: Pages 140, 187; Annie Leibovitz: Page 248; Sam Levi: Page 51; Dave Lewis/ Rex USA: Page 52; Peter Liepke: Page 37; Michael Lutch: Page 207; Andy Lyons/ All Sport: Page 44; Charlotte Macpherson: Page 47; Richard Mandelkorn: Page 113; David O. Marlow: Page 90; Mark Mathews: Page 25; Scogin Mayo: Page 26-27; Eamon McCabe: Page 281; Joseph Mehling: Page 98; Stephen Munday/ All Sport: Page 44; Gordon Munro: Page 33; C. O'Rear: Page 202; Peter Paige: Page 177; David Peterson: Page 272; Bill Phelps: Page 164; Tim Sneet Porter: Page 144; Gary M. Prior: Page 289; Retna: Page 278; Robert Reck: Page 196; Kevin Riley: Page 86; Nicolas Russell: Page 131; Thomas Hart Shelby: Page 100; Stephen Simons: Pages 250, 251, 271, 273, 282; Julie Skarratt: Page 142; John Spellman: Page 47; Burton Steel: Page 65; Ted Stefanski: Page 199; Stills: Page 247; John Swannell: Page 252; Ken Tannenbaum: Page 149; Scott Teitler: Page 53; Mario Testino: Page 52; Jay Thomas: Page 149; Bill Timmerman: Page 197; Gasper Triangale: Page 52; Terry Vine: Page 210; Edward Weston: Page 208; Charles White: Page 153; C. Wilder: Page 109; Robert Wright: Page 207; Zindman/ Fremont: Page 159.

CRAFT · ANTIQUES · ARCHITECTS AND INTERIOR DES
GAR BARS AND CLUBS · COLLEGES · COSMETIC SURGE
SHION · FITNESS · FLORISTS · GOLF CLUBS · HAIR AND
AWFIRMS · MUSEUMS · PARTY ORGANIZERS AND CATE
RIVATE CLUBS · PROPERTY CONSULTANTS · RESTAURAN
ECIALTY SHOPS · TRAVEL CONSULTANTS · WEALTH MAN
NTIQUES · ARCHITECTS AND INTERIOR DESIGNERS · A
ND CLUBS · COLLEGES · COSMETIC SURGEONS · CULIN
ORISTS · GOLF CLUBS · HAIR AND BEAUTY · HOTELS · J
USEUMS · PARTY ORGANIZERS AND CATERERS · POLO C
ROPERTY CONSULTANTS · RESTAURANTS · SCHOOLS · SP
NSULTANTS · WEALTH MANAGEMENT · WINE MERCHA
ND INTERIOR DESIGNERS · ART DEALERS · AUCTION HO
OSMETIC SURGEONS · CULINARY SCHOOLS · EMPLOYM
AIR AND BEAUTY · HOTELS · JEWELRY AND WATCHES · L
ND CATERERS · POLO CLUBS · PORTRAIT PAINTERS AND
ESTAURANTS · SCHOOLS · SECURITY CONSULTANTS · SP
ANAGEMENT · WINE MERCHANTS · WINE MAKERS · YAC
ESIGNERS · ART DEALERS · AUCTION HOUSES · CHAUFF
URGEONS · CULINARY SCHOOLS · EMPLOYMENT AGENC
EAUTY · HOTELS · JEWELRY AND WATCHES · LANDSCAP
ATERERS · POLO CLUBS · PORTRAIT PAINTERS AND PHC
ESTAURANTS · SCHOOLS · SECURITY CONSULTANTS · SP
ANAGEMENT · WINE MERCHANTS · WINE MAKERS · YAC
ESIGNERS · ART DEALERS · AUCTION HOUSES · CHAUFF
URGEONS · CULINARY SCHOOLS · EMPLOYMENT AGENC
EAUTY · HOTELS · JEWELRY AND WATCHES · LANDSCAP
ATERERS · POLO CLUBS · PORTRAIT PAINTERS AND PHC
ESTAURANTS · SCHOOLS · SECURITY CONSULTANTS ·
ANAGEMENT · WINE MERCHANTS · WINE MAKERS · YAC